M000101286

PROPERTIES, EVALUATION, AND CONTROL OF ENGINEERING MATERIALS

PROPERTIES, EVALUATION, AND CONTROL OF ENGINEERING MATERIALS

William A. Cordon

Professor of Civil and Environmental Engineering
Utah State University

McGraw-Hill Book Company

New York St. Louis San Francisco Auckland Bogotá Düsseldorf
Johannesburg London Madrid Mexico Montreal New Delhi
Panama Paris São Paulo Singapore Sydney Tokyo Toronto

This book was set in Times Roman.
The editors were Frank J. Cerra,
Madelaine Eichberg, and James W. Bradley;
the cover was designed by Joseph Gillians;
the production supervisor was Charles Hess.
The drawings were done by Santype Ltd.
Fairfield Graphics was printer and binder.

PROPERTIES, EVALUATION, AND CONTROL OF ENGINEERING MATERIALS

234567890 FGRFGR 7832109

Library of Congress Cataloging in Publication Data

Cordon, William A
Properties, evaluation, and control of
engineering materials.

Includes bibliographical references and index.
1. Materials. I. Title.
TA403.C64 620.1'1 78-25640
ISBN 0-07-013123-6

CONTENTS

Part 2 Materials Evaluation

PREFACE

This book is written for the student and practicing civil engineer, construction engineer, architect, contractor, and technologist. The material covered in Part One includes some elements of materials science as related to common structural materials; geology and mineralogy of rocks and aggregates; the physical and structural properties materials, along with their history, manufacture, and control.

The sequence of study starts with the smallest known particles of energy and matter and follows the development of materials through atomic and crystal or amorphous structure, natural materials, manufactured components, and finally the combination of materials as used in structural members and structures. A simple example of statistical quality control is included in Part One.

Part Two is devoted to laboratory testing, evaluation, and specifications of various materials.

The book can be used in several different courses of study. See Table 0-1. For civil engineering, architecture, and construction engineering, the book will serve as a text and a laboratory supplement for two lectures and one laboratory per week. Proposed laboratory schedules are presented in Appendix I.

For a study in plain concrete, only those chapters dealing with concrete will apply. Likewise, for courses in concrete technology, asphalt technology, and materials technology, certain chapters are applicable in each case.

Several chapters in the book are suitable as introductory material for graduate work. A graduate course can be developed by using appropriate chapters and supplementing them with outside reference material.

Table 0-1 Suggested uses of book in various courses of study

Type of course or profession	Chapters of book which apply
Civil engineering	All chapters
Architecture	All chapters
Construction engineering	All chapters
Plain concrete	1, 2, 3, 4, 5, 6, 11, 12, 13 Appendixes I to IV
Concrete technology	1, 3, 4, 5, 11, 12, 13 Appendixes I to IV
Asphalt technology	1, 3, 9, 11, 14 Appendixes I to IV
Materials technology	1, 3, 4, 5, 7, 8, 9, 10, 11, 12, 13, 14, 15, 16, 17 Appendixes I to IV
Introduction to graduate studies in concrete	1, 2, 3, 4, 6, 11, 12 All chapters
Reference book for practicing engineers, architects, and technologists	

The practicing civil engineer and architect engaged in design and construction personnel will find the book useful as a reference of current practices. The book emphasizes the significance of and reasons for testing and control of materials rather than detailed testing procedures.

William A. Cordon

CHAPTER

ONE

THE STUDY OF ENGINEERING MATERIALS

The subject of engineering materials involves several different areas of study. To a scientist, the mechanics and interactions among atoms and the basic atomic structure of materials are of greatest value. To a design engineer and architect, the performance of materials in structures and their ability to resist various stresses are of prime importance. To the construction engineer and contractor, the availability, suitability, and uniformity of specified materials are of greatest concern.

The emphasis placed upon each area of study changes as apparent needs develop. Before World War II greatest emphasis was placed on testing the behavior of common materials, and little effort was made to develop new materials. As the need for basic scientific research in materials became apparent during the war, the study of materials science became mandatory in many universities. The apparent consensus was that students should be taught basic materials science at the expense of more traditional courses in engineering materials and related courses in geology and mineralogy. The graduate engineer could then learn the practical aspects of materials through on-the-job training. Unfortunately for civil engineers, materials science texts were based primarily on metallurgy and contained little information regarding the physical properties of materials as used in design and construction.

Because of the change in emphasis, industry has found that many graduating civil engineers and architects are not properly trained to assume responsibility for the selection, evaluation, and control of common construction materials. Persistent problems of many engineering firms are related to the specification, evaluation, and control of the quality of the materials used. It is not uncommon for an engineer, architect, and owner to be faced with the dilemma of several unsatisfactory courses of action when materials fail to meet specification requirements. The problem is compounded when a decision is required of someone who does not have sufficient background in the significance of test results used in the evaluation of materials and adequacy of the structure produced.

1-1 COURSES OF STUDY IN ENGINEERING MATERIALS

Several types of university and technology courses deal with engineering materials. These usually fall into the following categories:

1. *Materials science.* A study of the atomic, molecular, and crystal structure and mechanics of materials and their influence on the behavior of materials. This field of study was pioneered by the metallurgist, and most texts emphasize metals.
2. *Strength of materials or mechanics of materials.* A study of the theoretical behavior of materials under stress. This is a traditional basic course in civil engineering.
3. *Structural materials.* A study of common materials used in structures with emphasis on physical and structural properties of materials, their evaluation, and their control.

The most appropriate materials course depends on the future aspirations of the students. For those planning graduate work and research, materials science and mechanics of materials are most appropriate. For those planning a career in architecture, structural design, and construction, courses in mechanics of materials and structural materials would be of greatest value. A course in structural materials is most valuable to civil engineers, architects, construction engineers, materials engineers, technologists, and contractors who will be involved in the selection, evaluation, and control of materials.

1-2 USE OF STRUCTURAL MATERIALS IN MODERN CONSTRUCTION

Any structure that exists is made from a variety of materials. This text is primarily concerned with common materials used in structures, i.e., concrete, steel, asphalt, and wood, with minor reference to other miscellaneous materials. Soil is discussed briefly, but soil is not considered a structural material as the term is used here. However, suitable soil is essential for the support of foundations for structures.

Table 1-1 shows that in large buildings steel and concrete are most prominent. Steel and concrete are companion materials in reinforced concrete, but reinforced concrete and steel also compete as structural members. Wood is used most often in smaller buildings and in homes with concrete in the foundations.

Concrete and asphalt compete in highway and airport pavement construction and, to some extent, in the lining of canals and small reservoirs.

Table 1-1 Materials most commonly used in structures

	Principal materials used in construction		
Structure	1	2	Miscellaneous
Buildings:			
High-rise building	Steel	Concrete	Wood, glass, plastics, clay
Commercial buildings	Concrete	Steel	Wood, glass, aluminum, clay
Homes	Wood	Concrete	Steel, aluminum, clay, plastics
Transportation:			
Highway pavements	Asphalt	Concrete	
Bridges	Concrete	Steel	Wood, aluminum
Airport pavements	Concrete	Asphalt	
Airport structures	Concrete	Steel	Wood, glass, aluminum, clay tile, plastics
Pipelines			
(*a*) Petroleum, gas	Steel		
(*b*) Water	Concrete	Steel	Wood
Water-control structures:			
Pipe	Concrete	Steel	Plastics, clay pipe
Canal linings	Concrete	Asphalt	
Dams	Concrete	Soil	
Irrigation structures	Concrete	Steel	
Sewage systems	Concrete	Clay	Plastics
Water treatment plants	Concrete	Clay	
Miscellaneous:			
Piers, waterfront structures	Wood	Concrete	
Tunnels	Concrete	Steel	
Sidewalks	Concrete	Asphalt	
Driveways	Concrete	Asphalt	
Decorative, outside walls	Brick	Wood	Concrete, stone, aluminum clay tile
Floors	Wood	Concrete	Asphalt, clay tile
Foundations	Concrete		Soil
Nuclear reactors	Concrete	Steel	

Note: The term "concrete" includes reinforced concrete.

Concrete and soil compete in dam construction, but nearly all water- and sewage-control structures are made of concrete.

Concrete and concrete materials will likely be used in some form in all civil engineering projects. More importantly, the design engineer, construction engineer, architect, contractor, and technologist may all be involved in the specifications and manufacture of concrete in the field. The responsibility of project personnel for the use of steel, wood, portland cement, asphalt cement, and miscellaneous materials is limited to understanding and selecting suitable products from those available. The final steps in manufacture of cast-in-place concrete take place as the concrete is specified, mixed, placed, finished, and cured on the job. An understanding of concrete specifications and the properties of concrete and concrete materials is therefore particularly important.

1-3 NATIONAL AND INTERNATIONAL ORGANIZATIONS THAT STUDY AND PROMOTE THE USE OF MATERIALS

Various organizations have been formed to bring together those individuals who are interested in the use of engineering materials. The professional organizations share technical and scientific knowledge, while the trade associations promote a given material and provide technical and practical information for its proper use. The following is a partial list of prominent organizations in the United States devoted to engineering materials. Other engineering societies such as the American Society of Civil Engineers, the American Society of Mechanical Engineers, the American Association of State Highway and Transportation Officials, and the Highway Research Board also have divisions and committees dealing with various materials.

1. *Professional organizations*
   - ASTM —American Society for Testing and Materials
   - ACI —American Concrete Institute
   - AIMMPE—American Institute of Mining, Metallurgical, and Petroleum Engineers
   - ASM —American Society for Metals
   - GSA —Geological Society of America, Engineering Geology Division
   - ACS —American Ceramic Society
   - NICE —National Institute of Ceramic Engineers
   - SPE —Society of Plastics Engineers
   - AAPT —Association of Asphalt Paving Technologists
2. *Trade associations*
   - AI —Asphalt Institute
   - NSGA —National Sand and Gravel Association
   - NRMCA—National Ready-Mixed Concrete Association
   - AISI —American Iron and Steel Institute
   - PCA —Portland Cement Association
   - NAA —National Ash Association
   - NSSCI —National Shale, Slate, and Clay Institute
   - RSI —Reinforcing Steel Institute
   - PCI —Prestressed Concrete Institute

1-4 STANDARD METRIC PRACTICE

A new system of measurement, the International System of Units (SI), is being adopted throughout the world. This system is a modern version of the meter, kilogram, second, ampere system, and its details are published and controlled by an international treaty organization. This discussion is based on ASTM Standard E 380, which presents the recommendations of the treaty organization. For a number of reasons, it is inevitable that a few units outside the system be used with it. It is this additional use of non-SI units that leads to controversy and difference between standards that define modern metric practice.

Since a wide variety of metric units have been in use for years in various parts of the world, it is natural that tradition would promote use of these old units in formerly metric countries. For this reason, many European and international standards also recognize a number of non-SI units.

As the world changes to standard SI units, it is important that the graduating engineers, architects, and technologists become familiar with and use the standard units. Where necessary, conversion from SI units to common English units can be readily made until such time as industry adopts standard units. Wherever possible, SI units are used in this book. Simple conversions to common units currently being used are also indicated.

To protect the new system from degradation and to cooperate with knowledgeable people all over the world who are recommending good unit use, the ASTM standard strongly urges the use of SI, plus a very limited group of non-SI units, the need for which is strong and is widely endorsed. The following units apply to the study of materials:

1. *Length.* The SI unit of length is the meter (m) with small lengths measured in centimeters (cm) and millimeters (mm). The kilometer (km) or hectometer (hm) is used for large measurements.
2. *Area.* The SI unit of area is the square meter (m^2). Large areas are properly expressed in square hectometers (hm^2) or square kilometers (km^2).
3. *Volume.* The SI unit of volume is the cubic meter (m^3). This unit, or one of the regularly formed multiples such as the cubic centimeter (cm^3), is preferred for all applications. The special name "liter" has been approved for the cubic decimeter, but use of this unit is restricted to the measurement of liquids and gases. No prefix other than milli- should be used with liter.
4. *Mass.* The SI unit of mass is the kilogram (kg). This unit, or one of the multiples formed by attaching an SI prefix to gram, is preferred for all applications. The megagram (Mg) is the appropriate unit for measuring large masses such as have been expressed in tons. However, the name "ton" has been given to several large mass units that are widely used in commerce and technology—the long ton of 2240 lb, the short ton of 2000 lb, and the metric ton of 1000 kg (also called the "tonne"). None of these terms are SI. The term "metric ton" should be restricted to commercial usage, and no prefixes should be used with it. Use of the term "tonne" is discouraged.

5. *Pressure and stress.* The SI unit of pressure and stress is the pascal (Pa), and with proper SI prefixes it is applicable to all such measurements. Old metric gravitational units for pressure and stress such as kilogram-force per square centimeter (kgf/cm^2) will not be used.

1-5 RECOMMENDATIONS CONCERNING MASS, FORCE, AND WEIGHT

The principal departure of SI from the gravimetric system of metric engineering units is the use of explicitly distinct units for mass and force. In SI, the name "kilogram" is restricted to the unit of mass, and the kilogram-force (from which the suffix "-force" was in practice often erroneously dropped) should not be used. In its place the SI unit of force, the newton (N), is used. Likewise, the newton rather than the kilogram-force is used to form derived units which include force; for example, the SI unit for pressure or stress is the pascal (N/m^2 = Pa).

Considerable confusion exists in the use of the term "weight" as a quantity to mean either force or mass. In commercial and everyday use, weight nearly always means mass; thus, when one speaks of a person's weight, the quantity referred to is mass. This nontechnical use of the term "weight" in everyday life will probably persist. In science and technology, the term "weight" of a body has usually meant the force that, if applied to the body, would give it an acceleration equal to the local acceleration of free fall. The adjective "local" in the phrase "local acceleration of free fall" has usually meant a location on the earth's surface. In this context, the "local acceleration of free fall" (g), sometimes referred to as "acceleration due to gravity equals 9.0665 m/s^2," is recommended. Because of the dual use of the term "weight" as a quantity, this term should be avoided in technical practice except when its meaning is completely clear. When the term is used, it is important to know whether mass or force is intended and to use SI units properly by using kilograms for mass or newtons for force.

Gravity is involved in determining mass with a balance or scale. When a standard mass is used to balance the measured mass, the direct effect of gravity on the two masses is canceled, but the indirect effect through the buoyancy of air or other fluid is generally not canceled. In using a spring scale, mass is measured indirectly, since the instrument responds to the force of gravity. Such scales may be calibrated in mass units if the variation in acceleration of gravity and buoyancy correlations are not significant in their use.

Confusion results in converting unit weight to the SI term "density." Density is the mass per unit volume (kg/m^3). Weight is not an SI unit but has been used (other than for scientific use) interchangeably with mass. Weight is a force in scientific use, and the unit weight is measured in newtons per unit volume (N/m^3). When kilograms per cubic meter is used, the correct term is density rather than unit weight.

The SI unit for loading or force is the newton (N), which is mass multiplied by acceleration. The corresponding SI term for psi (pounds per square inch) is the

Table 1-2 Prefixes and symbols used to form names and symbols of the decimal multiples

Multiplication factor	Prefix	Symbol
1 000 000 000 000 000 000 = 10^{18}	exa	E
1 000 000 000 000 000 = 10^{15}	peta	P
1 000 000 000 000 = 10^{12}	tera	T
1 000 000 000 = 10^{9}	giga	G
1 000 000 = 10^{6}	mega	M
1 000 = 10^{3}	kilo	k
100 = 10^{2}	hecto	h
10 = 10^{1}	deka	da
0.1 = 10^{-1}	deci	d
0.01 = 10^{-2}	centi	c
0.001 = 10^{-3}	milli	m
0.000 001 = 10^{-6}	micro	μ
0.000 000 001 = 10^{-9}	nano	n
0.000 000 000 001 = 10^{-12}	pico	p
0.000 000 000 000 001 = 10^{-15}	femto	f
0.000 000 000 000 000 001 = 10^{-18}	atto	a

pascal (Pa), or newtons per square meter. The recommended corresponding SI term for psi is the megapascal (MPa).

Although the general public will not readily convert to SI units, students, practicing engineers, architects, and technologists should lead the way in the adoption of standard SI units. This will help in the general acceptance of standard units. Table 1-2 gives useful SI symbols. Table 1-3 will be helpful in the conversion from SI units used in this text to common English units.

Table 1-3 Useful conversions when laboratory equipment is used which measure in English units

SI units to English units	English units to SI units
1 m = 1.0936 yd	1 yd = 0.9144 m
1 cm = 0.3937 in	1 in = 2.54 cm
1 m^3 = 1.3079 yd^3	1 yd^3 = 0.7649 m^3
1 m^3 = 35.313 ft^3	1 ft^3 = 0.0283 m^3
1 kg = 2.205 lb (mass)	1 lb (mass) = 0.4535 kg
1 kg/m^3 = 1.6855 lb/yd^3	1 lb/yd^3 = 0.5933 kg/m^3
1 kg/m^3 = 0.06243 lb/ft^3	1 lb/ft^3 = 16.02 kg/m^3
1 MPa = 145 psi	1 psi = 0.006895 MPa

Strength, MPa = total load on a 6 × 12 in cylinder, lb divided by 4100
Density, kg/m^3 = kilograms in a $\frac{1}{4}$-ft^3 container × 141.25
Density, kg/m^3 = pounds in a $\frac{1}{4}$-ft^3 container × 64.08
Density, kg/m^3 = specific gravity × 1000

QUESTIONS AND PROBLEMS

1 What changes have been made since World War II in the study of engineering materials?

2 Why is the study of construction materials important in modern construction?

3 What are the major areas in the study of engineering materials?

4 Why is concrete considered the most universal of all engineering materials?

5 What types of organizations study and promote the use of various materials?

6 What is the purpose of the SI system of measurements?

7 Why is there confusion in the use of terms for weight, mass, and force?

8 The term unit weight is a common measurement for weight per unit volume. What is the corresponding SI term for unit weight?

9 How would you express a persons weight in SI units?

10 Since testing machines show the total load on a test cylinder in pounds, will it be necessary to replace all of this equipment to convert to SI units?

11 Since the liter is not the standard SI unit of measure for 1000 cm^3, what unit should be used?

PART ONE

PROPERTIES OF ENGINEERING MATERIALS

CHAPTER

TWO

ATOMIC STRUCTURE OF COMMON MATERIALS

In order to understand the behavior and characteristics of materials, it is necessary to review simple concepts of atomic bonding and arrangement. The characteristics of each material such as hardness, strength, toughness, and density will depend on the kind and arrangement of atoms and whether there is a stable, strong, atomic attraction.

This text is not intended for use in materials science courses. Chapter 2 is presented to provide sufficient background information to better understand certain properties and behavior of common materials. The following are a few examples where atomic arrangement and bonding are of particular importance in understanding structural materials.

1. The formation and development of the properties of various minerals and rocks used as aggregates
2. The atomic arrangement of hydrated portland cement, which produces a rigid product, and the molecular structure of asphalt cement, which is flexible
3. The atomic bonding which produces the varied properties of different steels and metals
4. The atomic structure of rocks, which causes alkali-aggregate reaction in concrete

2-1 FUSION OF ATOMS

A theory on the fusion of atoms is explained in the following excerpts from "Of Stars and Man" by Ira Wolfert, The Readers Digest, May 1970, which cites Robert Jastrow's book *Red Giants and White Dwarfs*, Harper & Row, 1970.

> Radio telescopes and space probes have discovered charged particles blowing like winds through space. One particle is called a "proton." It has a charge of positive electricity. Another is called an "electron." It has a negative charge. Because of their opposite charges, they attract each other. When they come together, the electron is held in orbit around the proton. Together they make the simplest of the elements, the hydrogen atom. If enough atoms are present, the gravitational attraction each exerts on its neighbor is sufficient to hold the gas together. The bigger the mass of the hydrogen atoms, the stronger the gravitational force. For a gas cloud to congeal into a star, it has to be nearly 3000 times larger than our solar system.
>
> As the cloud is compressed, it begins heating up. When it reaches 100,000°F at its center, the hydrogen atoms collide so violently that they separate into plus and minus particles again.
>
> Finally, the ball is only about 1 million mi across, and the temperature at the core has risen to 20 million degrees. At this point, thermonuclear fusion begins. The protons are now smashing together so violently that they fuse to make the nucleus of a new element, helium. The process is similar to that which goes on in a hydrogen bomb and that which provides the energy of the sun. While bombs produce helium by the pound, the sun produces it at a rate estimated at about 564 million tons/s.
>
> When outward explosions from the center exactly balance the in-drawing gravitational force, the dimensions of the ball become stabilized. Our own sun, an average star, is in this state—its size is about 1 million mi in diameter.
>
> After the hydrogen at the star's core is transformed into helium, the nuclear explosions subside and gravity starts crushing the star again. This generates enough heat (200 million degrees) to produce a higher level of reaction, which fuses the helium nuclei into the nuclei of carbon atoms.
>
> If the star is large enough, it will go on to a series of collapses and ever hotter reactions. Through successive collapses and regenerations, a star can create the heavier elements found on planets like earth.
>
> When the central temperature goes up to 100 billion degrees, every possible nuclear reaction comes into play. It is in this last stage that the heaviest elements, those extending beyond iron, are produced. The star rebounds from the final collapse in a great explosion which disperses to space most of the elements manufactured in its interior during its lifetime.

2-2 FORMATION OF THE EARTH

When the star from which the earth was formed exploded, all the elements of the earth hurled into space as vapor. When the vapor congealed, it formed into a sphere of molten magma, a sphere being the most stable configuration of unrestrained liquid acted on only by the force of gravity of the mass.

As the earth's crust cooled, a variety of minerals were formed depending on the pressure involved, the rate of cooling, and the elements present. The molten material was without definite form, and the atoms could move about. As cooling progressed, atomic arrangements and crystallization took place. If cooling was slow, there was time to form long-order arrangement for crystals, whereas magma that was cooled rapidly produced noncrystalline or very fine-grained minerals.

The earth's interior is still molten, and occasionally magma reaches the surface through fissures during volcanic activity.

2-3 STRUCTURE OF ATOMS†

The atom of any element contains a nucleus of protons and neutrons surrounded by a given number of electrons. The electrons are charged particles with the charge taken to be negative. The protons are considered to carry a positive charge. Therefore the nucleus attracts one electron for each proton. The mass of an element depends on the protons and neutrons in its nucleus, but its behavior and characteristics are determined by the electrons.

2-4 ATOMIC NUMBER AND ATOMIC WEIGHT

The number of electrons attracted to the nucleus of an atom is called the "atomic number." The "atomic weight" is the total grams of 6.02×10^{23} atoms (Avogadro's number) and represents the number of atoms in a gram atom. A gram atom does not represent mass per volume, but is the mass of 6.02×10^{23} atoms. For example, 1 gram atom of oxygen contains 16.0 g, whereas a gram atom of silica contains 28.1 g.

2-5 ENERGY LEVEL OF ELECTRONS

The electrons attracted to a given atom are divided into groups or "quantum shells," depending on their level of energy. Each shell contains a maximum number of $2n^2$ electrons, where n is the shell number. The first, or K, shell is filled first and contains two electrons; the second, or L, shell contains $2 \times 2^2 = 8$; the third, 18; and the fourth, 32. An atom is most stable (less reactive) when each quantum shell contains $2n^2$ electrons. When this is not possible, an atom becomes stabilized with a minimum of eight electrons in the outer shell.

The electrons in the outer shell determine the behavior and characteristics of elements. For example, the stable, inert gas helium has two electrons which fill the first shell. Hydrogen, on the other hand, is very reactive since it has only one

† More complete information on this and related subjects can be found in materials science texts. This discussion is based on references at end of chapter.

Table 2-1† Electron arrangement for some elements found in common engineering materials

Element			Quantum shells (number of electrons at each energy level)					
Symbol	Atomic number	Atomic weight	*K*	*L*	*M*	*N*	*O*	*P*
H	1	1.008	1					
He	2	4.003	2					
C	6	12.011	2	4				
O	8	16.000	2	6				
Na	11	22.990	2	8	1			
Mg	12	24.312	2	8	2			
Al	13	26.980	2	8	3			
Si	14	28.086	2	8	4			
S	16	32.064	2	8	6			
Cl	17	35.453	2	8	7			
K	19	39.102	2	8	8	1		
Ca	20	40.080	2	8	8	2		
Fe	26	55.850	2	8	14	2		
Ni	28	58.710	2	8	16	2		
Cu	29	63.540	2	8	18	1		
Zn	30	65.370	2	8	18	2		
Ba	56	137.340	2	8	18	18	8	2

† Based on Table 2-1, Lawrence H. Van Vlack, *Elements of Materials Science*, Addison-Wesley, Reading, Mass., 1964.

electron in the first shell. It must combine with other elements to fill the first shell and reach a stable condition. Table 2-1 shows the electrons in each quantum shell for several elements found in common materials.

2-6 ATOMIC ATTRACTIONS

The engineering properties of any material depend on the atomic attractions which are present. Asphalt molecules, which have primary bonds within the molecule, for example, are only bonded together with weak secondary bonds (van der Waals forces); consequently, asphalt occurs as a liquid. Hardened portland cement paste has a combination of primary and secondary bonding and hence occurs as a solid. Rocks and minerals are hard and tough because they are bonded with primary atomic bonds. Most elements reach a more stable configuration in molecules by (1) receiving extra electrons from other atoms, (2) releasing electrons to other atoms, or (3) sharing electrons with other atoms.

2-7 PRIMARY BONDS

Primary bonds are the strongest of the atomic attractions and account for the strength and hardness of most structural materials.

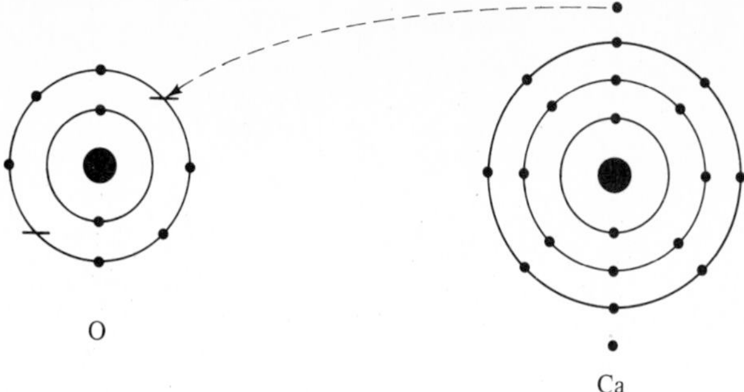

Figure 2-1 Ionic bonding. The oxygen atom borrows one of the extra electrons from the calcium atom to help fill its outer electron shell.

Ionic Bonds

Atoms with one and two electrons in their outer quantum shells release these outer electrons to atoms with vacancies in the outer shell and become positively charged ions. Atoms with vacancies in their outer shell which add the released electrons become negatively charged ions. There is an imbalance in each atom between the negative electrons and the positive protons. Attraction between negatively and positively charged ions develops a comparatively strong bond between neighboring ions of unlike charges. This is called "ionic bonding" (Fig. 2-1).

A negatively charged ion is attracted to all positively charged ions, and a positively charged ion is attracted to all negatively charged ions. This attraction is equal in all directions, which results in an accumulation of atoms. Under proper conditions, the atoms arrange themselves into crystals.

Covalent Bonds

The strongest force of atomic attraction is the covalent bond. An atom may acquire eight electrons in its outer shell by sharing electrons with an adjacent atom. The shared electron has strong attraction to both nuclei. The most notable example of such sharing is found in the carbon molecule, C.

The diamond is the hardest material found in nature, and it is composed entirely of carbon. Each carbon atom has four electrons in its outer shell, which it shares with four adjacent carbon atoms (Fig. 2-2). The strength of the covalent bonds in the diamond is demonstrated not only by its hardness but also by its high melting temperature.

Metallic Bonds

The third primary bond is the metallic bond. Metal atoms have only a few electrons in their outer shell (see Table 2-1). These outer electrons are not held firmly to the nucleus and are attracted to any positive ion. Since several positive ions are attracted to the same group of electrons (electron cloud), a bond develops among the ions.

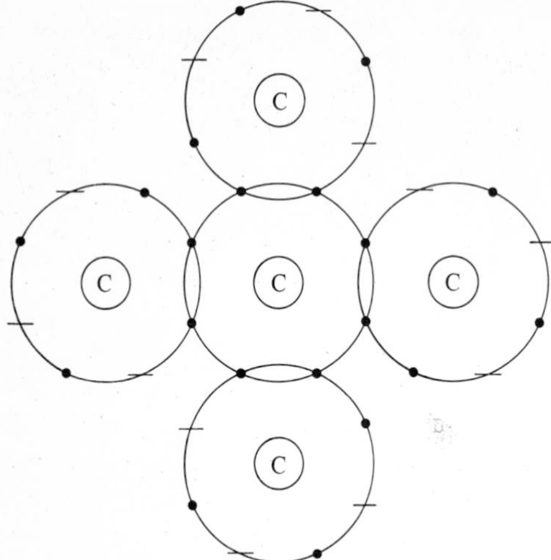

Figure 2-2 Covalent bonding. The carbon atom has four vacancies in its outer shell. By sharing electrons with four other atoms, its outer shell is filled with eight electrons.

Metallic bonding is the weakest of the primary bonds and allows the atoms to move their relative position. For this reason, under stress metals can permanently deform without fracturing. The free electrons give the metals high electrical conductivity, since they are free to move in an electric field. The mobility of the outer electrons also explains the thermal conductivity of metals.

2-8 SECONDARY BONDS (VAN DER WAALS FORCES)

The secondary bonds among elements are much weaker than primary bonds. Their presence and importance cannot be minimized, however, for without secondary bonding, liquids would not exist and many materials would have different characteristics.

Hydrogen Bridge

The atomic attraction that causes water to condense is known as the "hydrogen bridge." Two hydrogen atoms share their one electron with an oxygen atom in covalent bonding to form the water molecule. Since the one electron of hydrogen is shared with the oxygen atom, the exposed positive charge of its nucleus is attracted to electrons of other oxygen atoms (Fig. 2-3). This is one of the weakest of the atomic bonding forces, but it still causes water molecules to congeal into water.

Molecular Polarization

When any two or more atoms combine into a molecule, if the centers of all the positive nuclei and all the negative electrons do not coincide, an electrical dipole is formed with the center of the positive charges at one end and the center of the

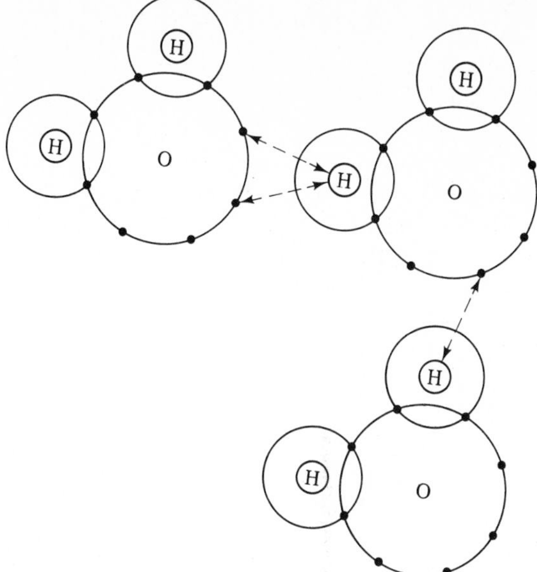

Figure 2-3 Hydrogen bridge. Exposed nucleus of the hydrogen atoms attracts electrons from other oxygen atoms.

negative charges at the other end. This dipole is attracted to other positive and negative charges; hence, the molecules are attracted to one another.

Dispersion Effect

The centers of the negative and positive charges of an atom coincide when electrons are symmetrical about the nucleus. Electrons move randomly, however, and may be concentrated at any given instant on one side of the nucleus. This causes momentary shift in the center of the negative charges and creates a weak attraction to other atoms momentarily polarized. If it were not for this attractive force, gases such as helium would not condense at any temperature.

Table 2-2 Atomic bonding of common materials

Material	Principal atomic bonding	Principal atomic arrangement
Mineral aggregates	Ionic and covalent	Crystalline
Portland cement concrete	Ionic, covalent, van der Waals	Crystalline
Clay products	Ionic and covalent	Amorphous
Steel	Metallic	Crystalline
Aluminum	Metallic	Crystalline
Asphalt (intermolecular)	van der Waals	Amorphous
Glass	Ionic, covalent	Amorphous

2-9 COORDINATION NUMBER

The "coordination number" refers to the number of neighboring atoms bonded to a given atom. The coordination number for carbon in a diamond, for example, is 4, because it is bonded to four other carbon atoms. There can be no more bonds since all vacancies in the outer shell are filled.

Two factors control the coordination number of an atom: (1) the number of possible atomic bonds and (2) the size of the atoms involved. In the silica tetrahedron, the size ratio for combined silicon and oxygen atoms is 0.39/1.32, or 0.3. There is not room for more than four oxygen atoms to bond with the silicon atom (Fig. 2-4). All atoms of a given metal are the same size, and the coordination number can be as much as 12 (see Table 2-3).

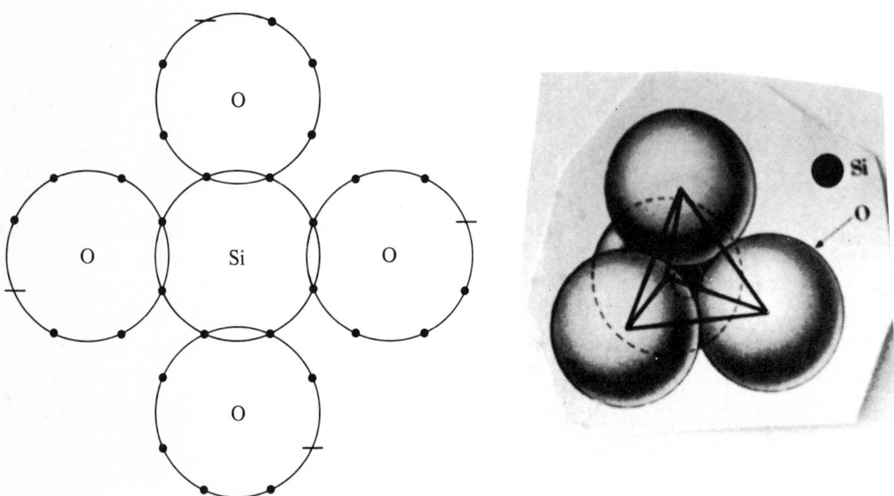

Figure 2-4 Silicate tetrahedron. These are strong covalent bonds between the silica and oxygen atoms. *(After Lawrence H. Van Vlack,* Elements of Materials Science, *Addison-Wesley, Reading, Mass., 1964.)*

Table 2-3† Atomic coordination versus atomic size ratio

Coordination number	Minimum ratio of atomic radii
3	0.155
4	0.225
6	0.414
8	0.732
12	1.0

† After Lawrence H. Van Vlack, *Elements of Materials Science*, Addison-Wesley, Reading, Mass., 1964.

In general, the coordination numbers of metals and ionic solids are governed by the relative size of the atoms and the coordination numbers of covalent solids by the limits of their electron sharing.

2-10 SILICATES

Many inorganic materials contain silicates which are found in most high-quality aggregates for concrete and asphaltic concrete. Probably the most widely known industrial silicate composition is portland cement. Many ceramics such as clay products and glass also contain silicates. Since silicates are an important component in many structural materials, it is important to discuss the atomic arrangement which explains the properties and behavior of these materials.

The silicate tetrahedron is thė primary building block of all silicate materials. One silicon atom fits among four oxygen atoms and shares electrons with each oxygen atom in strong covalent bonding (Fig. 2-4). Since each oxygen atom of the tetrahedron still has one vacancy in its outer electron shell, it will readily combine with other atoms. This deficiency is corrected when oxygen atoms share electrons with a second silicon atom.

Silicate Chains

The oxygen atoms are so strongly bonded to the silica atom in the silicate tetrahedron that they act as a unit in most silicates. The oxygen atoms of the tetrahedron will combine with other silicon atoms. When the silicon atoms of two tetrahedra share a common oxygen atom, the combination becomes Si_2O_7 (Fig. 2-5). If the combination of tetrahedra continues, a chain structure of almost infinite length is possible.

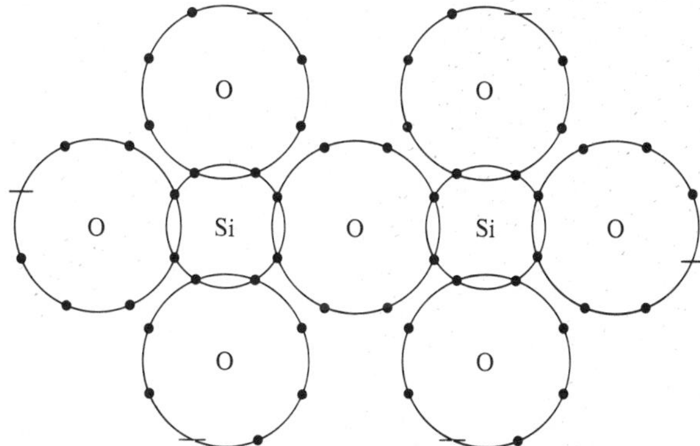

Figure 2-5 The starting of a silicate chain. Two silica atoms share a common oxygen atom.

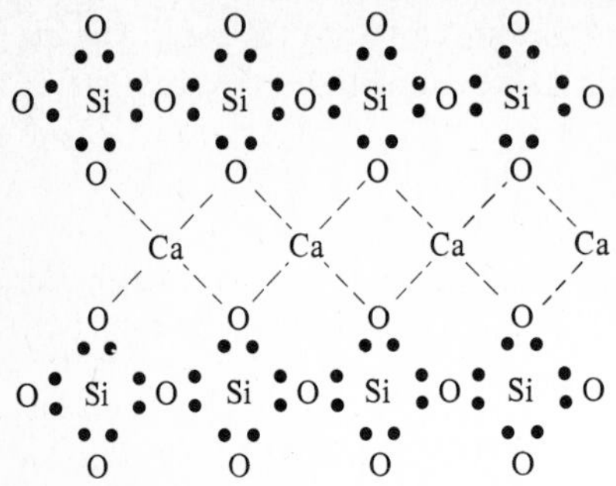

Figure 2-6 In portland cement, silicate chains are bonded together with calcium atoms in ionic bonding.

Other atoms combine with silicate chains. Portland cement, for example, contains calcium atoms which have two electrons in the outer shell. The calcium atom binds two silicate chains together by releasing its two outer-shell electrons intermittently to four oxygen atoms of four different tetrahedra (Fig. 2-6). Hydrated portland cement gel forms needlelike crystals. The chains are bound in one direction with covalent bonds which are stronger than the ionic bonds that bond the silicate chains.

Sheet Structures

Sheet structures are formed when oxygen atoms in the same plane, but not included in the chain structure, share the silica atom of other tetrahedra, resulting in two-dimensional growth. This produces flat, flaky materials like clay and mica. Only secondary bonds occur between sheets, which explains the characteristics of clay. Water forces the sheets apart, which accounts for high absorption. This, in turn, reduces the secondary bonding between the sheet, which destroys the structural strength of clays. Conversely, when clay dries out, the sheets come close together as the water leaves and the strength of thé clay returns, accompanied by high shrinkage.

Framework Structures

An extension of silicate tetrahedral units into three dimensions produces a framework structure. In these structures all the oxygen atoms of any particular tetrahedron are shared with a silicon atom of adjacent tetrahedra, and each silicon is shared by four oxygens. This results in two oxygen atoms for each silicon atom and produces SiO_2. Quartz is the most common form of the SiO_2 framework structure found in minerals. Quartz is a mineral, but it also occurs as a rock.

Amorphous Structures

Materials which do not have the long-range repetitive pattern of crystals are literally "without form." Such materials include gases, liquids, and glasses. Asphalt cement is the only major liquid structural material. Glass, the last of the three amorphous materials, is a hard solid and occurs in many natural volcanic rocks. These rocks are reactive with alkalies in portland cement, because some oxygen atoms of the silica tetrahedra have a vacancy in their outer shell. Chemically deposited silica is also amorphous and reactive with alkalies for the same reason. If crystallization had been completed, all oxygen atoms would be bound to two silica atoms and each silica atom would be shared by four oxygen atoms. The outer electron shell of all atoms would be filled, and the rock would be inert, such as quartz.

2-11 CARBONATES

Carbonates, particularly calcium carbonate, make up another group of important materials. Calcium carbonate, $CaCO_3$, is the atomic group that forms the mineral calcite and is found in such rocks as limestone, dolomite, coral, and marble. Atomic bonding in calcium carbonate is a combination of ionic and covalent bonding. The carbon atom shares electrons with three oxygen atoms. The calcium releases two electrons to two oxygen atoms of the carbonate ion, leaving the outer shell of the calcium ion filled with eight electrons (Fig. 2-7). Calcium carbonate is one of the most stable compounds of calcium, but since the carbon atom and the oxygen atoms have unfilled vacancies in their outer shell, $CaCO_3$ reacts readily with acids and breaks down into CaO and CO_2 at relatively low temperatures.

Calcium carbonate is one of the principal ingredients used in the manufacture of portland cement. Sound limestones, marble, and dolomite also produce concrete aggregates.

2-12 IRON

Iron atoms, all being the same size, have a maximum coordination number of 12 (Table 2-3) and fit into a uniform lattice arrangement bound together with metallic bonds. Pure iron is ductile and can be molded and drawn quite easily. This is possible because the relative position of an atom with respect to other atoms can change without breaking metallic bonding. A cubic unit of the lattice structure is used to identify the lattice arrangement of iron atoms. The sides of the cube are known as the "lattice constant," *a*, and *r* is the radius of the atoms.

Iron forms a face-centered cubic lattice above 723°C, and as it cools, it transforms into a body-centered cubic structure. Figure 2-8 shows each of these cubic structures, along with the relationship between the lattice constant and the size of the atoms.

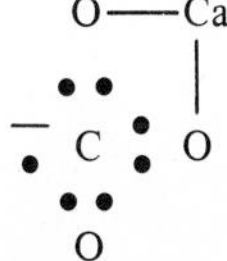

Figure 2-7 The atoms of calcium carbonate are bound with both covalent and ionic bonding.

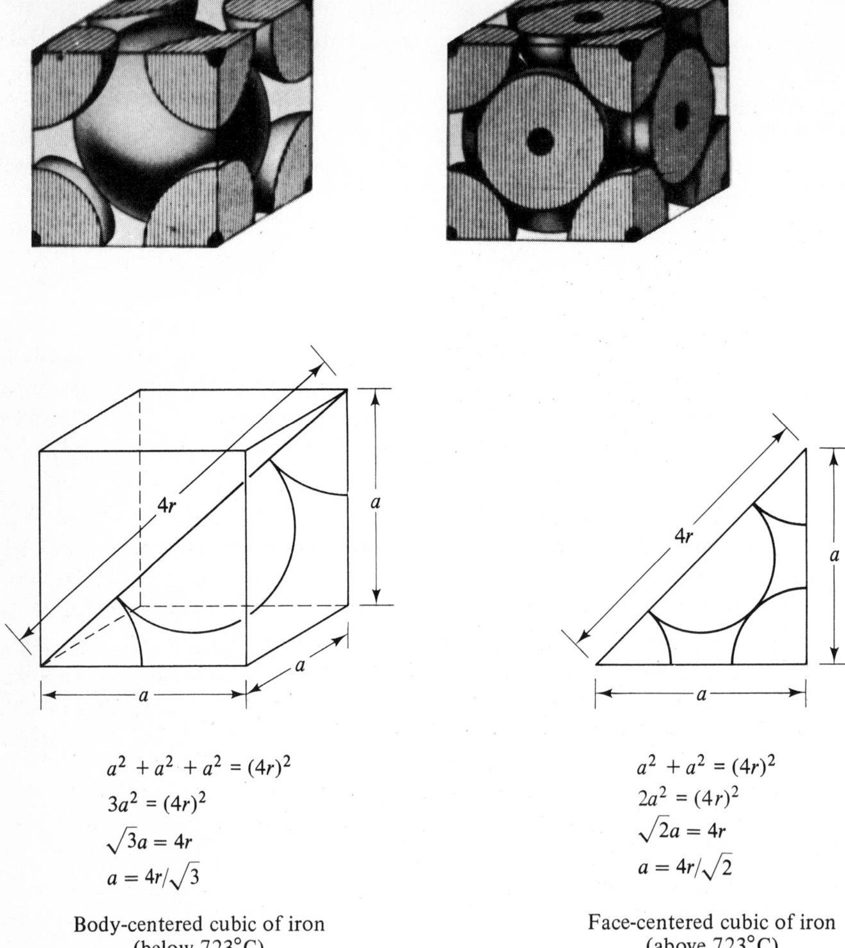

Figure 2-8 Cubic lattice structure of iron.

Atomic Packing

The "atomic packing factor" is the ratio of the volume of the atoms to the volume of the unit cell containing the atoms.

$$\text{Atomic packing factor} = n\frac{\frac{4}{3}\pi r^3}{a^3} \tag{2-1}$$

where r is the radius of the atom, a is the length of a side of the cube (lattice constant), and n is the number of atoms in the unit cell.

For the body-centered cube, the packing factor (PF) is

$$\mathrm{PF} = 2 \text{ atoms} \times \frac{4\pi r^3/3}{(4r/\sqrt{3})^3} = \frac{2 \times \frac{4}{3}\pi}{(4/\sqrt{3})^3} = 0.68 \qquad (2\text{-}2)$$

and for the face-centered cube it is

$$\mathrm{PF} = 4 \text{ atoms} \times \frac{\frac{4}{3}\pi}{(4/\sqrt{2})^3} = 0.74 \qquad (2\text{-}3)$$

2-13 STEEL

Steel is made from an alloy of iron and carbon. Carbon atoms are about the same size as the spacing of iron atoms in a face-centered cubic lattice structure and will fit among the iron atoms (Fig. 2.9). Steel is stronger, harder, and more brittle than iron, because the carbon atoms limit the slip planes in the lattice structure.

Above 723°C iron has a face-centered cubic structure, and as much as 2% carbon will go into solution with iron (Fig. 2-9). As the percentage of carbon increases, iron carbide, FeC_3, is formed. Iron carbide is very hard, due to strong atomic bonds other than metallic bonds. Below 723°C iron atoms change to a body-centered cubic structure. Even though there is a greater percentage of voids in a body-centered cubic structure, the voids are long and narrow at the ends. Carbon atoms do not fit in the voids of a body-centered cubic lattice and the solution of carbon in iron is very low. If steel above 723°C is cooled

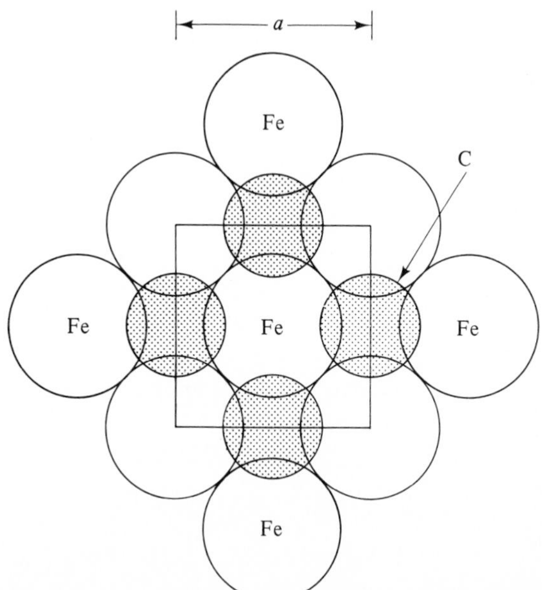

Figure 2-9 Carbon atoms will nearly fit in the voids of a face-centered cubic lattice of iron. Carbon will therefore go into solution with iron above 723°C. *(After Lawrence H. Van Vlack,* Elements of Materials Science, *Addison-Wesley, Reading, Mass., 1964.)*

rapidly, the face-centered cubic structure does not change and the carbon remains in the voids of the face-centered lattice structure. This produces harder steels. When mild steel cools slowly it is ductile. When it is quenched (tempered) it becomes hard and brittle.

2-14 ASPHALT

Asphalt cement is a highly complex combination of hydrocarbon compounds. The basic building block of the hydrocarbon compounds is the combination of two hydrogen atoms and one carbon atom bound with covalent bonds, H:C:H. This fills the outer electron shell of the hydrogen atoms but leaves two vacancies in the outer shell of the carbon atom. The carbon atom will combine with other hydrocarbon mers (units) into long-chain molecules terminating with a third hydrogen atom or other molecules (Fig. 2-10). Depending on the length of the chain and the terminal molecule, a whole family of hydrocarbon materials can be produced. This group in asphalt cement is sometimes referred to as the "oils" and includes the naphthenes and paraffins. These materials are thought to control the viscosity and flow of asphalts.

A second group called the "resins" is built around benzene rings (Fig. 2-11) and falls into the group of single- and multiple-ring aromatics. This group of hydrocarbons makes up about 70 percent of asphalt and is thought to furnish the adhesive and ductile properties of asphalt as the complex molecules develop.

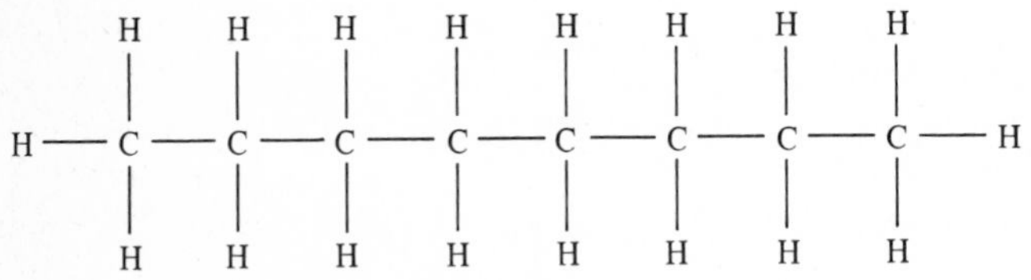

```
    H   H   H   H   H   H   H   H
    |   |   |   |   |   |   |   |
H — C — C — C — C — C — C — C — C — H
    |   |   |   |   |   |   |   |
    H   H   H   H   H   H   H   H
```

Figure 2-10 Paraffin hydrocarbon chain.

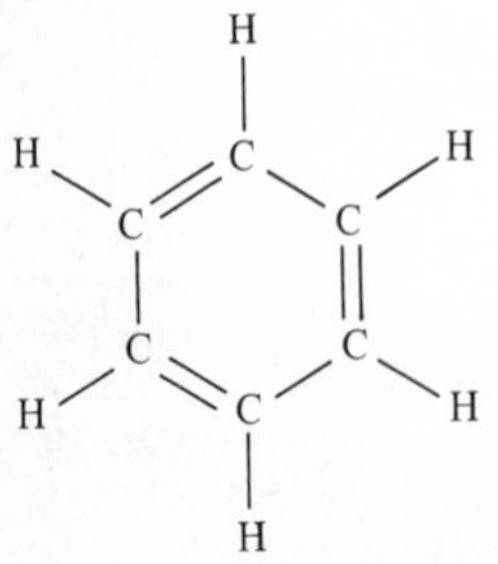

```
        H
        |
H       C       H
  \   //  \   /
    C       C
    |       ||
    C       C
  /   \\  /   \
H       C       H
        |
        H
```

Figure 2-11 Benzene ring.

The third major group of hydrocarbons is the asphaltenes, which have a variable and complex atomic arrangement. Asphaltenes occur in asphalt as a solid or powder and are thought to form a nucleus for the complex molecules. This nucleus is surrounded by the tacky, ductile resins or aromatics which are suspended in the oil medium.

The oil, resin, and asphaltenes develop into micelle units which are built up from complex molecules into colloids. Asphaltenes furnish the body or hardness to asphalt. Variations in the proportions of these groups and in the micelle development produce asphalt of varied properties.

2-15 POLYMERS

The most common polymers used in construction are plastics and the polyester and epoxy resins. The resins have been used extensively in research in treating portland cement concrete to improve strength and durability. The concrete, for example, is impregnated with unsaturated polyesters. The polymer chains are crosslinked by the addition of a catalyst, which reacts with the active end group of the polymer chain. By introducing unsaturated acids or alcohols along with a catalyst, the crosslinking is accomplished. The application of heat and/or radiation has also been used in crosslinking polymers.

Plastics

Nearly all plastics are built up with the carbon atom as the foundation and with a wide variety of hydrogen, oxygen, nitrogen, and other elements completing the molecule. Plastics have been developed by rearranging and building molecules which produce materials of desired properties. For example, ethylene, C_2H_4 (Fig. 2-12), can be made to join with other molecules to form a long-chain polymer. This is accomplished by subjecting the ethylene gas to the proper temperature and pressure and introducing catalysts. The process of addition mers (H—C—H units) is a form of polymerization. As this process progresses, there is a gradual increase in molecular weight and an increase in viscosity and boiling point until ethylene becomes the solid polyethylene, a flexible, inert, waxy solid. The molecule ethane will not polymerize (add mers) because the molecule is saturated. There are no vacancies in the outer electron shell of atoms of the molecule.

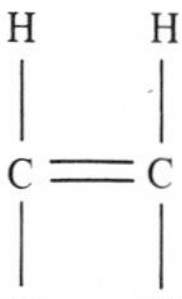

Figure 2-12 Ethylene molecule.

There are two ways to cause monomers to polymerize:

1. By linear addition, where similar molecules join together.
2. By condensation, where two different molecules interact with each other. This occurs with nylon, where adipic acid reacts with hexamethylene diamine and forms an extremely long chain with a molecule of water splitting off at each junction.

The types of materials which can be produced by polymerization and cross-linking of molecules are almost unlimited, as indicated by the new forms of plastics and resins introduced each year.

2-16 EPOXY RESINS

Epoxy resins have been known for a long time. In 1938 P. Caston of Switzerland and S. Greenlee of the United States discovered practical ways of using them. In about 1954 epoxy resins captured the interest of the construction industry. Epoxy resin compounds and, to a lesser extent, polyester resin compounds were found to be useful for certain phases of construction, repair, and maintenance.

The important properties of epoxy resins include:

1. High tensile strength
2. Adhesion to almost any other material
3. Chemical resistance
4. Electrical insulation
5. High thermal resistance

Epoxy resins are built around an epoxy group consisting of an oxygen atom sharing electrons with two carbon atoms in covalent bonding (Fig. 2-13).

The two carbon atoms have three vacancies in their outer electron shell which provide opportunities for polymerization, and the epoxy groups become part of other chemical groups in numerous ways. The most common manufacture is to combine by cooking, two intermediate products from petroleum distillation, epichlorhydrin and bisphenal. The higher the ratio of epichlorhydrin to bisphenal, the lower the viscosity of the final resin. A hardener is added at the time of use which completes the chemical process. The opportunity for linking and crosslinking of epoxy molecules with other chemicals explains the development of high tensile and compressive strengths and high chemical and thermal resistances.

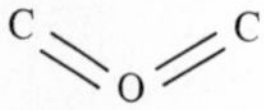

C O C

Figure 2-13 Epoxy group.

After hardening, epoxy resins are bound with strong primary atomic bonds; thus they are one of the few organic materials with this type of bonding.

Various chemical companies have a wide variety of their own particular proprietary formulations and provide instructions for their use.

2-17 SUMMARY

The development of an engineering material begins with its atomic structure. This chapter is not intended as a discussion of materials science but presents simple concepts which make the behavior of common materials easier to understand.

The structural properties of steel and concrete depend on atomic attraction. Primary atomic bonds are much stronger than secondary bonds (van der Waals forces) and are present in rocks, concrete, and steel. Only secondary bonds bind molecules of asphalt together, which makes asphalt a viscous liquid. Steel is much harder and stronger than iron because the addition of carbon limits the slip planes in the lattice structure.

Most rocks and soils are composed of silicates and carbonates which are also the primary ingredients of portland cement.

Alkali-aggregate reaction is a major problem in concrete durability. An aggregate is reactive with alkalies when they contain SiO_2 that is not completely crystallized. This is called "amorphous silica," and it is reactive because the outer electron shells of some oxygen atoms are not completely filled.

Most organic materials such as plastics do not have primary atomic bonding among molecules. Plastics and epoxy and polyester resin molecules can be cross-linked with primary bonds. This produces high strength with chemical and thermal resistance.

REFERENCES

1. Van Vlack, Lawrence H.: *Elements of Materials Science*, Addison-Wesley, Reading, Mass., 1964.
2. Guy, A. G.: *Essentials of Materials Science*, McGraw-Hill, New York, 1976.
3. Asphalt Institute: Information Series No. 106.
4. ACI Publication SP 21: "Epoxies with Concrete."
5. Wolfert, Ira: "Of Stars and Man," *Readers Digest*, May 1970.
6. Hansen, Charles: unpublished notes.

QUESTIONS AND PROBLEMS

1 How many iron atoms are there per gram?

2 SiO_2 has a density of 2.65 g/cm^3.

(*a*) How many atoms are present per cubic centimeter?

(*b*) Per gram?

3 Sketch the valence-shell electron structure of SiO_4.

4 Prove that 0.155 is the minimum ratio of atomic radii for a threefold coordination number.

5 What determines the density of an atom?

6 How are hydrogen atoms fused into helium atoms?

7 The sun gives off energy through fusion. Have we accomplished fusion on the earth?

8 List the various atomic bonds from the strongest to the weakest.

9 What is the difference between SiO_2 in quartz and SiO_2 in glass?

10 Name some silicate sheet structures in common materials.

11 Explain why CaO (quicklime) is unstable in water.

12 What is the atomic structure of hydrated portland cement?

13 What is an amorphous atomic arrangement? What significance does it have in concrete durability?

14 (*a*) What is the alloy of iron and carbon?
(*b*) Why is steel harder than iron?

15 (*a*) Name the three important chemical groups in asphalt cement.
(*b*) What influence does each group have on the properties of asphalt cement?

16 What is a polymer?

17 Why are epoxy resins important in modern construction?

CHAPTER

THREE

MINERALS, SOILS, ROCKS, AND AGGREGATES

The origin of any material will fall into the broad classification of animal, vegetable, or mineral. Most materials used by the civil engineer, with the exception of wood, are composed of minerals. Even asphalt and coal, which were originally animals and plants, have been altered extensively. They are now considered to be part of the earth's crust and are organic minerals.

3-1 FORMATION OF MATERIALS OF THE EARTH'S CRUST

As the earth's crust cooled, a variety of minerals were formed, depending on the pressure involved, the rate of cooling, and the elements present. In the molten state, the atoms could move about. The molten material was without definite form and came under the general classification magma. As cooling progressed, atomic arrangements and crystallization took place. If cooling was slow, there was time to form long-order arrangement for crystals, whereas magma that was cooled rapidly on the surface produced noncrystalline or fine-grained minerals. Some minerals are formed by alternation of other minerals.

The earth's interior is still molten, and occasionally magma reaches the surface through fissures during volcanic activity (Fig. 3-1). Some of the most famous volcanoes which are still active are Mauna Loa and Kilauea, in the Hawaii Volcanoes National Park.

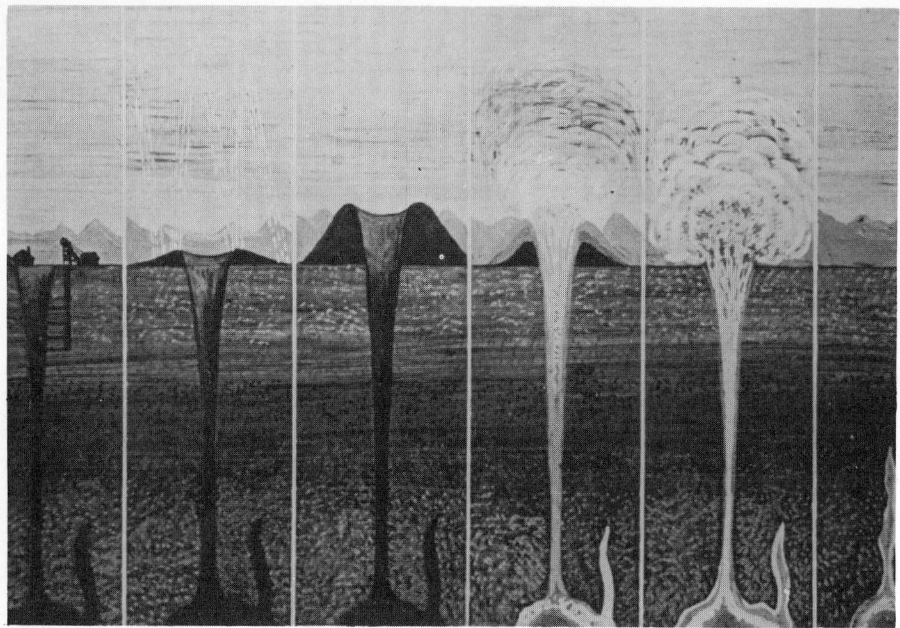

Figure 3-1 Diagram of various phases of volcanic activity.

3-2 MINERALS

Adequate treatment of the science of mineralogy is not within the scope of this text. However, a brief discussion of the makeup of various minerals and rock types is presented to introduce the engineer, architect, and technologist to basic minerals and rock types that may be used as aggregates for concrete and asphaltic concrete.

Table 3-1 lists some of the common minerals and gives their chemical composition and recognizable characteristics. With this information, the classification of various common rock types is more meaningful.

Table 3-1 Classification of common minerals

Silicate minerals		
Mineral	Chemical composition	Characteristics
Quartz	SiO_2	Colorless, with a glassy luster. Crystalline, but lacks visible cleavage, hard, resists weathering and abrasion and is, therefore, an important constituent of many high-quality rocks.

Table 3-1 Classification of common minerals (contd.)

Silicate minerals		
Mineral	Chemical composition	Characteristics
Opal	$SiO_2 \cdot nH_2O$	Hydrous silica. Resinous to glassy luster, variable color. Found in sedimentary rocks, especially some cherts; amorphous and reactive with alkalies in portland cement paste.
Chalcedony	SiO_2	Properties between quartz and opal. Microscopic fibers of quartz plus submicroscopic pores filled with water and air. Frequently a constituent of chert. Reactive with alkalies in portland cement paste.
Glass	SiO_2	Clear, appears black in obsidian, amorphous. Quickly chilled in liquid state. Noncrystalline, reactive with alkalies.
Feldspars		
Orthoclase (potash)	Potassium aluminum silicates	Feldspars are the most abundant rock-forming minerals in the earth's crust. They are found in all major rock groups—igneous, sedimentary, and metamorphic. Slightly softer than quartz; cleavage in two directions. Particles show several smooth surfaces. Colorless with glossy luster.
Plagioclase (soda lime)	Sodium and calcium aluminum silicates	
Hornblende	Silicates of iron and magnesium	Dark green to black color. Occurs in various types of igneous and metamorphic rocks.
Augite	Silicates of iron and magnesium	Pyroxene group.
Biotite	Silicates of iron and magnesium	Dark mica, clear flakes or plates.
Muscovite	Silicates of iron and magnesium	Colorless or light green mica. Perfect cleavage in one direction. Vermiculite formed by alteration of mica.
Clay		
Micas	Hydrous aluminum, magnesium, and iron silicates that may contain calcium, potassium, or sodium	Clay is usually defined by its particle size (less than 0.002 mm). Clay minerals are major constituents of clay and shales and may be disseminated in seams and pockets of carbonate rocks and in altered and weathered igneous and metamorphic rocks. Clays are usually deleterious in concrete.
Kaolin group		
Montmorillonite (expansive clay)		
Portland cement (hydrated)	$CaO \cdot SiO_2 \cdot H_2O$†	Color gray, soft. Produced by hydration of portland cement.
Iron oxides (iron ores)		
Magnetite	Fe_3O_4	Black, heavy, and magnetic. Found in many dark igneous rocks and in sediments.

Table 3-1 Classification of common minerals (contd.)

Mineral	Chemical composition	Characteristics
Iron oxides (iron ores)		
Hematite	Fe_2O_3	Heavy, reddish color when powdered. Often found in red-colored rocks.
Goethite	FeO(OH)	Found in limonite, a weathering product which frequently contains water and impurities such as clay minerals.
Ilmenite	$FeTiO_3$	Found in many dark, igneous rocks.
Carbonate minerals		
Calcite	Calcium carbonate, $CaCO_3$	Relatively soft, can be scratched with a knife. Breaks into fragments with smooth, parallelogram-shaped sides.
Dolomite	Calcium and magnesium carbonate, $CaCO_3$, $MgCO_3$	Similar but slightly harder than calcite. Rhombohedral cleavage, soluble in acid.
Sulfates and sulfides		
Gypsum (hydrous)	Hydrous calcium sulfate, $CaSO_4 \cdot 2H_2O$	Soft, white or colorless. Also occurs as impurity in carbonate rocks and shales.
Gypsum (anhydrous)	Calcium sulfate, $CaSO_4$	Resembles dolomite. Anhydrite is harder than hydrous gypsum.
Sulfate alkalies	Na_2SO_4	Sulfate alkalies may attack hardened concrete, causing deterioration.
Iron sulfides		
Pyrite and marcasite	FeS_2	Frequently found in igneous, sedimentary, and metamorphic rocks. Color is brass yellow (fool's gold). Marcasite is light yellow.
Pyrrhotite	$Fe_{1-x}S$	Bronze brown, metallic luster

† Principal compound in portland cement. Other compounds of aluminum, iron, and gypsum are also present.

3-3 SOILS

Nearly all engineering projects involve the use of soil as either a foundation material or a construction material. When it is used as a foundation material, the engineer must assess the *in situ* properties of the soil in order to select the type of foundation system that will be required for the particular structure. As a construction material, soil is used for many applications such as earth dams, highway embankments, site-grading operations, and trench backfill. For these applications the remolded properties of the soil are important. In order to work with soil either as a construction material or as a foundation material, it is essential to have an understanding of the important engineering properties of soils and how they vary with soil type and environmental conditions. The basic principles of soil behavior can be learned in a course in soil mechanics, but practical experience and a knowledge of precedents are essential for engineers working with soil as an engineering material.

A basic understanding of soil behavior has enabled engineers to develop many methods to improve soil properties. These methods include mechanical procedures such as compaction as well as using various soil additives such as portland cement, lime, and other additives involving chemical reactions.

Soil Properties

The important engineering properties of soil include permeability, compressibility, and shear strength. The permeability of soil is a measure of the ease with which water flows through soil. It must be determined for use in earth dam design and for the design of various subsurface drainage systems. Compressibility is used to describe the settlement characteristics of soils. It is important in predicting the amount that a given structure will settle as a result of compression of the foundation soils. In addition to the magnitude of settlement, the rate at which a given structure will settle is also important. Settlement rate varies with soil type and the stratification in the soil profile. Determination of the shear strength of soil is important in assessing the stability of embankments, the lateral pressure against retaining structures, and the ultimate bearing capacity of foundations. It is greatly dependent on soil type, moisture condition, stress history, and density.

Soil Classification

In general, soils can be grouped into two broad classifications: (1) coarse-grained soils and (2) fine-grained soils. Coarse-grained soils are mainly composed of sands and gravel, and fine-grained soils are composed of silts and clays. The generally accepted particle size ranges for these soils are shown in Table 3-2. Soils are considered coarse-grained if more than 50 percent of the material by weight has a particle size greater than 0.075 mm and fine-grained if more than 50 percent of the material has a particle size less than 0.075 mm.

Table 3-2 Particle size range of various soil types

Soil type	Particle size range, mm
Gravels	4.75 to 150
Sand	0.075 to 4.75
Silt	0.002 to 0.075
Clay	Less than 0.002

Coarse-grained soils generally tend to be more permeable, less compressible, and of higher strength than fine-grained soils. However, these properties for coarse-grained soils are greatly dependent on the percentage and nature of the fine fraction (material less than 0.075 mm). The behavior of fine-grained soils depends on moisture conditions, the stress history of the soil, and the amount of clay in the soil. The strength is much greater and the compressibility is much less for dry silts and clays, and for silts and clays that have been subjected in the past to very high stress (such as those found in glaciated areas), than for saturated silts and clays that have not been subject to high stresses in the past. The type of clay mineral that makes up the clay fraction of soil has a large effect on the behavior of the soil. For example, the clay mineral mortmorillonite has an expanding lattice, and it can expand significantly when the moisture content of the soil is increased.

Classification Systems

Several soil classification systems have been developed for engineering purposes. In each system soils are grouped in accordance with their behavior under various physical conditions. The most popular classification system used by soil and foundation engineers is the Unified Soil Classification System (ASTM D-2487). In this system soils are divided into three groups: (1) coarse-grained soils, (2) fine-grained soils, and (3) highly organic soils. The coarse-grained soils are classified mainly on the basis of grain size with some modifications for the nature of the fine fraction. Fine-grained soils are classified by the Unified Soil Classification System in accordance with their behavior at various moisture contents. This behavior is characterized by simple laboratory tests referred to as the Atterburg Limits Tests (ASTM D-423 and D-424). A summary of the Unified Soil Classification System is shown in Table 3-3. Table 3-4 shows a use chart that can be used in a general way to characterize the soil properties of various soils and to indicate their desirability for various uses. Soil classification systems can be very useful to engineers because they offer guidance for making general evaluations of the behavior of soils. However, blindly using a classification system or a use chart such as that of Table 3-4 without an understanding of soil mechanics can lead to disastrous results.

3-4 ROCKS

The minerals discussed in the previous section have definite chemical composition and usually specific crystalline structure. Most rocks are composed of several minerals, but may be only one mineral. Some quartzites are composed exclusively of the mineral quartz, and certain limestones are composed exclusively of the mineral calcite. Individual sand grains frequently are composed of particles of rock, but they may be composed of a single mineral, particularly in the finer sizes.

Although all natural rocks were at one time igneous (formed by the action of fusing heat), much of the earth's crust has gone through additional changes.

Table 3-3 Unified soil classification†

Soil	Group symbols	Description
Coarse-grained soil		
Gravel		
Clean gravel	GW	Well-graded gravels, gravel-sand mixtures, wide range in grain sizes, little or no fines.
	GP	Poorly graded gravels, gravel-sand mixtures, mostly one size, little or no fines.
With fines	GM	Silty gravels, poorly graded gravel-sand-silt mixtures, nonplastic fines.
	GC	Clayey gravels, poorly graded gravel-sand-clay mixtures, plastic fines.
Sands		
Clean sand	SW	Well-graded sands, gravelly sands, wide range in grain size, little or no fines.
	SP	Poorly graded sands, gravelly sands, mostly one size, little or no fines.
With fines	SM	Silty sands, poorly graded sand-silt mixtures, nonplastic fines.
	SC	Clayey sands, poorly graded sand-clay mixtures, plastic fines.
Fine-grained soil		
Silts and clays (liquid limit > 50)	ML	Inorganic silts and very fine sands, rock flour, silty or clayey fine sands with slight plasticity. None to slight dry crushing strength.
	CL	Inorganic clays of low to medium plasticity. Includes gravelly, sandy, and silty clays. Lean clays, medium to high dry crushing strength.
	OL	Organic silts and silt clays at low plasticity. Slight to medium dry crushing strength.
Silts and clays (liquid limit < 50)	MH	Inorganic silts, micaceous or diatomaceous fine sandy or silty soils. Elastic silts, slight to medium dry crushing strength.
	CH	Inorganic clays of high plasticity, fat clays. High to very high dry crushing strength.
	OH	Organic clays of medium to high plasticity. Medium to high dry crushing strength.
Organic soils	P	Peat and other highly organic soils. Identified by color, odor, spongy or fibrous texture.

† Used by U.S. Bureau of Reclamation and U.S. Corps of Army Engineers.

Table 3-4 Engineering use chart for soils

Typical names of soil groups	Group symbols	Important properties: Permeability when compacted	Shearing strength when compacted and saturated	Compressibility when compacted and saturated	Workability as a construction material
Well-graded gravels, gravel-sand mixtures, little or no fines	GW	Pervious	Excellent	Negligible	Excellent
Poorly graded gravels, gravel-sand mixtures, little or no fines	GP	Very pervious	Good	Negligible	Good
Silty gravels, poorly graded gravel-sand-silt mixtures	GM	Semipervious to impervious	Good	Negligible	Good
Clayey gravels, poorly graded gravel-sand-clay mixtures	GC	Impervious	Good to fair	Very low	Good
Well-graded sands, gravelly sands, little or no fines	SW	Pervious	Excellent	Negligible	Excellent
Poorly graded sands, gravelly sands, little or no fines	SP	Pervious	Good	Very low	Fair
Silty sands, poorly graded sand-silt mixtures	SM	Semipervious to impervious	Good	Low	Fair
Clayey sands, poorly graded sand-clay mixtures	SC	Impervious	Good to fair	Low	Good
Inorganic silts and very fine sands, rock flour, silty or clayey fine sands with slight plasticity	ML	Semipervious to impervious	Fair	Medium	Fair
Inorganic clays of low to medium plasticity, gravelly clays, sandy clay, silty clays, lean clays	CL	Impervious	Fair	Medium	Good to fair
Organic silts and organic silt-clays of low plasticity	OL	Semipervious to impervious	Poor	Medium	Fair
Inorganic silts, micaceous or diatomaceous fine sandy or silty soils, elastic silts	MH	Semipervious to impervious	Fair to good	High	Poor
Inorganic clays of high plasticity, fat clays	CH	Impervious	Poor	High	Poor
Organic clays of medium to high plasticity	OH	Impervious	Poor	High	Poor
Peat and other highly organic soils	PT	—	—	—	—

Note: Low number indicates preferred soil.
After Department of Interior, U.S. Bureau of Reclamation, Earth Manual, Denver, Colorado, 1963.

Relative desirability for various uses†									
Rolled earth dams			Canal sections		Foundations		Roadways		
							Fills		
Homogeneous embankment	Core	Shell	Erosion resistance	Compacted earth lining	Seepage important	Seepage not important	Frost heave not possible	Frost heave possible	Surfacing
—	—	1	1	—	—	1	1	1	3
—	—	2	2	—	—	3	3	3	—
2	4	—	4	4	1	4	4	9	5
1	1	—	3	1	2	6	5	5	1
—	—	3 if gravelly	6	—	—	2	2	2	4
—	—	4 if gravelly	7 if gravelly	—	—	5	6	4	—
4	5	—	8 if gravelly	5 erosion critical	3	7	8	10	6
3	2	—	5	2	4	8	7	6	2
6	6	—	—	6 erosion critical	6	9	10	11	—
5	3	—	9	3	5	10	9	7	7
8	8	—	—	7 erosion critical	7	11	11	12	—
9	9	—	—	—	8	12	12	13	—
7	7	—	10	8 volume change critical	9	13	13	8	—
10	10	—	—	—	10	14	14	14	—
—	—	—	—	—	—	—	—	—	—

Table 3-5 Classification of common igneous rocks

Rock type	Common name	Principal mineral composition	Characteristics	Typical physical properties†		
				Specific gravity	Percent absorption	Abrasion loss (%)
Medium-to-coarse-grained igneous Intrusive—slowly cooled	Granite	Quartz Feldspar (orthoclase) Mica	Medium- to coarse-grained. Quartz and feldspar light color. Mica usually dark. Produces nonreactive aggregate of good quality. Extremely coarse-grained granite is called pegmatite.	2.65	0.3	38
	Syenite	Feldspar (orthoclase and plagioclase) Mica Augite	Medium- to coarse-grained, light-colored feldspar; dark-colored hornblende and mica. Nonreactive. Produces good-quality aggregates.	2.74	0.4	24
Darker ↓	Diorite	Feldspar (plagioclase) Hornblende Ferromagnesian minerals	Darker in color. Nonreactive. Produces good-quality aggregates.	2.92	0.3	21
	Gabbro	Feldspar (plagioclase) Augite Hornblende Ferromagnesian minerals	Black in color. Nonreactive. Produces good-quality aggregates.	2.96	0.3	18
	Diabase	Augite Feldspar (plagioclase) Iron	Dark, heavy, nonreactive. Good-quality aggregates.	2.96	0.3	18
Fine-grained igneous Extrusive—rapid cooling	Basalt	Feldspar (plagioclase) Augite Iron	Color black. Hard and tough. Lava flows may be vesicular or massive. Nonreactive unless volcanic glass is present.	2.86	0.5	14

Lighter ↓	Andesite	Feldspar (plagioclase) Augite Hornblende Iron Glass	Lighter in color than basalt. Greater abundance of feldspar. Reactive if glass is present.			
	Trachyte	Feldspar (orthoclase) Mica Quartz Hornblende Glass	Softer and lighter. Not considered good aggregate.			
	Rhyolite	Feldspar (orthoclase) Quartz Kaolin Glass	Various light colors. Soft and does not usually produce good aggregates. Usually reactive with alkalies.			
Volcanic glass	Obsidian and pitchstone	Glass	Suddenly chilled. Few or no crystals. Dense, dark, natural glass.	2.5	0.2	+50
	Perlite	Glass with 2 to 5 percent water	Onionlike structure with a pearly luster. When heated, perlite puffs to become an artificial pumice.	2.5	0.3	+50
	Pumice and pumicite	Glass	Pumice is a glassy froth. Elongated, tubular voids. Pumicite is windblown deposits of fine particles of glass.			
Volcanic ash and cinders	Scoria	Feldspar (plagioclase) Augite Iron Hornblende	Volcanic froth, spherical voids. May be glassy, but usually has the composition of basalt.			
	Tuff	Consolidate Ash	May be glassy, fine particles from a volcano.			

† Physical properties determined by ASTM tests C-127, C-535, and C-131, discussed in Chap. 12.

Rocks are classified according to origin into three major divisions: igneous, sedimentary, and metamorphic. These three major groups are subdivided into rock types according to mineral and chemical composition, texture, and internal structure. *Igneous* rocks are formed from molten rock either above or below the earth's surface. *Sedimentary* rocks are formed at the earth's surface by the accumulation and consolidation of sediments of existing rocks. *Metamorphic* rocks are formed from existing rocks by additional crystallization when there is sufficient heat, pressure, or shearing forces in the earth's crust. Not only igneous rocks, but also sedimentary and metamorphic rocks may be weathered and eroded to form new sedimentary rocks. Metamorphic rocks may also go through additional metamorphic crystallization.

Igneous Rocks

Igneous rocks (Table 3-5) may be divided into two broad classes: extrusive and intrusive rocks. *Extrusive* rocks were formed as magma was forced to the surface of the earth and then cooled. These lava flows are commonly basalt (Fig. 3-2), but they include a wide range of chemical and mineralogical compositions. Andesites and rhyolites are widespread, and tuffs and volcanic ash are fragmental materials also ejected from volcanoes. In general, the basalt group of rocks is dark in color; forms columnar, massive, or vesicular structure; and is fine-grained (Fig. 3-2).

Figure 3-2 Vesicular basalt showing air voids in this type of lava.

Figure 3-3 Granite showing crystals of mica (black), feldspar (grey), and quartz (white).

Figure 3-4 Obsidian, black volcanic glass.

Table 3-6 Classification of common sedimentary rocks

Rock type	Common name	Principal mineral composition	Characteristics	Typical physical properties		
				Specific gravity	Percent absorption	Abrasion loss (%)
Sediments mechanically deposited, unconsolidated	Clay	Variable	Mineral grains (less than 0.002 mm).			
	Silt		Mineral grains (0.002 to 0.075 mm).			
	Sand		Mineral grains and rock fragments 0.075 to 4.75 mm in size.			
	Gravel		Rock fragments 4.75 to 75 mm in size.			
	Cobbles		Rock greater than 75 mm in size.			
Sediments mechanically deposited,	Clay stone and shale	Various clays	Consolidated clay.	1.8 to 2.5		
consolidated, or bonded with interstitial cementing material	Siltstone	Various silts	Consolidated silt.			
	Sandstone	Quartz Feldspar Calcite	Grains may be bonded together with quartz, feldspar, opal, or calcite.	2.54	1.8	38
	Quartzitic sandstone	Quartz	Abundance of quartz grains with some crystallization between grains.	2.65	0.4	28
	Graywackes	Quartz and feldspar grains in shale or slate matrix	Gray to greenish gray common type of sandstone.			
	Arkose	Feldspar Quartz	Coarse-grained sandstone derived from granite			
	Conglomerate	Variable	Consolidated or bonded gravel or cobbles.	2.68	1.2	
	Breccia	Variable	Consolidated or bonded angular fragments.	2.57	1.8	

Chemically deposited (siliceous precipitate)	Chert	Cryptocrystalline quartz, chalcedony, opal, or combinations of all three	Fine-grained, hard (scratches glass), tough, usually gray to black, white to brown, occasionally green, red, or blue. Waxy to greasy luster. Porous varieties. Lighter in color; chalky surface. Chert may be reactive with alkalies.	2.50 to 2.65	1.0 to 1.6	26
	Jasper		Dense red, dense yellow, or brown or green chert.			
	Flint		Dense black or gray chert.			
	Agate		Clear chert variegated with blotches of coloring.			
	Petrified wood		Wood cells replaced and filled with various cherts.			
Chemically deposited (carbonate precipitate)	Limestone	Calcite	Softer than silica rocks. Reacts with acid. Light colors usually gray.	2.66	0.9	36
	Dolomite	Calcite Dolomite	Similar to limestone. Usually occurs as a combination of calcite and dolomite. Carbonate-alkali reaction may occur where large crystals of dolomite are scattered in a fine-grained matrix of calcite or clay.	2.70	1.1	35
	Marl	Calcite clay	Clayey limestone or calcareous shale.			
	Caliche	Calcite soil	Soil bonded with calcite.			
	Coquina	Calcite	Limestone from shells.			

Intrusive rocks were formed from magma below the surface of the earth, and since they cooled slowly under pressure, they had time to form larger crystals. The texture of igneous rocks as a group, therefore, depends largely on the rate of cooling, ranging from very coarse-textured granites (Fig. 3-3) and pegmatites to glassy textured rocks such as obsidian (Fig. 3-4).

The lavas of the Columbia Plateau in Washington, Oregon, and Idaho are examples of extrusive basaltic rocks which have been cooled quickly. The granite cores of many of the ranges within the Western mountains are typical examples of intrusive rocks which have been cooled slowly. The so-called trap rock ridges occurring in various sections of the Piedmont region in the East, throughout the length of the Connecticut Valley, and even in the Palisades along the Hudson River are also examples of igneous rocks. The ordinary commercial variety of "trap rock" is basalt, diabase, or gabbro.

Sedimentary Rocks

There are many types of sedimentary rocks (Table 3-6), the most common being sandstone, limestones (Fig. 3-5), and shales. These rocks are derived primarily from the disintegration of other rocks; and since they are deposited as sediment, they are known as sedimentary rocks. Marine animals and precipitation play an important part in formation of limestone.

Figure 3.5 Limestone showing different patterns as the lime was chemically deposited.

Table 3-7 Classification of common metamorphic rocks

Rock type	Common name	Principal mineral composition	Characteristics	Typical physical properties		
				Specific gravity	Percent absorption	Abrasion loss (%)
Recrystallized siliceous rocks	Quartzite	Quartz	Very hard, dense, coarse-grained. Various colors. Crystallized from sandstone. Produces excellent aggregates.	2.69	0.3	28
	Gneiss: (*a*) Granite (*b*) Hornblende	Quartz Feldspar Mica Hornblende	Coarse-grained, banded dark and light colors, usually gray to black.	2.74	0.3	45
	Schist: (*a*) Mica (*b*) Hornblende (*c*) Chlorite	Mica Feldspar Hornblende Chlorite Quartz	Micaceous, semiparallel laminations of mica, various colors depending on minerals. Gray to black. Sometimes green.	2.85	0.4	38
	Slate	Quartz Mica	Crystallized from shale. Fine-grained, dense dark splits into thin plates.	2.74	0.5	20
	Phyllite	Clay Mica Chlorite Feldspar	Intermediate between slates and schists. Silky sheen on surface of cleavage plane.	2.80	0.4	30
	Amphibolite	Hornblende Feldspar (plagioclase)	Medium- to coarse-grained. Parallel alignment of hornblende gives schistosity.	3.02	0.4	35
	Serpentine	Ferromagnesian minerals; silicates of iron and magnesium	Relatively soft light to dark green to almost black. Soft.	2.62	0.9	19
Recrystallized carbonate rocks	Marble	Calcite	Crystallized limestone. Relatively soft, various colors, translucent, bonded, coarse-grained.	2.63	0.2	47

Figure 3-6 Granite gneiss showing bands of quartz.

Metamorphic Rocks

Metamorphic rocks (Table 3-7) are igneous or sedimentary rocks that have crystallized with heat and pressure from their original texture and structure (Fig. 3-7). Metamorphic rocks are usually dense and hard and may be massive, but are frequently foliated and tend to break into flat particles. Rock formed from sediment may be banded with differing minerals (Fig. 3-6). Certain phyllites and slates are reactive with alkalies in portland cement.

3-5 DISTRIBUTION OF SOILS, ROCKS, AND AGGREGATES†

For the purpose of discussing the distribution of natural soils and rock types, the continental United States is divided into regions, each of which has a reasonable continuity of mineral types as well as similarity of material characteristics (Fig. 3-8). The boundaries between these several areas are necessarily arbitrary. For the most part, they are natural boundaries indicating a general change in the characteristics of the soil and rock types. In addition, they may represent

† Symposium on Mineral Aggregates, ASTM STP No. 83, 1948.

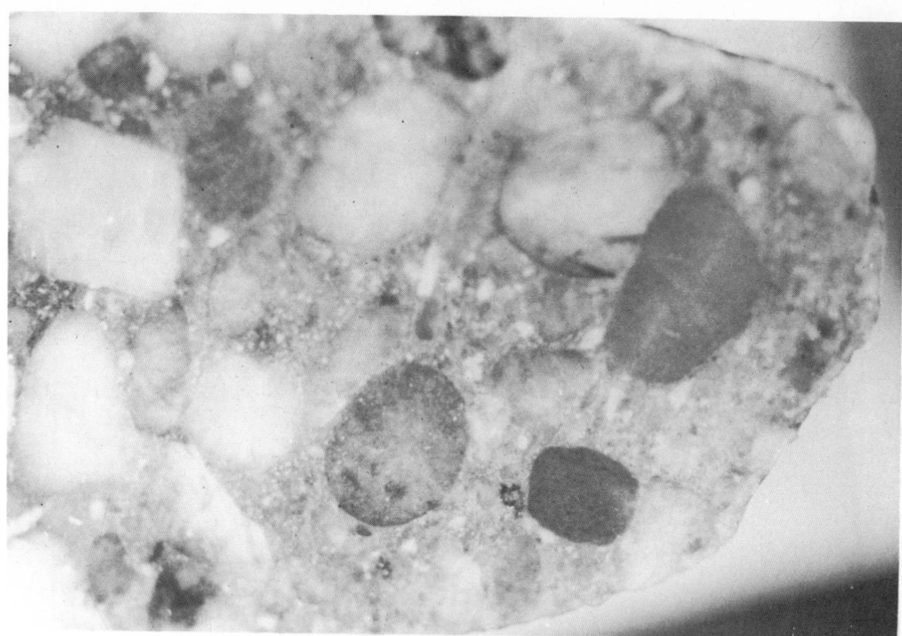

Figure 3-7 Quartzite showing gravel and sand that has recrystallized into quartz (upper photograph) and white quartz (lower photograph).

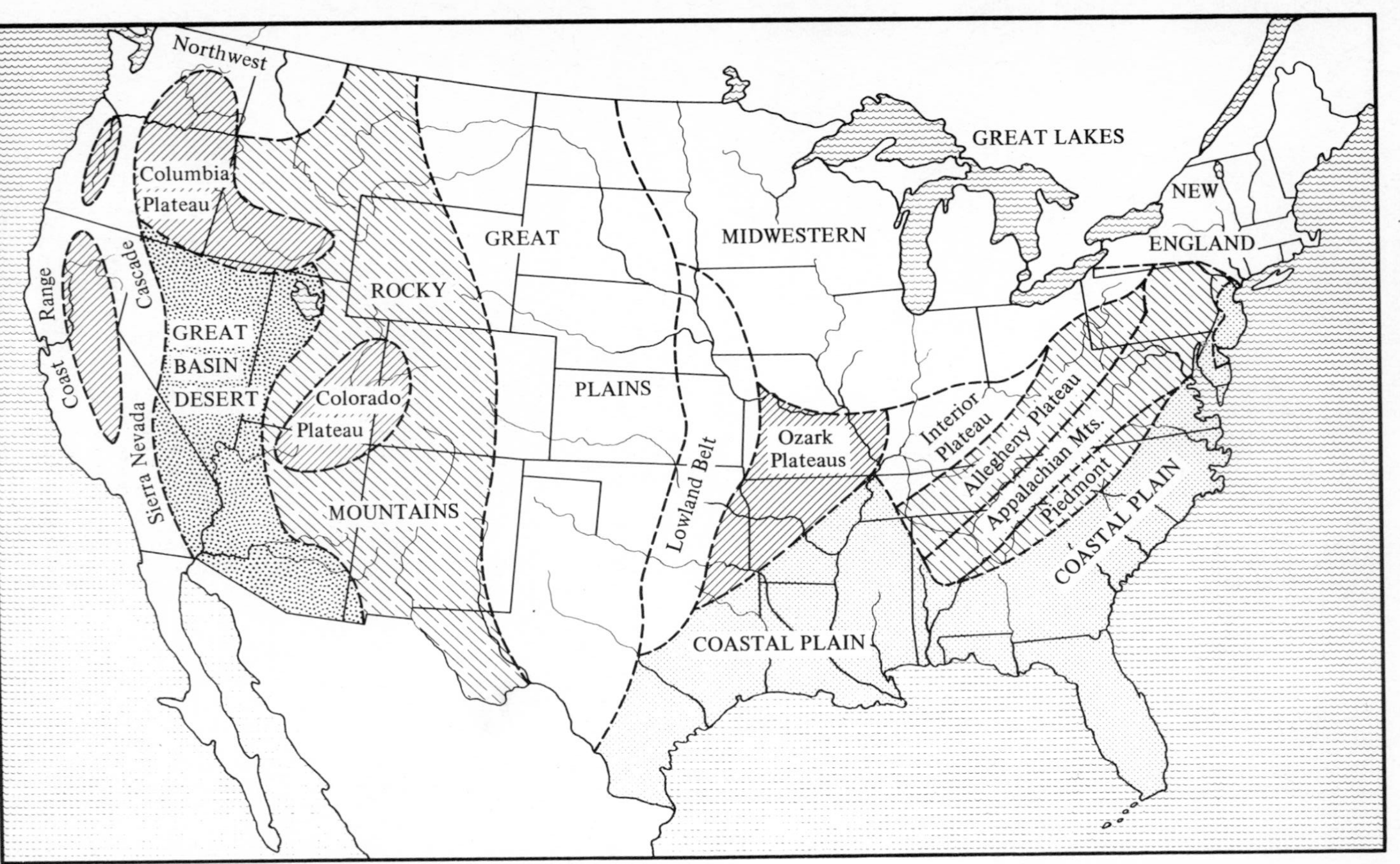

Figure 3-8 Rock and soil regions of continental United States.

striking changes in topography. In a broad sense, the origin of the material plays an important part in fixing the boundaries of the regions.

1. Northern New England states
2. Coastal Plain
3. Piedmont area, Blue Ridge and Appalachian Mountains
4. Interior Plateau, Allegheny Plateau
5. Ozark plateaus
6. Lowland Belt
7. Great Lakes and Midwestern area
8. The Great Plains
9. The Rocky Mountains
10. The Colorado Plateau
11. The Great Basin and desert areas
12. The Columbia Plateau
13. Northwest area
14. Central California and Willamette Valleys
15. The Sierra Nevada, Cascade, and Pacific Coast Mountains
16. The Pacific Coast Range

Northern New England

The bedrock materials in nearly all the northern New England states are primarily metamorphic materials of high quality. Glaciers passed over very hard materials of the Canadian shield in the North and covered the bedrock materials about 15 to 20 ft. The drift materials which are found throughout the New England states are generally coarse-textured.

Gravels are widespread and occur in terraces paralleling the major streams. The glacial gravels are composed primarily of hard, metamorphic, crystalline rocks of the Canadian shield and similar bedrock materials of the New England states themselves. Soft sandstones have been found in some deposits.

Bedrock materials are quarried extensively throughout the New England states. Marble is quarried in Vermont and occurs in Maine, Massachusetts, and Connecticut. Limestone is also quarried in several sections of this area, particularly in the limestone valleys of the Tectonic Mountains in western Massachusetts and Connecticut. Granite quarries are found along the entire coast of the New England states.

Coastal Plain

The Coastal Plain extends from Long Island south along the entire Atlantic Coast, from Florida along the entire Gulf of Mexico to the Mexican border, and includes the lower Mississippi drainage area and all the eastern portion of Texas.

Surface materials of the Atlantic and Gulf Coastal Plain consist almost entirely of unconsolidated, water-deposited sand, clays, and some gravels. Limestone occurs in some sections of Florida, as well as in Georgia, Alabama, and Louisiana. Soft chalk occurs in long, narrow belts in Texas, Alabama, and Tennessee.

Generally speaking, the gradation of the sediments becomes finer as they go toward the sea. The extreme eastern and the extreme southern portions of the Coastal Plain, therefore, have a limited supply of coarse aggregates. The gravel materials are mostly quartz, with chert predominating in northwestern Alabama. Limestone is found in the gravels of Tennessee and Kentucky, but even here chert materials predominate. Cherty gravels abound along the Tennessee and Cumberland Rivers, while the so-called Lafayette gravels occur in more or less isolated remnants, on the higher lands in the Coastal Plain in Georgia, Alabama, Mississippi, Tennessee, and Kentucky, and particularly in eastern Texas.

Florida "lime rock" covers the entire northwestern quarter of the Florida peninsula, and an outcrop of calcite caprock overlain by gypsum and hydrite occurs in Louisiana.

Piedmont, Blue Ridge, and Appalachian Mountains

The unconsolidated sediments of the Coastal Plain are in striking contrast to the old or bedrock materials of the Piedmont area and the Blue Ridge and Appalachian mountain ranges. The Piedmont province is bordered on the east and south by the Coastal Plain and on the west, for the most part, by the Blue Ridge Mountain province.

The Piedmont area consists almost entirely of hard metamorphic and granitic rocks, although some soft shells, limestones, and igneous rocks are found. The primary source of mineral aggregates in this region is granite and trap rock, although limestone is quarried in North and South Carolina, Virginia, and Maryland. The Piedmont portion of Pennsylvania and New Jersey is among the largest producers of trap rock because of the close proximity to several large cities.

The Appalachian Mountain region just west of the Piedmont consists of a narrow belt of deformed rocks lying between the ridge and valley province on the west and the Piedmont province on the east. The mountainous belt extends from northern Georgia northeast into Pennsylvania. The rocks in this area are often faulted and metamorphic.

Just west of the Blue Ridge Mountains extending from Montgomery, Alabama, northward into Pennsylvania, the topography consists essentially of many long, narrow ridges with intervening valleys. Limestone is the prevailing aggregate.

Allegheny Plateau

The Allegheny Plateau is an area of interbedded rock materials tilted somewhat and dissected. The region covers most of eastern Ohio, most of western and northern Pennsylvania, most of West Virginia, and the eastern portion of Tennessee and northern Alabama. The bedrock materials are primarily sandstones and shales, although some thin beds of high-grade limestones are to be found. River gravels are important sources of supply of mineral aggregates in the upper reaches of the Ohio, as well as the Allegheny, Monongahela, and Kanawha rivers.

Interior Plateau

The interior low plateau consists essentially of flat-lying limestone. The region includes the Kentucky bluegrass region, the Nashville Basin, the Highland Rim, and the Pennyroyal districts of western Kentucky and south central Indiana. Good-quality limestones are plentiful throughout this region, although cherty limestones predominate in many areas. Principal streams include the Tennessee and Cumberland Rivers, both of which contain large quantities of gravel, largely of cherty character.

Ozark Plateaus

The Ozark plateaus, which cover a large portion of southern Missouri and northern Arkansas, consist essentially of limestone plateaus, although interbedded sandstones as well as igneous rocks, including granite, occur in both Missouri and Arkansas. Limestone is a principal source of mineral aggregate, but the limestones, as well as some of the river gravels, are frequently cherty.

Lowland Belt

The area between the Ozarks on the east and the Great Plains on the west, extending from central Texas into the glacial region of Kansas and Iowa, is an important lowland belt. Rock materials consist primarily of interbedded sandstones and shales, although beds of limestone are frequently the only available source of supply of bedrock materials for mineral aggregates. In both Texas and Oklahoma, limestone is an important source of crushed stone. In eastern Nebraska and Kansas, limestone is the important source of crushed rock, particularly in the region around Kansas City. The Cottonwood Falls Limestone is particularly important in east-central Kansas.

Great Lakes and Midwestern Area

Several states around the Great Lakes and some of the northern Plains states consist generally of a deep deposit of glacial debris. Natural sand and gravel deposits are abundantly available in outwash plains and in the glacial terraces of several streams, including the Mohawk, Susquehanna, Wabash, Illinois, Minnesota, Wisconsin, Missouri, and portions of the Mississippi rivers. The quality of these glacial gravels is generally good, although the presence of shale, limonite, soft sandstone, chert, and other undesirable materials makes the processing of some deposits impracticable for commercial use. Streams which flowed from the previous ice sheets, such as the Ohio and Scioto rivers, frequently contain glacial gravels of great economic importance.

Lake beaches are the only sources of granular materials in wide expanses of North Dakota, South Dakota, and Minnesota, where large glacial lakes have resulted in the deposition of fine-grained soils to great depths.

Throughout much of Ohio, Indiana, Wisconsin, Michigan, Iowa, and Minnesota, limestone and dolomite quarries are the primary source of aggregates where the drift cover is missing or is shallow. In contrast, in Minnesota and in that portion of the Dakotas east of the Missouri River, glacial drifts cover much of the surface; consequently, rock available for quarrying is exposed only along the streams.

Great Plains

The Great Plains of the United States cover a large area extending from the Rocky Mountains eastward some 400 miles and from the Mexican border north to the Canadian border. Sections of Texas, Oklahoma, New Mexico, Colorado, Kansas, Nebraska, Wyoming, North and South Dakota, and Montana are included in this region. The area is mostly a grass-covered plain.

The vast expanses of the Great Plains are covered in part with semigranular to granular outwash materials, apparently derived from the Rocky Mountains. Sands are abundant, and in some sections gravel occurs also. In addition, much of the Wyoming basin and large sections of Montana are covered with a thin veneer of gravel consisting apparently of old outwash remnants. One particularly large area of gravel deposits is found in central Montana near Lewiston. Similarly, a veneer of gravel frequently occurs on the vast rock terraces along the Yellowstone River. Although some sections of the Plains contain bedrock materials, these consist mostly of shales, poorly consolidated sandstones, and chalks. In some instances, reasonably good limestones can be found. Bedrock materials suitable for development of a good supply of mineral aggregates are practically nonexistent except in and around mountain uplifts in Wyoming and Montana, including the Black Hills uplift in South Dakota and Wyoming. In the Edwards Plateau in central Texas, massive limestone is available. In the Texas mineral region, as well as in the mountains in Oklahoma, granites also occur.

Practically none of the bedrock formations, which include limestones, sandstones, and similar materials, are suitable as concrete aggregates. Natural sand and gravel are the principal source of mineral aggregates. The coarser sizes of gravel are in short supply in most of the deposits in the Great Plains area. Extensive use is made of what is called "sand-gravel aggregate," which is composed predominantly of sand passing the no. 8 sieve and the finer sizes of gravel.

Rocky Mountain Area

The Rocky Mountains, which border the Great Plains on the east and the Great Basin and desert areas on the west, contain a wide variety of sedimentary, metamorphic, and igneous rocks (Fig. 3-9). Unlimited supplies of gravel, sand, and

Figure 3-9 Teton Mountains in Wyoming.

Figure 3-10 Sandstone formations, Canyon Lands National Park.

bedrock materials are available. The northern Rockies in Idaho and western Montana consist of metamorphic crystalline rocks, and gravels consisting primarily of quartzitic sandstone can be found in abundance. Recent volcanic activity is in evidence in southern Idaho, southern Utah, and northern Arizona, which has produced surface deposits of basalt and other igneous rocks.

Colorado Plateau

The Colorado Plateau consists of a series of flat-topped, high plateaus surrounded by deeply cut canyons and escarpments (Fig. 3-10). Bedrock materials for the most part are recent soft shales and sandstones, although some hard limestone and some igneous rocks are found. A deep layer of Navaho Sandstone covers much of this area (Fig. 3-11). Good-quality stream gravels can be found along the Colorado River and its tributaries.

Figure 3-11 Tributaries to the Colorado River cut deep, narrow canyons through the deep bed of sandstone at Lake Powell.

Figure 3-12 Terraces left by ancient Lake Bonneville.

Great Basin and Desert

Bordering on the Rocky Mountains on the west is a vast desert country which covers much of Nevada and large portions of Utah, Arizona, Mexico, California, Oregon, and southern Idaho. Topographically, this region consists of a series of mountain ranges, with an almost countless number of flat, filled-in valleys and basins extending between the mountain ranges. In effect, the mountains are burying themselves in their own debris. During glacial times some of these basins became filled with water. With changes in the overflow outlets, lakes assumed various elevations for long periods. The result was a series of granular terraces along many of the mountain slopes which now constitute an excellent source of gravel and sand.

The Great Salt Lake is all that remains of Lake Bonneville, which at one time covered much of northern Utah and southern Idaho. The outlet of Lake Bonneville ran through southern Idaho into Snake River and on to the Pacific Ocean. The level of the lake dropped below the elevation of the outlet, and Lake Bonneville dried up to what is now Great Salt Lake. Many terraces and benches were formed during the existence of Lake Bonneville and can be seen along the mountains in much of northern Utah (Fig. 3-12). Sands and gravels are composed predominantly of quartzitic sandstones with lesser amounts of granite, limestone, and various igneous rocks.

There is an unlimited supply of many types of suitable bedrock materials in the Rocky Mountain area and in the Great Basin and desert areas.

Northwest

The glacial features of northern Idaho and Washington and northwestern Montana are different from those of other glacier-covered states. In Idaho the glacial materials consist primarily of outwashes from tongues of ice which extended southward into the north-south valleys. These outwash materials are mostly sands and gravels which overlie older valley fillings. The gravels occur in extensive terraces in most of the valley sections of northern Idaho. In Washington glaciation was more general.

In addition to the large supply of glacial gravels in portions of these Northwestern states, granites, basalts, and many other hard, durable rocks are available in abundant supply for use as high-quality mineral aggregate sources.

Columbia Plateau

The Columbia Plateau lies between the Rocky Mountains on the east and the Sierra Nevada and the Cascade Mountains on the west in the states of Washington, Oregon, and Idaho. For the most part, this plateau consists of a basalt rock area;

Figure 3-13 Dry Falls at lower end of the Grand Coulee, Washington.

Figure 3-14 East abutment of Grand Coulee Dam showing exposed granite bedrock.

however, glacial outwash gravels and sands of considerable extent occur in the northern portion of the plateau. This vast region contains a variety of igneous rocks, some of which are suitable for use as crushed aggregates. Basalt flows occur in great abundance east of the Columbia River and along this river to its mouth (Fig. 3-13). Most of the basalt is fresh and of high quality for the manufacture of road-building materials. Basalt formations vary from large column structures to so-called massive basalt. One extensive deposit of rounded basalt gravel and sand was located on the east bank of the Columbia River, near Grand Coulee Dam, although the dam abutment was granite bedrock (Fig. 3-14). The deposit of basalt supplied high-quality aggregates for over 11 million yd of concrete used in the dam.

Central California and Willamette Valleys

The Great Valley of California and the Willamette Valley in Oregon consist of long, wide valleys which have been filled in extensively. The floor of the Great Valley of California is covered with alluvium, which may be sand, gravel, or silty clay. As the mountains are approached, the texture becomes coarser until, in some sections, extensive granular alluvial fans are found. Igneous as well as metamorphic rocks are abundant in sections of the valleys as well as in the adjacent mountains.

Sierra Nevada, Cascade, and Pacific Coast Mountains

Like the Rocky Mountains, the mountains of Washington, Oregon, and California contain an abundance of sand and gravel and bedrock materials. Granites, basalts, and other igneous rock types suitable for use as mineral aggregates are widespread. In California sand and gravels are used extensively, while dredge tailings from gold mines are used as a source of mineral aggregates.

3-6 AGGREGATES

An "aggregate" is defined as a granular material, such as natural sand and gravel or manufactured sand and gravel, which when bound together into a conglomerate mass by a cement, forms concrete or mortar.

Table 3-8 General classification of materials used as aggregates

Aggregate	Size	Origin	Use
Natural sand (fine aggregate)	Smaller than no. 4 sieve	River-worn or glacial deposits.	Concrete, mortar, asphaltic concrete.
Natural gravel (coarse aggregate)	Larger than no. 4 sieve	River-worn or glacial deposits.	Portland cement concrete only. Asphaltic concrete requires crushed, angular aggregate particles.
Manufactured aggregates:			
Processed sand (fine aggregate)	Smaller than no. 4 sieve	Bedrock or larger pieces of rock.	Concrete, mortar, asphaltic concrete.
Crushed gravel (coarse aggregate)	Larger than no. 4 sieve	Bedrock or larger rock.	Concrete, asphaltic concrete.
Lightweight aggregates:			
Expanded shale, slate, or clay	Smaller than about 15 mm	Oil shale, shale, slate, or treated clay. Expanded in kiln or sintered.	Lightweight structural concrete.
Scoria	Smaller than about 15 mm	Crushed volcanic cinders.	Lightweight concrete; medium strength.
Pumice	Smaller than about 12 mm	Volcanic glass froth.	Lightweight concrete; medium strength.
Perlite	Smaller than 5 mm	Expanded from crushed perlite rock.	Insulating concrete, low to medium strength.
Vermiculite	Smaller than 12 mm	Expanded from mica rock.	Insulating concrete, low strength.
Heavyweight aggregates:			
Sand (fine aggregate)	Smaller than no. 4 sieve	Manufactured from heavy rock such as barite, magnetite, limonite, or hematite ores. Steel punching and lead have also been used.	High-density concrete for radiation shielding.
Gravel (coarse aggregate)	Larger than no. 4 sieve		

Classification of Aggregates

A variety of granular materials used as aggregates to make concrete aggregates are divided into groups, depending on their initial state, particle size, and density. Aggregates are selected depending on the properties of concrete required (Table 3-8).

Quality of Aggregates

Aggregate quality is based on such properties as strength, toughness, hardness, durability, particularly resistance to freezing and thawing action, surface characteristics, and chemical stability. Desirable properties will vary, depending on whether aggregates are to be used in portland cement concrete or in asphaltic concrete (Tables 3-9 and 3-10). In asphaltic concrete, for example, resistance to abrasion is of first importance since the stability of asphaltic concrete pavements depends on loads being distributed through point-to-point contact of aggregate particles. When the aggregates wear, the stability and skid resistance are reduced. Some aggregates tend to be susceptible to "stripping," or failure of bond between

Table 3-9 Properties of typical rock types for concrete aggregates

Type of rock	Mechanical strength	Durability	Chemical stability	Surface characteristics	Presence of undesirable impurities
Igneous					
Granite, syenite, diorite	Good	Good	Good	Good	Possible
Felsite	Good	Good	Questionable	Fair	Possible
Basalt, diabase, gabbro	Good	Good	Good	Good	Seldom
Peridotite	Good	Fair	Questionable	Good	Possible
Sedimentary					
Limestone, dolomite	Good	Fair	Fair	Good	Possible
Sandstone	Fair	Fair	Good	Good	Seldom
Graywackes	Good	Fair	Good	Good	Seldom
Chert	Good	Poor	Poor	Fair	Likely
Conglomerate, breccia	Fair	Fair	Good	Good	Seldom
Shale	Poor	Poor	Fair	Good	Possible
Argillites	Poor	Poor	Fair	Poor	Possible
Phyllites	Fair	Fair	Fair	Poor	Possible
Metamorphic					
Gneiss, schist	Good	Good	Good	Good	Seldom
Quartzite	Good	Good	Good	Good	Seldom
Highly granulated quartzite	Fair	Good	Good	Fair	Seldom
Marble	Fair	Good	Good	Good	Possible
Serpentinite	Fair	Fair	Good	Fair to poor	Possible
Amphibolite	Good	Good	Good	Good	Seldom
Slate	Good	Good	Good	Poor	Seldom

Table 3-10 Desirable properties of rocks for asphaltic concrete aggregates

Rock type	Hardness, toughness	Resistance to stripping†	Surface texture	Crushed shape
Igneous				
Granite	Fair	Fair	Fair	Fair
Syenite	Good	Fair	Fair	Fair
Diorite	Good	Fair	Fair	Good
Basalt (trap rock)	Good	Good	Good	Good
Diabase (trap rock)	Good	Good	Good	Good
Gabbro (trap rock)	Good	Good	Good	Good
Sedimentary				
Limestone, dolomite	Poor	Good	Good	Fair
Sandstone	Fair	Good	Good	Good
Chert	Good	Fair	Poor	Good
Shale	Poor	Poor	Fair	Fair
Metamorphic				
Gneiss	Fair	Fair	Good	Good
Schist	Fair	Fair	Good	Fair
Slate	Good	Fair	Fair	Fair
Quartzite	Good	Fair	Good	Good
Marble	Poor	Good	Fair	Fair
Serpentine	Good	Fair	Fair	Fair

† Aggregates that are hydrophilic (water-loving) tend to strip more readily since water more easily replaces an asphalt film. Freshly crushed aggregates with many broken ionic bonds also tend to strip more readily.

the aggregate surface and the asphalt cement, that exposes the aggregate to freezing and thawing action.

The stability of portland cement concrete pavements is mainly dependent on the hardened paste; consequently, hardness and toughness of aggregates are not as important as in asphaltic concrete. Aggregate reaction with the cement alkalies is a unique problem with portland cement concrete. A rough, somewhat porous surface texture enhances the bond between the aggregate particle and the hardened paste.

Strength of Various Rock Types

The compressive strength of concrete may or may not depend on the strength of the aggregate particles. This relationship is discussed in Chap. 6. The strength of the aggregates is important in some concretes. Table 3-11 shows the approximate compressive strength (in MPa) of various aggregate types. The aggregate types are listed in descending order of strength.

Table 3-11 Compressive strength of common rock types used as aggregates

	Approximate strength range, MPa
Quartzite	423 to 124
Basalt	377 to 201
Schist	297 to 91
Granite	257 to 115
Limestone	241 to 93
Gneiss	235 to 94
Sandstone	240 to 94

3-7 LIGHTWEIGHT AGGREGATES

Lightweight aggregates have been used for many years. The first lightweight aggregate was cinders or clinkers from high-temperature industrial furnaces, which gave the name "cinder blocks" to common lightweight masonry units.

Lightweight aggregates which were manufactured to produce high-strength concrete were first introduced in the United States for concrete ships built during World War I. These were built to supplement the use of plate steel in the construction of ships and barges. High-quality, lightweight aggregates were developed during World War II for the same purpose. Additional aggregates have been developed for use in decks for large suspension bridges and for high-rise buildings where weight is critical.

Many different types and brands of lightweight aggregates are in use today (Table 3-12).

Concretes made with lightweight aggregates are often used as a suitable substitute for natural, normal-weight aggregates. The capability of producing manufactured aggregates for concrete is of increasing importance as sources of natural aggregates become depleted or unavailable.

Expanded Shale, Clay, and Slate

Expanded shale, clay, and slate aggregates are made by heating certain prepared clays, shales, and slate to the fusion point where they become soft and expand because of entrapped expanding gases. Examples of such aggregates are shale expanded and crushed and shale sized, then expanded.

Shale expanded and crushed The raw shale is crushed to pass through a screen having $1\frac{1}{2}$-in openings. After expansion it is crushed to desired sizes. Very good structural concrete was made with "haydite" aggregate used in the construction of ships during World War II.

Table 3-12 Lightweight aggregates

Type	Source or manufacture	Concrete produced†
Expanded shale, slate, or clay	Crushed oil shale and slate or processed clay expanded in a rotary kiln or by sintering	Structural (medium to high strength)
Expanded slag	Molten slag expanded with water and steam	Structural (medium to high strength)
Scoria	Porous volcanic lava	Semistructural (medium strength)
Cinders	Cinders or clinkers from industrial furnaces	Semistructural (medium strength)
Pumice	Porous volcanic glass	Semistructural (medium strength)
Tuff	Consolidated volcanic ash	Semistructural concrete (lower strength)
Expanded vermiculite	Vermiculite ore crushed and expanded in kiln	Insulation (low strength)
Expanded perlite	Perlite ore crushed and expanded in kiln	Insulation (low strength)

† The properties of some lightweight concretes can be improved with proper combinations of lightweight aggregates and in combination with natural heavy aggregates.

Shale sized and then expanded The shale is crushed to the desired size before heating. The resulting product is fused to the point where it has a tight skin and high strength. Very good structural concrete can be produced that has densities varying from 1440 to 1600 kg/m^3 (Fig. 3-15).

Processed Clay, Shale, or Fly Ash

The prepared material is extruded through a die to form cylinders which are cut to approximately 1 to 2 cm. The small cylinders which are sprayed with fuel oil become spherical in shape and expand when heated in a rotary kiln. Pellets below 6 mm in size are formed by controlling the water so that pellets of the desired size are formed during the mixing process. "Gravelite" was the trade name of one of the early aggregates of this type which was used in construction of the San Francisco Bay Bridge.

Pellet-shaped, expanded-clay aggregate Pellets of the desired size from a die press are passed through a revolving cylinder in which they are rounded and coated with powdered refractory clay that has a higher fusion temperature than the main

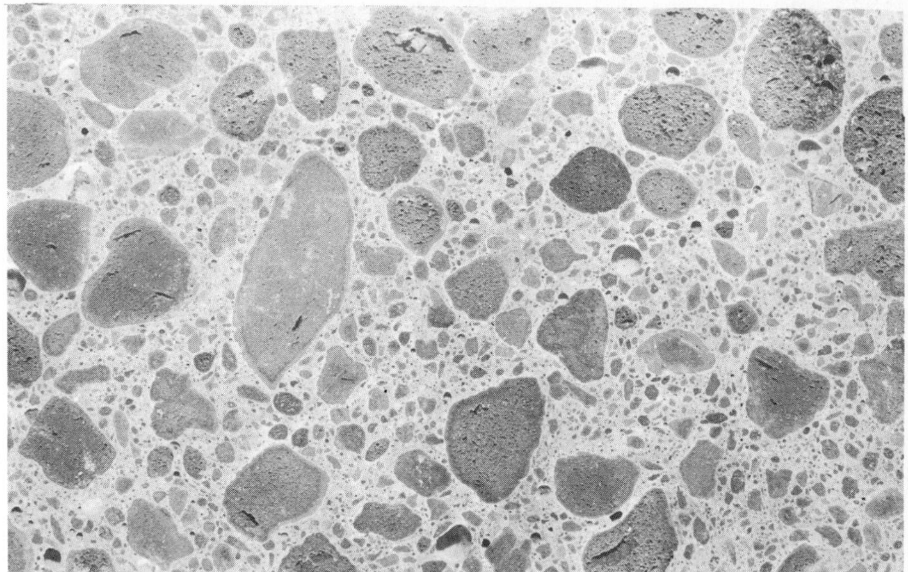

Figure 3-15 Section of concrete made with expanded shale aggregate showing the porosity of the aggregate particles (1.5 times magnification).

body of the pellet. The pellets are then expanded in a rotary kiln at a temperature above the fusion point of the pellet but below that of the refractory coating. In another process, raw shale is crushed and screened to desired sizes and coated with powdered limestone. As it is heated in a rotary kiln, the lime coating combines with the shale to form a thin, hard coat of calcium silicate.

Sintered Aggregate

There are several processes of producing lightweight aggregate by mixtures of coal and shale, clays, cinders, fly ash, slag, or ashes in moving grates exposed to flames under forced drafts. The resulting product is then crushed to desired sizes.

Expanded Slag

Blast furnace slag is naturally a heavy, glassy rock similar to some igneous rocks. Slag can be expanded into lightweight aggregate by being mixed with water while it is still molten.

When molten slag is poured into water, the violent reaction creates small, porous pieces called "granulated slag." Water can be controlled and introduced from paddles which cut through a stream of molten slag. In this case, larger pieces of porous slag are produced.

3-8 NATURAL, LIGHTWEIGHT AGGREGATES

Pumice, scoria, volcanic cinders, tuff, and diatomite are the only common natural rocks that are light and strong enough to be used as lightweight aggregate without processing other than crushing and screening to size. Diatomite is the only one that is not volcanic.

Pumice

The most widely used of the natural, lightweight aggregates is pumice. It is a highly vesicular, frothlike volcanic glass which is usually white-gray to yellow in color, but may be red, brown, or even black. It is found in large beds in volcanic areas of the Western United States. The quality of structurally weak pumice having high absorption characteristics may be improved by calcining at temperatures near the point of fusion.

Scoria

A highly vesicular lava in which the vesicles are rounded in cross section, as contrasted to pumice where the vesicles are tube shaped and approximately parallel, is scoria. Scoria aggregate resembles industrial cinders and is usually red to black.

Tuff

Tuff is a soft, volcanic rock which was consolidated after being deposited as fragments of volcanic ash.

3-9 INSULATING AGGREGATES

Two lightweight aggregates produce concrete that is light and porous and has good resistance to heat transfer. This type of concrete is used in roof decks and in composite outside walls. These aggregates are also used as loose insulation fill.

Perlite

Perlite ore is crushed into particles fine enough to pass through about a no. 16 sieve. When expanded in either a rotary or a vertical kiln, perlite will expand, as the combined water is released, into fibrous glass particles up to 10 times their original volume (Fig. 3-16). Concrete made with perlite has low density and good insulation properties.

Figure 3-16 Expanded perlite aggregate (6 times magnification).

Exfoliated Vermiculite

Vermiculite is a micaceous, laminated mineral that will exfoliate as layers of combined water are converted to steam. The expanded particles resemble small accordions (Fig. 3-17). This aggregate also has good insulation and low density.

3-10 SUMMARY

The earth's crust is sometimes given the general classification of soil. Soil considered as an engineering material is that portion between the original bedrock and the surface. Soil not only is important for foundations and soil structures but also furnishes minerals and raw materials for other engineering materials:

1. *Minerals.* Minerals are the basic materials that make up soils and rocks.
2. *Rocks.* Rocks may be composed of one or several minerals.
3. *Aggregates.* Aggregates are rocks that are suitable to use in concrete and asphaltic concrete.

Figure 3-17 Expanded vermiculite (6 times magnification).

4. *Lightweight aggregates.* Lightweight aggregates are generally porous and are used to reduce dead loads and structures and for insulation.

The distribution of soils, rocks, and aggregates throughout the United States is varied and indicates the geologic transformations of the continent.

REFERENCES

1. Legg, F. E., Jr.: *Concrete Construction Handbook*, McGraw-Hill, New York, 1974.
2. Cordon, W. A.: *Mineral Aggregates*, Utah State University Press, Logan, Utah, 1970.
3. Woods, K. B.: ASTM STP No. 83, "Symposium on Mineral Aggregates."
4. Price, W. H., and W. A. Cordon: "Tests of Lightweight-Aggregate Concrete Designed for Monolithic Construction," *ACI Journal*, April 1949.
5. Expanded Shale, Slate, and Clay Institute: "Lightweight Aggregates."
6. Perlite Institute: "Perlite Design Manual."
7. ASTM C-294: "Constituents of Natural Mineral Aggregates," 1975.
8. Rhoads, R., and R. C. Mielenz: ASTM STP No. 83, "Petrographic and Mineralogic Characteristics of Aggregates."
9. Dunn, I. S., L. R. Anderson, and F. W. Kiefer: *Fundamentals of Geotechnical Analysis*, Wiley, New York, 1979.

QUESTIONS AND PROBLEMS

1 Explain the difference between a mineral and a rock.

2 How are minerals formed?

3 Is quartz a mineral or a rock type?

4 Explain the difference between opal, chalcedony, and chert.

5 What is a soil?

6 What is the difference between rocks and soil?

7 What determines the classification of a soil?

8 Name the three general classifications of rocks and explain each.

9 What is meant by trap rock?

10 Where in the United States is limestone most abundant?

11 Where can glacial deposits be found in the United States?

12 Where has the most recent volcanic action occurred in the United States?

13 In what areas is there a problem in finding suitable granular materials and aggregates?

14 List the properties that make a good (*a*) concrete aggregate, (*b*) aggregate for asphaltic concrete.

15 What rock types make the best aggregates for (*a*) concrete, (*b*) asphaltic concrete?

16 Is abrasion resistance important for aggregates for (*a*) asphaltic concrete, (*b*) portland cement concrete? Explain.

17 What is meant by chemical stability?

18 What is stripping?

19 Explain why aggregates should be properly graded.

20 What lightweight aggregates are used for high-strength structural concrete?

21 Explain how it is possible to obtain a rough estimate of the insulating value of a concrete without making a thermal conductivity test.

22 Why is lightweight concrete important?

CHAPTER

FOUR

INORGANIC CEMENTS

Important inorganic cements in use today are all compounds of calcium. Calcium, one of the most abundant elements in the earth's crust, combines with several different elements to produce cementing materials. Calcium hydroxide produces mortar and lime, calcium sulfate produces plaster, and calcium silicate produces portland cement and pozzolanic cement.

4-1 HISTORY OF INORGANIC CEMENTS

Egyptians were first to use lime mortar in building the pyramids. Limestone ($CaCO_3$) was calcined in primitive kilns, driving off CO_2 gas. The lime was then mixed with water, sand, and straw to produce lime mortar. Such lime kilns were also used by the early pioneers of the West (Fig. 4-1).

The Romans are credited with the discovery of hydraulic cement, a cement which will set under water. It is also known that the Greeks used a hydraulic cement. The Romans made hydraulic cement by mixing lime paste with a pozzolanic volcanic ash. A pozzolan is an amorphous silica which hardens as a calcium silicate hydrate, similar to hydrated portland cement, by reacting chemically with alkalies in the presence of water. The name is derived from the Italian town Pozzuoli, where a suitable pozzolan composed of glassy volcanic tuff was found. Pozzolanic cement was used in such notable structures as the Pantheon and the Colosseum. It was also used in aqueducts and the Appian Way. Many of these structures are still in existence today, which indicates the high quality and durability of concrete made by the Romans (Fig. 4-2). Ancient ruins in Mexico, Central

Figure 4-1 Remains of an old lime kiln built in the early days of the West.

America, and South America show that ancient Americans were skilled in the use of inorganic cements.

Cement technology was essentially lost during the Middle Ages, after the fall of the Roman Empire, and it was not until the eighteenth century that hydraulic cements were again used. In 1756, John Smeaton was commissioned to rebuild the Eddystone lighthouse off the coast of Cornwall, England. A lime-pozzolan mortar was recognized as being necessary for underwater construction. Previous structural failures of the Eddystone lighthouse prompted Smeaton to experiment, and he found that better limes were made from limestone containing considerable clay. Smeaton is credited with being the first to recognize hydraulic lime, which was the forerunner of natural cement. A patent was issued to James Parker of England in 1796 for a hard-burned impure lime. Parker called his product Roman cement, and it attained wide use. Natural cements were made from clay-bearing limestone which were hard-burned and after cooling were ground into a fine powder. These impure limestones were known as *cement rocks*, from which natural cements were produced. Natural cements were used quite extensively in the United States in the late 1820s. The most important U.S. construction during this period was the Erie Canal.

Figure 4-2 Section of an old Roman concrete aqueduct built on the Rhine River 2000 years ago. The cement was composed of lime and a local pozzolan.

Joseph Aspdin, an English brick mason, was granted a patent in 1824 for portland cement, so named because the hardened cement resembled a premium limestone quarried on the Isle of Portland. The cement was composed of clay and lime heated to the point of fusion and then, after cooling, ground into a fine powder. Although much improved, modern portland cement is basically the same today.

4-2 LIME MORTAR

When limestone ($CaCO_3$) is heated to about 650°C, CO_2 gas is driven off, leaving calcium oxide (CaO). Calcium oxide reacts with water, producing calcium hydroxide, $Ca(OH)_2$, which is the cement of lime mortar and which provides plasticity and cohesiveness to masonry mortars and plaster. As calcium hydroxide is exposed to the atmosphere, it reacts with CO_2 and returns to limestone ($CaCO_3$), thus completing a reversible cycle and producing a hard cement.

Manufacture: $$CaCO_3 + \text{heat} \rightarrow CaO + CO_2 \tag{4-1}$$

Quicklime: $$CaO + H_2O \rightarrow Ca(OH)_2 \quad \text{(slaked lime)} \tag{4-2}$$

Lime cement hardening: $$Ca(OH)_2 + CO_2 \rightarrow CaCO_3 + H_2O \tag{4-3}$$

4-3 PLASTER

Gypsum is a hydrous form of calcium sulfate, namely $CaSO_4 \cdot 2H_2O$. The atomic bonds in the sulfate crystals are weak; and when heated, the water of crystallization is driven off, leaving anhydrous $CaSO_4$, which is common plaster. When plaster is mixed with water, the reaction is reversed and hard gypsum is produced.

Manufacture: $$CaSO_4 \cdot 2H_2O + \text{heat} \rightarrow CaSO_4 + 2H_2O \tag{4-4}$$

Cement hardening: $$CaSO_4 + 2H_2O \rightarrow CaSO_4 \cdot 2H_2O \tag{4-5}$$

4-4 PLASTER OF PARIS

When only part of the water of crystallization is driven off, a hydrous form of gypsum, "plaster of Paris," is produced. When plaster of Paris is mixed with water, the reaction is reversed rapidly and the plaster of Paris sets within about 20 min.

Manufacture: $$CaSO_4 \cdot 2H_2O + \text{heat} \rightarrow CaSO_4 \cdot \tfrac{1}{2}H_2O + \tfrac{3}{2}H_2O \tag{4-6}$$

Cement hardening: $$CaSO_4 \cdot \tfrac{1}{2}H_2O + \tfrac{3}{2}H_2O \rightarrow CaSO_4 \cdot 2H_2O \tag{4-7}$$

4-5 POZZOLANIC CEMENT

Pozzolanic cement is produced from a reaction among alkalies, hydrated lime, and finely ground amorphous silica. As discussed in Chap. 2, when SiO_2 is not completely crystallized, the outer electron shells of some oxygen atoms in the silica tetrahedra are not completely filled, making the SiO_2 reactive with alkalies.

Hardening: $$SiO_2 + Ca(OH)_2 \rightarrow CaO \cdot SiO_2 + H_2O \tag{4-8}$$

4-6 MASONRY CEMENT

A more cohesive and plastic mortar is required for masonry construction, but strength is not as important. Masonry cements are produced by grinding $CaCO_3$ (usually limestone) with the portland cement clinker. The limestone is softer than the clinker and grinds very fine, producing a plastic and cohesive cement.

Masonry cement can also be produced by adding hydrated lime, $Ca(OH)_2$, to portland cement.

4-7 EXPANSIVE CEMENTS

Although not new, the first commercial use of expansive cement in the United States was on the West Coast in 1963. The purpose of the cement is to compensate for normal drying shrinkage. There are three types of expansive cements:

1. *Type K*. A mixture of portland cement plus anhydrous calcium sulfoaluminate ($4CaO \cdot 3AlSO_3 \cdot SO_3$), calcium sulfate ($CaSO_4$), and lime (CaO).
2. *Type M*. A mixture of portland cement, calcium aluminate cement, and calcium sulfate.

The compounds of type *K* and type *M* expansive cements may be burned separately and the clinker ground with the portland cement clinker or added to the kiln and burned with the portland cement clinker.

3. *Type S*. A portland cement containing excess amount of tricalcium aluminate and calcium sulfate.

4-8 WHITE CEMENT

White cement is made by carefully selecting raw ingredients to eliminate or greatly reduce iron and manganese, which give portland cement its gray color. White cement has essentially the same concrete-making properties as regular portland cements.

4-9 ALUMINOUS CEMENT

Aluminous cements are made by mixing bauxite rather than siliceous materials with limestone in the kiln. Calcium aluminates are composed of mainly $CaO \cdot Al_2O_3$ rather than calcium silicates. This type of cement is useful for refractory mortar, for rapid set and high early strength, and in areas where chemical attack is a problem.

A mixture of aluminous cement and portland cement will give a rapid set in concrete. The time of set can be regulated by varying the proportions of portland and aluminous cements.

4-10 PORTLAND CEMENT

Portland cement is produced by grinding together clay-bearing and lime-bearing materials (usually clay and limestone) and heating to about 1500°C. At 650°C the limestone separates into CO_2 gas and calcium oxide (CaO). When the silica

Table 4-1 Chemical reactions in the hydration of portland cement

$2(3CaO \cdot SiO_2)$ (Tricalcium silicate)	+	$6H_2O$ (Water)	=	$3CaO \cdot 2SiO_2 \cdot 3H_2O$ (Tobermorite gel)	+	$3Ca(OH)_2$ (Calcium hydroxide)
$2(2CaO \cdot SiO_2)$ (Dicalcium silicate)	+	$4H_2O$ (Water)	=	$3CaO \cdot 2SiO_2 \cdot 3H_2O$ (Tobermorite gel)	+	$Ca(OH)_2$ (Calcium hydroxide)
$4CaO \cdot Al_2O_3 \cdot Fe_2O_3$ (Tetracalcium aluminoferrite)	+	$10H_2O$ (Water)	+	$2Ca(OH)_2$ (Calcium hydroxide)	=	$6CaO \cdot Al_2O_3 \cdot Fe_2O_3 \cdot 12H_2O$ (Calcium aluminoferrite hydrate)
$3CaO \cdot Al_2O_3$ (Tricalcium aluminate)	+	$12H_2O$ (Water)	+	$Ca(OH)_2$ (Calcium hydroxide)	=	$3CaO \cdot Al_2O_3 \cdot Ca(OH)_2 \cdot 12H_2O$ (Tetracalcium aluminate hydrate)
$3CaO \cdot Al_2O_3$ (Tricalcium aluminate)	+	$10H_2O$ (Water)	+	$CaSO_4 \cdot 2H_2O$ (Gypsum)	=	$3CaO \cdot Al_2O_3 \cdot CaSO_4 \cdot 12H_2O$ (Calcium monosulfoaluminate)

After L. E. Copeland and Stephen Brunauer, *Chemistry of Cement*. Scientific American, April 1964.

reaches the point of fusion, the atoms are able to move about and the CaO combines chemically with SiO_2 and small amounts of Al_2O_3 and Fe_2O_3, producing portland cement clinker. The clinker is then ground to a fine powder, and a small amount of gypsum is added. When mixed with water, the portland cement hydrates and produces tiny calcium silicate crystals. About 75 percent of portland cement clinker is composed of calcium silicates. Calcium compounds of aluminum (Al_2O_3), iron (Fe_2O_3), and gypsum ($CaSO_4$) are of secondary importance. The principal reactions in the manufacture and hardening of portland cement are as follows:

Manufacture: $$SiO_2 + CaCO_3 + \text{heat} \rightarrow CO_2 + CaO \cdot SiO_2 \qquad (4\text{-}9)$$

Hardening: $$CaO \cdot SiO_2 + H_2O \rightarrow CaO \cdot SiO_2 \cdot nH_2O + Ca(OH)_2 \qquad (4\text{-}10)$$

Complete chemical reactions in the hydration of portland cement are shown in Table 4-1.

Although the manufacturing process of producing portland cement is simple, a modern cement plant uses complex and sophisticated equipment and processes (Fig. 4-3).

Composition of Portland Cement

Although about 75 percent of portland cement is composed of calcium silicates, the remaining compounds are important in determining the type and properties of the cement. The four most important compounds are shown in Table 4-2.

Tricalcium silicate Tricalcium silicate hydrates rapidly and produces early strength and early heat of hydration. Tricalcium silicate is produced in a kiln when the charge contains an abundance of lime, and hence the greater amount of CaO in the reaction.

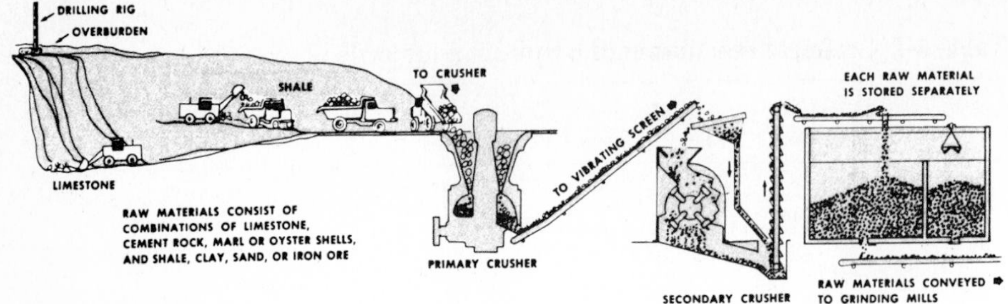

1. Stone is first reduced to 5-in.-size, then to ¾ in., and stored.

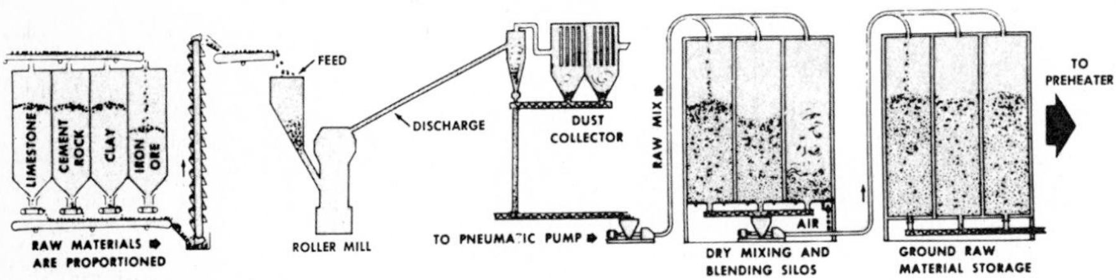

2. Raw materials are ground to powder and blended.

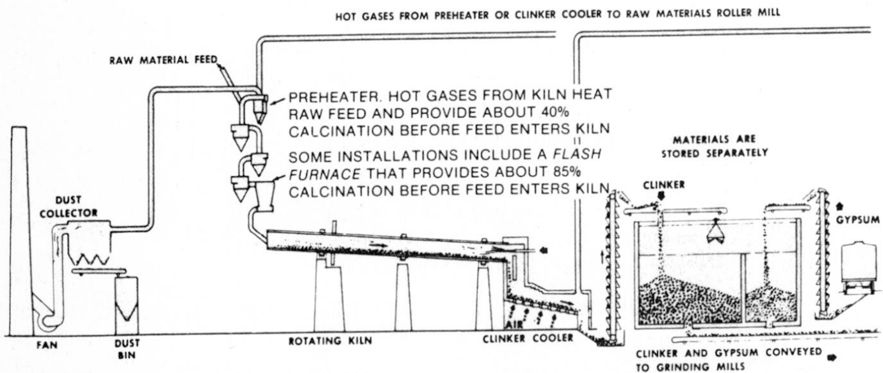

3. Burning changes raw mix chemically into cement clinker. Note four-stage preheater, flash furnaces, and shorter kiln.

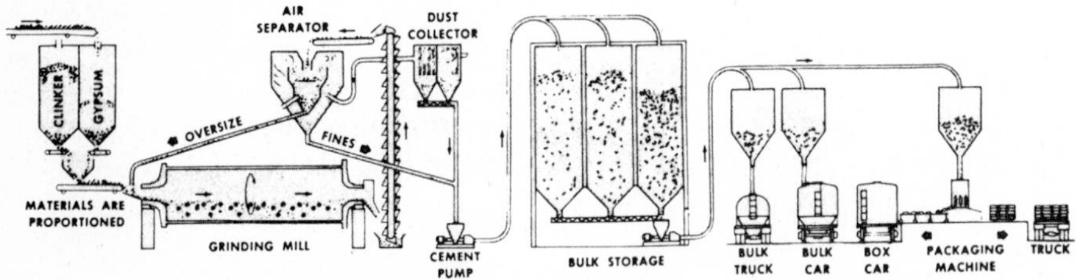

4. Clinker with gypsum is ground into portland cement and shipped.

Figure 4-3 Flowchart showing the styles in the manufacture of portland cement. (*Portland Cement Association.*)

Table 4-2 Principal compounds of portland cement

Industry code	Compound	Chemical formula
C_3S	Tricalcium silicate	$3CaO \cdot SiO_2$
C_2S	Dicalcium silicate	$2CaO \cdot SiO_2$
C_3A	Tricalcium aluminate	$3CaO \cdot Al_2O_3$
C_4AF	Tetracalcium aluminoferrite	$4CaO \cdot Al_2 \cdot Fe_2O_3$

Dicalcium silicate Dicalcium silicate hardens slowly and is responsible for strength increase in concrete at later ages. The heat of hydration is liberated slowly. More dicalcium silicate is produced when the raw materials contain less lime.

Tricalcium aluminate Tricalcium aluminate hydrates rapidly and liberates a large amount of heat. If this reaction were not controlled, concrete would set so rapidly that it could not be used in modern construction. A small amount of gypsum ($CaSO_4 \cdot 2H_2O$) interground with the cement clinker retards the hydration reaction of tricalcium aluminate so that the calcium silicates can set first.

After hydration, tricalcium aluminate will react principally with sodium and magnesium sulfate, found in soil and water, which causes the concrete to disintegrate. Moderate sulfate-resisting cement limits the percentage of tricalcium aluminate to 8 percent. This compound is limited to 5 percent in sulfate-resisting cement.

Tetracalcium aluminoferrite The addition of iron or iron ore to the raw materials lowers the percentage of tricalcium aluminate and thus aids in the manufacture of type II and type V cements. The iron reacts with the tricalcium aluminate, producing the tetracalcium aluminoferrite. This compound does not add significantly to the properties of concrete, but does cause the charge in the cement kiln to liquefy at lower temperature (lowers the point of fusion), thus reducing the energy required in cement manufacture.

Types of Portland Cement

The properties of portland cement can be altered by changing the percentages of each of the compounds contained in the clinker. There are five common types of non-air-entraining cements recognized today (Table 4-3).

1. *Type I.* Normal production of any cement plant without restriction of the compound composition.
2. *Type II.* Modified to limit the percentage of tricalcium aluminate and tricalcium silicate—moderate sulfate resistance and moderate temperature rise.
3. *Type III.* Tricalcium silicate and tricalcium aluminate are increased, and dicalcium silicate is very low. Cement is ground very fine to increase the surface area of cement particles, which produces more rapid hydration. Type III cement is produced for high early strength.

Table 4-3 Typical calculated compound composition and fineness of portland cements

Type of portland cement	Compound composition, percent†				Fineness, cm^2/g‡
	C_3S	C_2S	C_3A	C_4AF	
I	50	24	11	8	1800
II	42	33	5	13	1800
III	60	13	9	8	2600
IV	26	50	5	12	1900
V	40	40	5	9	1900

† The compound compositions shown are typical. Deviations from these values do not indicate unsatisfactory performance. For specification limits see ASTM C-150.

‡ Fineness as determined by Wagner turbidmeter test (Chap. 13).

Source: Portland Cement Association.

4. *Type IV*. Tricalcium silicate and tricalcium aluminate are reduced to very low levels, and dicalcium silicate is increased to reduce the heat of hydration. This cement was developed for use in large dams where low temperature rise was critical, but is not manufactured today since similar properties can be obtained with type II cement plus a pozzolan.
5. *Type V*. The tricalcium aluminate is limited to 5 percent. The combination of 2 times the amount of tricalcium aluminate plus the tetracalcium aluminoferrite and related compounds is limited to 20 percent. This cement is designed to have minimum reaction with sodium and magnesium sulfates.

4-11 LOW-ALKALI CEMENT

The term "low-alkali cement" refers to the amount of alkalies, sodium and potassium oxide (Na_2O and K_2O), found in portland cement. Calcium oxide, one of the principal compounds of portland cement, reacts with SiO_2 to produce hardened cement. Sodium and potassium oxides also combine with amorphous SiO_2, but the silica gel produced is unstable in concrete and causes expansion and cracking. The term "alkali-silica reaction" refers to the reaction between K_2O and Na_2O and aggregate particles containing amorphous SiO_2.

Specifications for low-alkali cement limit $Na_2O + 0.658K_2O$ to 0.6 percent as a principal precaution against alkali-aggregate reaction.

4-12 POZZOLAN

Although a pozzolan is not a compound of portland cement, the replacement of a portion of cement with a pozzolan changes the properties of the various types of cement.

1. *Reduces temperature rise.* Pozzolanic action occurs very slowly, and consequently the temperature rise is much smaller. Type II cement with a pozzolan will exhibit similar temperature-rise properties as type IV cement.
2. *Reduces alkali-aggregate expansion.* A pozzolan is an active, amorphous silica and reacts readily with any alkali in the presence of moisture. The pozzolan, being a very finely divided silica, readily consumes the K_2O and Na_2O from the cement, completely dispersing the expansive silica. Consequently, the alkalies are not available to react with reactive aggregates.
3. The harmful effects of tricalcium aluminate can be reduced by use of a pozzolan. For example, if the pozzolan is used to replace 30 percent of the portland cement, the percentage of tricalcium aluminate in the total cementing material would also be reduced by 30 percent.

One disadvantage in the use of a pozzolan in concrete is the requirement for a longer period of moist curing for the pozzolanic action to be completed.

4-13 PORTLAND-POZZOLAN CEMENT

When the calcium silicates hydrate, hydrated lime is one of the products of hydration (Table 4-1). This leaves a reactive soluble salt in the concrete mass and is responsible for the white encrustations and efflorescence which appear on hydraulic structures where the lime has leached to the surface and reacted with CO_2.

A double cementing action takes place when portland-pozzolan cement is used or when a pozzolan is added to concrete with portland cement.

First reaction: $$CaO \cdot SiO_2 + H_2O \rightarrow CaO \cdot SiO_2 \cdot nH_2O + Ca(OH)_2 \quad (4\text{-}11)$$

Second reaction: $$Ca(OH)_2 + SiO_2 \rightarrow CaO \cdot SiO_2 + H_2O \quad (4\text{-}12)$$

4-14 COMMERCIAL POZZOLANS

Pozzolans may be interground with the portland cement clinker or may be added with the portland cement when the concrete is proportioned. The following types of pozzolans are in use in the concrete industry.

1. *Fly ash* is the flu dust that is precipitated in the smokestacks of coal-burning power plants. It is composed of the fine particles of shale in the coal which form tiny spheroids of glass when exposed to the hot flame of the furnace (Fig. 4-4).
2. *Blast furnace slag* contains the lime used in flux and the silicate impurities of iron ore. In portland blast furnace slag cement, the slag is mixed with the portland cement clinker before grinding.
3. *Ground pumice* and other volcanic rocks which contain a natural volcanic glass are used as pozzolans.
4. *Opaline cherts* contain a very reactive amorphous silica and are finely ground to make a pozzolan.
5. *Calcined clay* becomes pozzolanic when it is heated sufficiently to break up the crystal structure of the SiO_2 into amorphous silica.

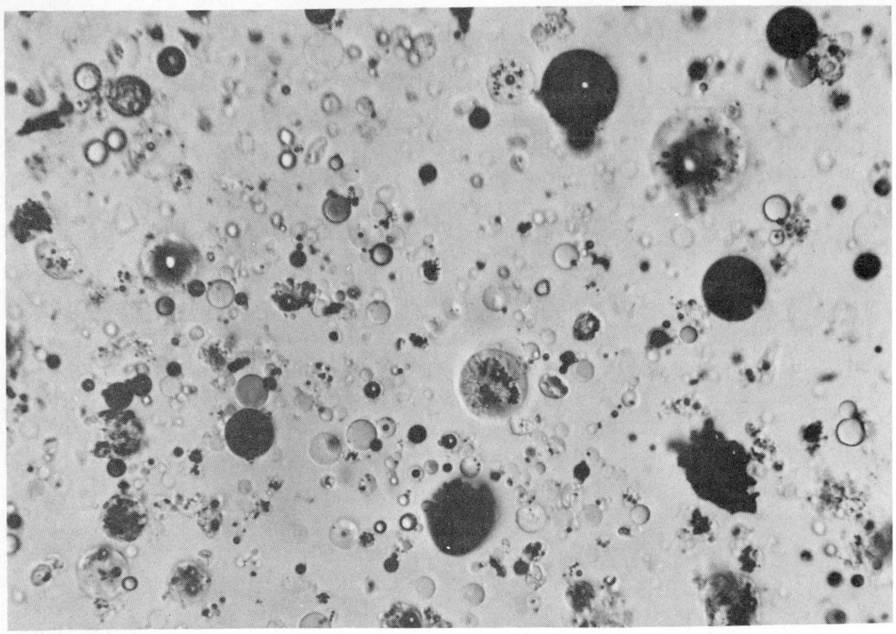

Figure 4-4 Photomicrograph of a typical fly ash showing the large percentage of spherical glass particles.

4-15 SUMMARY

Inorganic cements have been used in construction since prehistoric times. All common cements used today are compounds of calcium:

1. Lime
2. Plaster
3. Plaster of Paris
4. Portland cement
5. Pozzolan cement

Portland cement is by far the most important cement and is manufactured from two of the most abundant minerals found in the earth's crust, $CaCO_3$ and SiO_2.

The various types of portland cement are produced by varying the composition of the four principal compounds.

Pozzolans are becoming increasingly important in the manufacture of portland cement and as an admixture in concrete, since they provide a simple means of improving the properties of concrete.

REFERENCES

1. "Design and Control of Concrete Mixtures," *Portland Cement Association Bulletin*, 11th ed.
2. Cordon, William A.: "Article on Concrete," *Encyclopedia Americana*, 1974.
3. Brunauer, Stephen, and E. L. Copeland: "The Chemistry of Concrete," *Scientific American*, April 1964.
4. U.S. Bureau of Reclamation: *Concrete Manual*, 8th ed., 1975.

QUESTIONS AND PROBLEMS

1 Explain the importance of the element calcium in inorganic cements.

2 How did the Romans produce inorganic cements?

3 Show the difference between plaster and plaster of Paris.

4 How are the following special cements made?
- (*a*) White cement
- (*b*) Aluminous cement
- (*c*) Expansive cement
- (*d*) Masonry cement

5 What is Portland cement?

6 Why is a small amount of gypsum added with portland cement clinker at the time of grinding?

7 Show the reactions when limestone is burned, slaked, and hardened into cement.

8 What are the principal compounds of portland cement?

9 Explain the effect each of the compounds of portland cement has on the properties of concrete.

10 Explain where each of the different types of portland cement might be used.

11 Explain the difference between low-alkali cement and cement which resists the attack of sulfate alkalies.

12 Why are pozzolans used with portland cement in concrete?

13 Name the natural materials from which pozzolans can be made.

14 What type of portland cement is produced if no restrictions on compound composition are placed on the plant production?

CHAPTER
FIVE

CONCRETE

5-1 CONCRETE AND ITS USES

"Concrete" is defined as a composite material which consists essentially of a binding medium within which are embedded particles or fragments of aggregate. In portland cement concrete, the binder is a mixture of portland cement and water. Asphalt and other cements are used to make various types of concrete, but common usage of the term "concrete" refers to portland cement concrete.

Today, portland cement concrete is the most versatile and widely used structural material. It is used in dams, canals, aqueducts, and other structures to control and convey water. It is used in highways, streets, pavements, and sidewalks; thus, it is a major material in the transportation industry. Concrete is used almost exclusively for foundations of buildings, bridges, and other structures. It is used in buildings, bridges, and all types of miscellaneous structures. Where concrete is not used as the primary structural material, it is employed for fireproofing, waterproofing, and soundproofing and for architectural and decorative floors, walls, and panels. Concrete is also important in construction of atomic energy facilities because of its shielding properties.

Concrete is of such importance that almost without exception every civil engineering structure uses concrete in some form. Materials required to make portland cement and concrete are nonstrategic, nonpolluting, and plentiful throughout the earth, since they are composed of the earth's crust. Concrete may become more important in the future as the supply of more strategic materials becomes exhausted.

The three principal requirements for concrete, listed in the order of importance, are

1. Quality
2. Workability
3. Economy

5-2 QUALITY OF CONCRETE

The quality of concrete is measured by its strength, durability, and dimensional stability.

1. *Strength.* Hardened concrete must have sufficient strength to resist stresses from loads which may be imposed on a structure. The strength must also be sufficiently high to allow for variations in concrete mixtures.
2. *Durability.* Concrete must be able to withstand forces of deterioration such as freezing and thawing, wetting and drying, erosion, and chemical attack.
3. *Dimensional stability.* Quality concrete should have a minimum of shrinkage or expansion because of either outside forces or chemical reactions within the concrete itself.

5-3 WORKABILITY OF CONCRETE

Plastic concrete mixtures must be sufficiently workable to be mixed, transported, and placed properly without excessive effort and expense. Concrete which cannot be placed properly will not produce quality structures regardless of the quality of the mixture.

Concrete which may be considered workable for one structure may not be suitable for another. Concrete containing an excess of cement or other fines and a high percentage of entrained air will be plastic and easy to remold. This mixture would not be suitable to place around tunnel linings or flow under blockouts because of its lack of mobility. On the other hand, a mixture containing too much water may have high mobility but insufficient plasticity to prevent segregation of the coarse aggregate particles from the mortar. Concrete for pavements or dams, where there is ample room for compaction and vibration equipment, requires a minimum of mobility and plasticity. Workable concrete has a combination of the following characteristics.

1. *Plasticity.* Plasticity is that property of a concrete mixture which allows it to be molded and moved with a minimum of force and without segregation. A concrete mixture with plasticity has minimum resistance against shearing forces.
2. *Mobility.* The capacity for a concrete mixture to readily respond to vibration and move into and completely fill all parts and corners of a form is defined as "mobility."

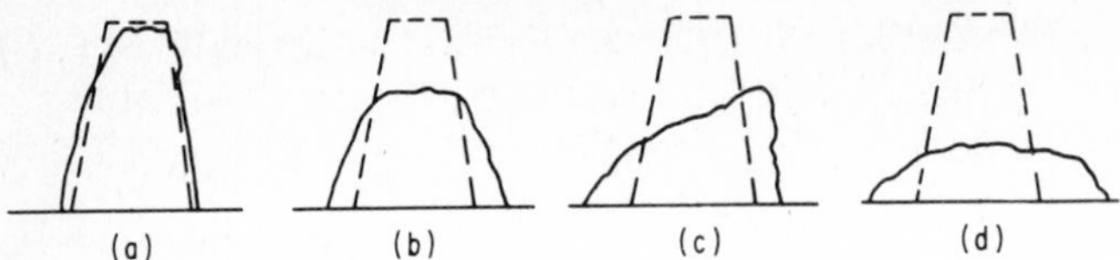

Figure 5-1 The slump of concrete is an indication of workability.

3. *Slump*. Slump is a common field control test (ASTM C-143) for concrete mobility. It is the subsidence of fresh concrete upon removal of a 12-in truncated cone form (Fig. 5-1).

5-4 ECONOMY OF CONCRETE MIXTURES

The economy or cost of production of concrete is an important consideration in the overall cost of construction. If concrete is to compete successfully with other construction materials, costs must be held to a minimum. Economy must be sacrificed, however, to provide adequate quality and workability. An optimum combination of ingredients is one that will provide required quality and workability at minimum cost. An economical concrete mixture is generally one that makes maximum use of aggregates without sacrificing needed workability and holds the amount of the more expensive paste to a minimum.

5-5 INFLUENCE OF EACH INGREDIENT ON THE PROPERTIES OF CONCRETE

The proportions of ingredients used in concrete must be carefully balanced to produce an optimum mixture for the purposes intended. Too much or too little of any one ingredient may have an adverse effect on one of the important properties of the resulting concrete (Table 5-1).

Aggregates

Most of the rocks found in the earth's crust can be used as aggregate in concrete. Because of the variety of physical and chemical characteristics among aggregates,

Table 5-1 Influence of each principal ingredient on the properties of concrete

Ingredient	Quality	Workability	Economy
Aggregate	Increases	*Decreases*	Increases
Portland cement	Increases	Increases	*Decreases*
Water	*Decreases*	Increases	Increases

their influence on concrete mixtures is also varied. Physical characteristics such as particle size distribution, particle shape, surface texture, and hardness influence this behavior. Chemical composition and reactivity influence the properties of hardened concrete.

The maximum amount of aggregate possible should be used in concrete mixtures. Aggregate generally increases both the quality and the economy of concrete. Each cubic meter of portland cement–water paste will cost approximately 4 times as much as each cubic meter (solid volume) of aggregate. Aggregates also have greater dimensional stability, particularly less drying shrinkage, than portland cement paste.

Workability requirements limit the amount of aggregate that can be used in concrete mixtures. Aggregate particles, in effect, float in the paste of the mixture; and when there is insufficient paste to fill the voids in the aggregate particles, the mixture becomes granular, crumbly, and unworkable because of particle interference. Table 5-2 lists the factors which influence the amount of aggregate that can be used.

Table 5-2 Factors which influence the aggregate content of fresh concrete

Factor	Comment
Slump	As the aggregate content increases, with no changes in the paste content, the slump decreases.
Grading	Proper grading of aggregate particles decreases the volume of voids among the aggregate particles, which permits a greater aggregate content in a mixture, without particle interference.
Entrained air	Entrained air, in effect, increases the volume of paste and permits an increase in aggregate content at the same slump.
Particle shape and surface texture	There is usually a smaller volume of voids in rounded, smooth aggregates.
Water-reducing admixtures	Dispersing agents commonly referred to as water-reducing admixtures make the paste more fluid by releasing water trapped by the cement. This permits an increase in the aggregate content at a given slump.
Viscosity of paste	An increase in viscosity of paste decreases the allowable aggregate content.
Temperature	High temperature increases the viscosity of paste and reduces the aggregate content for the same slump.

Portland Cement

Portland cement and water react chemically and produce a calcium silicate hydrate. It takes a comparatively small amount of water (estimated to be about 30 percent of the cement) to complete the hydration reaction. A paste with this much water, however, is stiff and unworkable, and an additional amount of water is required for sufficient fluidity of the paste and workability of the concrete. The ratio of water to cement (w/c ratio) determines the quality of the paste and, to a large extent, controls the quality of concrete. It follows that additional cement added to concrete improves the quality by reducing the w/c ratio.

In lean concrete, additional amounts of portland cement improve the workability of the concrete. This trend is limited, however, and an excessive amount of cement tends to make concrete mixtures sticky and lacking in mobility. Hardened concrete containing excessive cement and water will have increased drying shrinkage.

Water

Water is essential to hydrate portland cement and provides workability to concrete mixtures. Too much water added to the mixture is detrimental to the quality of concrete. More water than the amount required to hydrate portland cement dilutes the paste, separates the calcium silicate gel crystals, and weakens the gel structure. Uncombined water leaves capillary voids in the paste, which are involved in most freezing and thawing mechanisms. The proportion of water to cement is critical in producing quality, and the ratio of aggregate to paste is critical in obtaining workability and volume stability.

Admixtures

An admixture is any material added to concrete in addition to the three principal ingredients—aggregates, portland cement, and water. Admixtures are used in concrete to improve one or more of the principal requirements for concrete mixtures. For example, air-entraining agents improve durability and plasticity, but air entrainment reduces strength. This type of admixture should always be used where freezing and thawing deterioration is a problem, but reduces the strength unnecessarily in structural concrete not exposed to freezing and thawing in a saturated condition. Water-reducing admixtures increase workability and quality by more efficient use of the water in a concrete mixture. By reducing the water, these admixtures densify the concrete and decrease capillary voids and permeability.

Admixtures which retard or accelerate the time of set or strength gain do not generally influence the properties of plastic concrete. Table 5-3 lists admixtures in common use in concrete.

Table 5-3 Admixtures in general use in concrete

Admixture	Approximate amount used per cubic meter of concrete	Purpose
Air-entraining agents	13 to 28 g of solids	Improve durability Improve workability Permit use of additional aggregate
Water-reducing agents	0.3 to 1 kg	Increase slump Reduce *w/c* ratio Permit use of additional aggregate at the same slump and same *w/c* ratio
Pozzolans	30 to 120 kg	Reduce alkali-aggregate reaction Reduce temperature rise Reduce permeability Increase sulfate resistance
Accelerating agents	1.2 to 6 kg	Accelerate hydration and setting of cement Produce early strength
Retarding agents	0.3 to 1 kg	Retard hydration and setting of cement

5-6 PROPORTIONING CONCRETE TRIAL MIXES

Properly proportioned ingredients of concrete provide a balance between reasonable economy and requirements for workability, strength, durability, and appearance. The required properties are usually governed by specification limits, which reflect conditions and requirements for concrete performance.

Numerous methods have been proposed for proportioning concrete mixes involving relationships among the grading of aggregates, volume of voids within the mixture, amount of water, and quantity of portland cement. In 1918, it was discovered that the ratio of the amount of water to the amount of cement in a concrete mix varied with the strength of concrete. Since that time it has been found that many other variables influence the strength of concrete; but, other things being equal, the water-cement ratio provides a basis for predicting strength and, to some extent, other desirable properties of concrete.

In the early 1940s the remarkable benefits of entrained air to the freezing and thawing durability of concrete were recognized. The durability of concrete can be increased tenfold by the use of small amounts of an air-entraining agent in a concrete mixture. In recent years the use of other admixtures has increased.

The *w/c* ratio–strength relationship and the use of entrained air are considered to be the two major discoveries in concrete technology in this century.

The American Concrete Institute recommends the following steps to be used in arriving at a trial concrete mix (ACI Standard 211.1). Proportions calculated by these methods, or by any method for that matter, must always be considered a preliminary trial mix subject to revision on the basis of actual behavior of the ingredients used.

STEP 1 *Choice of slump:* The amount of subsidence or slump of concrete measured upon removal of the standard slump cone is an indication of the consistency, wetness, and, to some extent, workability of the mix. Table 5-4 indicates slump ranges recommended when vibration is used to consolidate the concrete. Mixes of the stiffest consistency that can be placed efficiently should be used.

STEP 2 *Choice of maximum size of aggregate:* Well-graded aggregates containing large sizes will contain less voids than aggregates of small sizes. Consequently, less sand, cement, and water is required to fill the voids in the coarse aggregate.

The largest aggregate that is economically available and consistent with the dimensions of the structure and the limitations of the mixing and placing equipment should be used. ACI Committee 211 recommends that aggregate should not exceed one-fifth of the narrowest dimension between the sides of forms, or three-fourth's the minimum clear spacing between reinforcing bars. In slab work, the largest size aggregates should be less than one-third the depth of the slab.

It has been found that for high-strength concrete with low water-cement ratios somewhat higher strengths can be obtained if the maximum size of aggregate is reduced. The strength is increased because smaller-sized aggregates provide additional surface area to bond with the paste (see Sec. 6-1).

STEP 3 *Estimating the quantity of mixing water and entrained air:* The amount of mixing water required to produce a given slump or consistency of concrete varies with different aggregates and cement, the grading of aggregates,

Table 5-4 Recommended slumps for various types of construction

	Slump, cm	
Types of construction	Maximum	Minimum
Reinforced foundation walls and footings	8	2
Plain footings, caissons, and substructure walls	8	2
Beams and reinforced walls	10	2
Building columns	10	2
Pavements and slabs	8	2
Heavy mass concrete	8	2

Source: ACI 211.

Table 5-5 Approximate mixing-water requirements for different slumps and maximum sizes of aggregates

Slump, cm	Water requirements, kg/m^3 of concrete for indicated maximum sizes of aggregate, mm†							
	10	12.5	20	25	40	50‡	70‡	150‡
Non-air-entrained concrete								
3 to 5	205	200	185	180	160	155	156	125
8 to 10	225	215	200	195	175	170	160	140
15 to 18	240	230	210	205	185	180	170	—
Approximate amount of entrapped air in non-air-entrained concrete (%)	3	2.5	2	1.5	1	0.5	0.3	0.2
Air-entrained concrete								
3 to 5	180	175	165	160	145	140	135	120
8 to 10	200	190	180	175	160	155	150	135
15 to 18	215	205	190	185	170	165	160	—
Recommended average total air content (%)	8	7	6	5	4.5	4	3.5	3

† The quantities of mixing water are for use in computing cement contents for trial batches. They are maxima for reasonably well-shaped, angular coarse aggregates graded within limits of accepted specifications.

‡ The slump values for concrete containing aggregate larger than 40 mm are based on slump tests after removal of particles larger than 40 mm by wet sieving.

Source: ACI 211.

temperature, and many other variables. One of the primary reasons for making trial mixes is to determine the water requirement for particular materials. Table 5-5 provides estimates of the required mixing water for concrete made with various maximum sizes of aggregate with and without air entrainment. These are average values and can be used only as preliminary estimates. Recommended air contents shown in Table 5-5 are those which will produce approximately 9 percent air in the mortar portion of all concrete mixtures. Experience has indicated that adequate durability is obtained by using these air contents.

STEP 4 *Selection of water-cement ratio:* The required water-cement ratio is usually determined by strength requirements, although other factors such as durability and finishing properties may govern. Because of the variation be-

Table 5-6 Relationships between water-cement ratio and compressive strength of concrete

	Water-cement ratio, by weight	
Compressive strength at 28 days, MPa†	Non-air-entrained concrete	Air-entrained concrete
45	0.38	—
40	0.43	—
35	0.48	0.40
30	0.55	0.46
25	0.62	0.53
20	0.70	0.61
15	0.80	0.71

† Values are estimated average strengths for concrete containing not more than the percentage of air shown in Table 5-5. For a constant water-cement ratio, the strength of concrete is reduced as the air content is increased.

Strength is based on 15 × 30 cm cylinders moist-cured 28 days at 23 ± 1.7°C in accordance with Section 9(b) of ASTM C-31, "Making and Curing Concrete Compression and Flexure Test Specimens in the Field." Cube strengths will be higher by approximately 20 percent.

Relationship assumes the maximum size of aggregate is about 20 to 30 mm; for a given source, strength produced by a given water-cement ratio increases as maximum size decreases; see Sec. 6-7.

Source: ACI 211.

tween strength and water-cement ratio among different materials, it is highly desirable to have this relationship established for the particular materials under investigation. Table 5-6 shows approximate, conservative values of the *w/c* ratio–strength relationship for average conditions. It would be unusual if the values shown in Table 5-6 were realistic for any given group of materials. ACI Committee 318, "Building Code," recommends that the strength–*w/c* ratio relationship be established for specific materials being considered. This can be accomplished by referring to previous records. When such records are not available, laboratory tests should be made to determine the strength of concrete with three different *w/c* ratios (three-point curve, Fig. 5-2). Although the relationship between strength and the *w/c* ratio is not a straight line, it can be assumed to be straight within the narrow range being considered.

Although air entrainment is one of the most important factors in determining the freezing and thawing durability of concrete, it is also known that concrete with low water-cement ratios is more durable than concrete with high water-cement ratios. The capillary voids left by excess water in cement paste provide sources for freezing and thawing deterioration mechanisms to operate. Table 5-7 shows the recommendation for maximum *w/c* ratios for extreme exposure conditions.

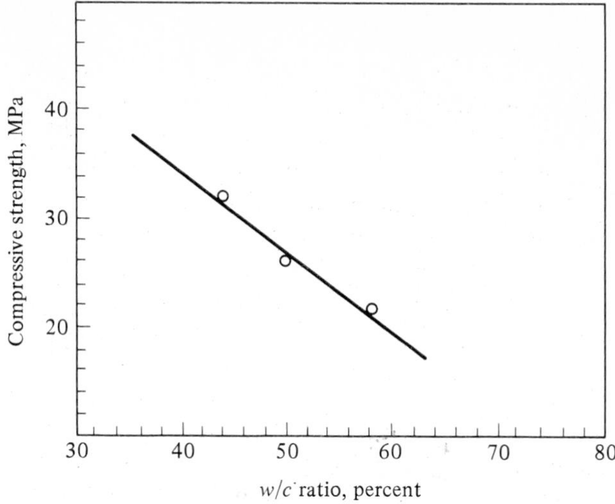

Figure 5-2 The relationship between strength and w/c ratio can be determined with a three-point curve.

STEP 5 *Calculation of cement content:* A predetermined amount of cement required per cubic yard of concrete may be previously established for a given concrete. The amount of cement can also be estimated from determinations made in steps 3 and 4. The required cement content is equal to the estimated mixing-water content (step 3) divided by the water-cement ratio (step 4).

Table 5-7 Maximum permissible water-cement ratios for concrete in severe exposures†

Type of structure	Structure wet continuously or frequently and exposed to freezing and thawing‡	Structure exposed to seawater or sulfates
Thin sections (railings, curbs, sills, ledges, ornamental work) and sections with less than 3-cm cover over steel	0.45	0.40§
All other structures	0.50	0.45§

† Based on the report of ACI Committee 201, "Durability of Concrete in Service."

‡ Concrete should also be air-entrained.

§ If sulfate-resisting cement (type II or type V of ASTM C-150) is used, permissible water-cement ratio may be increased by 0.05.

Source: ACI 211.

Table 5-8 Proportion of dry-rodded coarse aggregate per unit of volume of concrete

Maximum size of aggregate, mm	Proportion of dry-rodded coarse aggregate† per unit of concrete for different fineness moduli‡ of sand			
	2.40	2.60	2.80	3.00
10	0.50	0.48	0.46	0.44
12.5	0.59	0.57	0.55	0.53
20	0.66	0.64	0.62	0.60
25	0.71	0.69	0.67	0.65
40	0.76	0.74	0.72	0.70
50	0.78	0.76	0.74	0.72
70	0.81	0.79	0.77	0.75
150	0.87	0.85	0.83	0.81

† Based on aggregates in dry-rodded condition as described in ASTM C-29 for unit weight of aggregate.

These values are selected from empirical relationships to produce concrete with a degree of workability suitable for usual reinforced construction. For less workable concrete, such as required for concrete pavement construction, they may be increased about 10 percent. For more workable concrete, such as may sometimes be required when placement is to be by pumping, they may be reduced by up to 10 percent.

‡ Fineness modulus of sand equals the sum of ratios (cumulative) retained on sieves with square openings of 0.149, 0.297, 0.595, 1.19, 2.38, and 4.76 mm.

Source: ACI 211.

STEP 6 *Estimation of the coarse-aggregate content:* Previous experience and laboratory tests have established the maximum quantity of coarse aggregate that can be used in a concrete mix having satisfactory workability. Table 5-8 shows the quantity of coarse aggregate that generally may be used per unit of concrete. The dry-rodded density of coarse aggregate is determined by laboratory tests, and the values shown in Table 5-8 are those proportions of the dry-rodded density that can be used in an equal unit volume of concrete.

STEP 7 *Estimation of fine-aggregate content:* At the completion of step 6, all ingredients of the concrete have been estimated except the fine aggregate. If the density of concrete (kg/m^3) is assumed or can be estimated from experience, the required kilograms of fine aggregate is simply the difference between the density of concrete and the combined kilograms of all other ingredients. The density of concrete is often known with reasonable accuracy from previous experience with similar materials. Table 5-9 gives estimated values for the density of concrete based on an average specific gravity and maximum size of the aggregate.

Table 5-9 First estimate of density of fresh concrete

Maximum size of aggregate, mm	First estimate of concrete density, kg/m^3	
	Non-air-entrained concrete	Air-entrained concrete
10	2285	2190
12.5	2315	2235
20	2355	2280
25	2375	2315
40	2420	2355
50	2445	2375
70	2465	2400
150	2505	2435

Source: ACI 211.

5-7 EXAMPLE OF A TRIAL-MIX DETERMINATION

Mix Proportion

Mix proportioning is best illustrated by a typical example (Table 5-10).

Laboratory Batch Weights

Obviously, it is not practical to mix 1 m^3 of concrete in the laboratory. A convenient-size batch can be based on a constant weight of cement of 6 kg. This will provide sufficient concrete (about 1 ft^3) for slump, unit weight, and strength tests.

By simple proportion, the batch weights are computed by multiplying the trial mix by $\frac{6}{364} = 0.0165$ (Table 5-11).

It is recommended that the sand and coarse aggregate be saturated surface dry (*SSD*) for laboratory tests. Otherwise, adjustments in the batch weights will be necessary (see Sec. 5-10).

Observation and Adjustment of the Trial Mix

During the time the trial batch is being mixed, the appearance is checked for harshness and for whether the mix is too sandy or too rocky. This will serve as a basis for adjusting the sand percentage (Fig. 5-3).

Table 5-12 gives several approximate rules for adjusting a concrete trial mix. Since the density will not vary significantly with small adjustments, these adjustments can be made among ingredients as long as the total combined ingredients (kg/m^3) equal the density of the concrete (kg/m^3).

Table 5-10 Example of trial-mix computations

Type of structure—reinforced concrete building	
Maximum size of aggregate	20 mm
Slump	10 cm
Water content (Table 5-5)	200 kg/m^3
Water-cement ratio (Table 5-6)	0.55
Cement content $= \frac{200}{0.55}$	364 kg/m^3
Coarse aggregate:	
Dry-rodded bulk density = 1762.5 kg/m^3	
Proportion of coarse aggregate per unit of concrete (Table 5-8) = 0.64	
Coarse-aggregate content = 0.64 × 1762.5 = 1128 kg/m^3	
Density of concrete (Table 5-9) = 2355 kg/m^3	
Water	200
Cement	364
Coarse aggregate	1128
Total except sand	1692
Sand content = 2355 − 1692	663 kg/m^3
Sand percentage $= \frac{663}{663 + 1128} = 37\%$	
Batch weights of trial mix	
Water	200 kg/m^3
Cement	364
Sand	663
Coarse aggregate	1128
Total	2355 kg/m^3

Recommended Tests

The following tests and test specimens should be made with the fresh-mixed concrete (see Chap. 12):

1. Slump
2. Density, kg/m^3
3. Strength specimens
4. Percent air

Table 5-11 Batch weights for a laboratory-size batch

Cement	0.0165 × 364 =	6.0
Water	0.0165 × 200 =	3.3
Sand	0.0165 × 663 =	10.9
Coarse aggregate	0.0165 × 1128 =	18.6
Total		38.8 kg

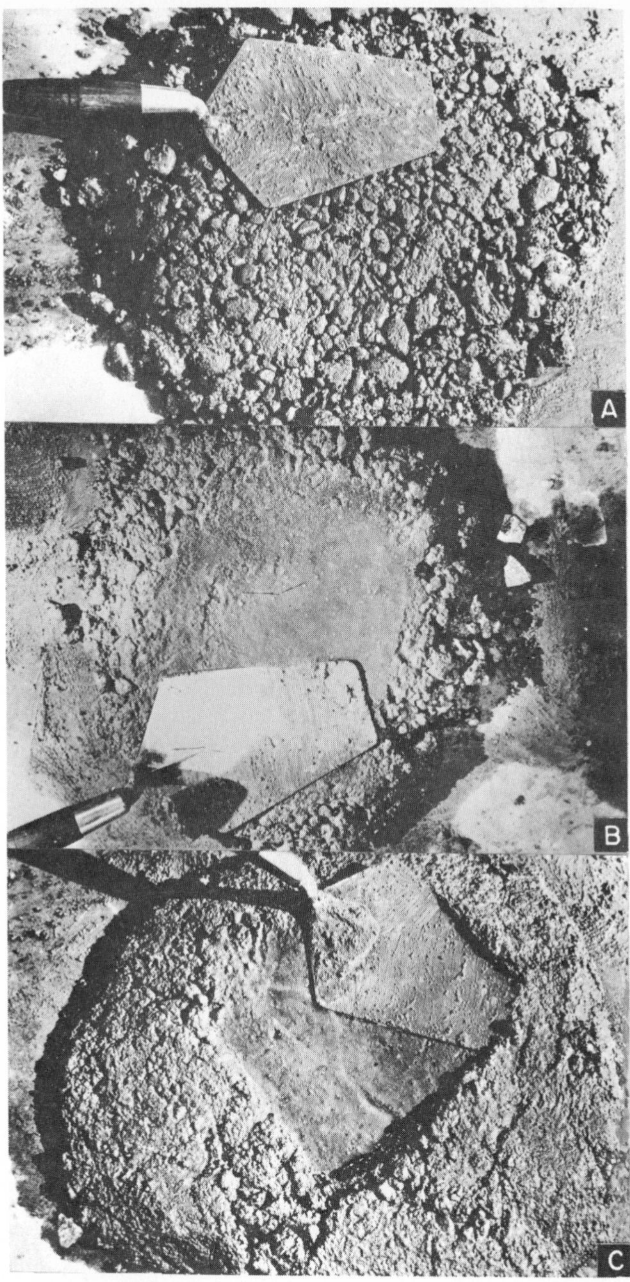

Figure 5-3 Appearance of fresh concrete. (A) Undersanded. (B) Properly sanded. (C) Oversanded. *(Portland Cement Association.)*

Table 5-12 Approximate rules for adjusting trial mixes

Changes in proportions of ingredients	Water content	Sand content
For each 1 cm increase or decrease in slump	Increase or decrease 1 percent	
For each 1 percent increase or decrease in air content		Decrease or increase 1 percent
For each 1 percent increase or decrease in percent of sand	Increase or decrease 1 percent	

5-8 EVALUATION AND ADJUSTMENT OF TRIAL MIXES

The trial mix, selected from Tables 5-4 to 5-9, is based on materials with average properties. Aggregates, cements, and admixtures vary from average, and it is necessary to adjust the values shown in the tables for actual job materials. It may also be desirable to evaluate the relative cost of using various combinations of available materials.

Evaluation Chart

The first trial mix will give specific data on the materials used. It would be unusual if the measured slump turned out to be the same as the estimated slump. It is advisable to make a second mix in which the slump is increased or decreased by subtracting or adding a small amount of aggregate. The slump and aggregate

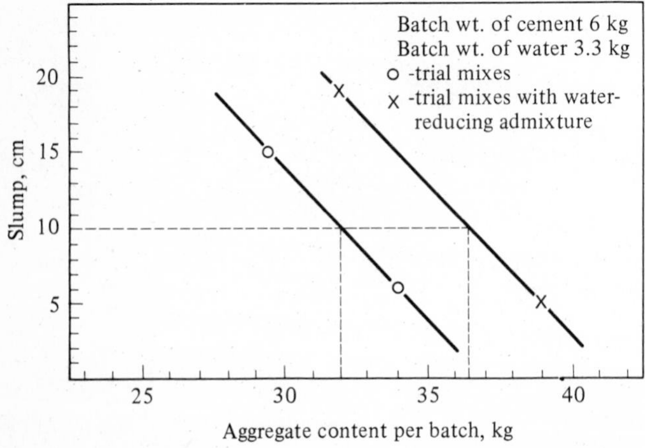

Figure 5-4 Evaluation chart showing the relationship between aggregate content and slump.

content are plotted on an evaluation chart (Fig. 5-4), which will establish the relationship between them. In our example, with 29.5 kg of aggregate the first trial mix produced a slump of 15 cm (Fig. 5-4). In the second trial it was found that 34 kg of aggregate could be added to 6 kg of cement and 3.3 kg of water to produce a slump of 6 cm (Fig. 5-4).

From Fig. 5-4 it is possible to select accurately the kilograms of aggregate for any desired slump. In our example, for a slump of 10 cm, 32 kg of aggregate can be used with 6 kg of cement and 3.3 kg of water, resulting in our adjusted mix.

Selection of Most Economical Combination of Ingredients

The more aggregate used with a given amount of cement, the more economical the concrete. The evaluation chart (Fig. 5-4) indicates the economy in using lower slumps. Other combinations of materials can also be plotted on Fig. 5-4, such as mixes made with more or less sand, different gradings of aggregate, different cements, different aggregates, and various admixtures. The position of each line on the chart will indicate the relative economy of using each different combination of materials. For example, a water-reducing admixture increased the aggregate from 32.0 kg to 36.4 kg (Fig. 5-4) for a 10-cm slump.

5-9 CONVERSION OF ADJUSTED LABORATORY BATCH WEIGHTS TO BATCH WEIGHTS FOR 1 m^3 OF CONCRETE

The batch weights for 1-m^3 volume will depend on the density of the concrete. In our example the density of concrete was found to be 2250 kg/m^3. Our adjusted trial batch weights from Fig. 5-4 are as follows:

Cement	6
Water	3.3
Aggregates	32
Total	41.3 kg

$$\text{Batches per cubic meter} = \frac{2250}{41.3} = 54.48$$

The final adjusted batch weights per cubic meter are as follows:

Cement	6 × 54.48 =	327
Water	3.3 × 54.48 =	180
Sand	11.8 × 54.48 =	643
Gravel	20.2 × 54.48 =	1100
Total		2250 kg/m^3

5-10 ADJUSTMENT FOR AGGREGATE MOISTURE CONDITIONS IN THE FIELD

It is assumed that the aggregates in a concrete mix are saturated surface dry (SSD) and will neither add water to nor absorb water from the added mixing water. In the field this is rarely the case, and it is necessary to adjust mix proportions for free water or absorption. The computation of adjustment for surface moisture or absorption on an SSD basis is as follows.

1. *Free-moisture computation*

$$SSD + SSD \times M = W$$

$$SSD(1 + M) = W$$

$$SSD = \frac{W}{1 + M} \qquad (5\text{-}1)$$

where SSD = saturated surface dry aggregate, kg
M = percent moisture/100
W = amount of wet aggregate, kg

2. *Adjustment of batch weight of sand.* Adjustment of batch weight of sand in our trial batch, assuming 5 percent moisture, is

$$643(SSD \text{ sand}) \times 1.05 = 675.2 \text{ kg/m}^3 \qquad \text{(wet sand)}$$

The batch weight of water should be decreased by

$$675.2 - 643 = 32.2 \text{ kg}$$

3. *Adjustment for absorption*

$$SSD - SSD \times A = D$$

$$SSD = \frac{D}{1 - A} \qquad (5\text{-}2)$$

where A = absorption
D = dry weight of aggregate

Table 5-13 Final batch weights adjusted for moisture and absorption

Cement	=	327
Water	180 − 32.2 + 11 =	158.8
Sand	643 + 32.2 =	675.2
Coarse aggregate	1100 − 11 =	1089.0
Total		2250.0 kg/m^3

Adjustment of previous batch weights, assuming the coarse aggregate is dry and will absorb 1 percent moisture, is

$$1100(SSD \text{ sand}) \times (1 - 0.01) = 1089 \text{ kg/m}^3 \qquad \text{(dry sand)}$$

The coarse aggregate will absorb 1100 − 1089 = 11 kg of water from the mix, and this should be added to the batch weight of water, see Table 5-13.

5-11 PROPORTIONING LIGHTWEIGHT AGGREGATE CONCRETE

The same principles apply to proportioning lightweight aggregate concrete and heavyweight concrete as to normal-weight concrete: the density of concrete (kg/m^3) must equal the combined sum of the ingredients (kg/m^3).

STEP 1 *Estimating cement content:* Because of the high and variable absorption values of the aggregates, it is difficult to accurately determine the w/c ratio of the paste in lightweight concretes. It is recommended, therefore, that the first step in proportioning lightweight concrete mixes be to estimate the required cement contents for a trial mix. Any estimate covering the broad spectrum of lightweight concretes must, of necessity, be approximate. ACI Standard 211.2 gives approximate relationships in Table 5-14. These may vary greatly depending on the type of aggregate used.

STEP 2 *Estimating water content:* The amount of mixing water that should be added to lightweight concrete is the minimum amount that will permit the concrete to be properly placed, consolidated, and finished. Until a trial mix is made with specific aggregates, in the condition they will be used, a rough estimate of the required water may be made, as shown in Table 5-15.

STEP 3 *Calculating aggregate content:* After the quantity of all other ingredients has been estimated, the quantity of lightweight aggregate can be computed by subtracting the sum of all ingredients except aggregates from the density of the lightweight concrete. Estimates of the density of various lightweight aggregate concretes are shown in Table 5-16.

Table 5-14 Approximate relationship between strength and cement content

Compressive strength, MPa	Cement content, kg/m^3
17	250–420
21	280–450
28	330–500
35	390–560

Table 5-15 Approximate water content for lightweight concretes

Type and condition of aggregate	Water content, kg/m^3
Structural aggregates	
SSD	180
Dry	195
Insulation aggregates	
SSD	200
Dry	300

Table 5-16 Approximate density of lightweight aggregate concretes

Type of aggregate	Approximate density, kg/m^3
Expanded shale, clay, or slate	1360 to 1850
Expanded slag	1440 to 1920
Scoria	961 to 1440
Pumice	800 to 1280
Perlite	320 to 800
Vermiculite	240 to 640

STEP 4 *Trial-mix computations*

Estimated density of concrete (Table 5-16)		1600 kg/m^3
Estimated cement content (Table 5-14)	400	
Estimated water content (Table 5-15)	195	
Total without aggregate		595 kg/m^3
Estimated aggregate content		1600 − 595 = 1005 kg/m^3

5-12 ADJUSTMENT OF TRIAL MIX

It would be more by coincidence than by design if a trial mix, based on approximate estimates, were to produce the desired concrete. An evaluation chart similar to that proposed for normal-weight concrete (Fig. 5-4) is recommended. By making trial mixes with various amounts of aggregate, a close approximation of the actual mix can be made. If only one trial mix is made, it is recommended that a portion of the mixing water be held out and only a sufficient amount of water be added to produce the desired slump. The mix can then be adjusted to actual conditions.

Example Assume that the trial mix, computed in step 4, actually required 180 kg/m^3 of water to produce a desired slump at 10 cm. The density was found to be 1425 kg/m^3.

Sum of ingredients in batch:

Cement	400
Water	180
Aggregate	1005
Total	1585 kg/m^3

Density: 1425 kg/m^3

$$\text{Batches per cubic meter} = \frac{1425}{1585} = 0.899$$

Actual amount of each ingredient per cubic meter:

Cement	$400 \times 0.899 =$	359.6
Water	$180 \times 0.899 =$	161.8
Aggregate	$1005 \times 0.899 =$	903.6
Total		1425.0 kg/m^3

The kilograms of ingredients can be adjusted to fit more nearly the desired mix as long as their total sum equals the density of the concrete.

5-13 PROPORTIONING HEAVYWEIGHT CONCRETE

There is little difference between proportioning heavyweight concrete and normal-weight concrete. The specific gravity of the aggregate, and hence the density of the concrete, is much greater. Estimates of w/c ratio, water, cement, and coarse-aggregate contents can be made as discussed in Sec. 5.6 (steps 1 through 4).

STEP 5 *Estimating the density:* Because of the heavy aggregates, the density of the heavyweight concrete is higher than that of normal-weight concrete. Table 5-17, adapted from ACI Standard 211.1, shows the approximate density of concretes using various heavyweight aggregates.

STEP 6 *Estimating aggregate content:* The estimated content of heavyweight aggregate is equal to the difference between the estimated density of concrete and the cement and water content.

Table 5-17 Approximate density of various heavyweight concretes

Aggregate	Specific gravity	Approximate density of concrete, kg/m^3
Hydrous iron ores, limonite, and goethite	3.4 to 3.8	2880 to 3120
Barite ore, barium sulfate	4.0 to 44	3280 to 3600
Iron ores, ilmenite, hematite, and magnetite	4.2 to 4.8	3440 to 3840
Metallic iron, punchings, pellets, etc.	6.5 to 7.5	4970 to 5600

Example Assume:

Water content (Table 5-5) 200 kg/m^3

w/c ratio (Table 5-6) 0.55

Cement content $\dfrac{200}{0.55} = 364\ kg/m^3$

Total 564 kg/m^3

Density of concrete (Table 5-17) = 3600 kg/m^3

Total aggregate content:

$$3600 - 564 = 3036\ kg/m^3$$

For the first trial, an estimate of about 40 percent fine aggregate and 60 percent coarse aggregate will be within the workable range.

STEP 7 *Trial-mix proportions:*

Cement		364
Water		200
Sand	$0.40 \times 3036 =$	1214
Coarse aggregate	$0.60 \times 3036 =$	1822
Total		3600 kg/m^3

5-14 ADJUSTMENT AND EVALUATION OF HEAVYWEIGHT CONCRETE MIXES

An evaluation chart similar to Fig. 5-4 can be made for heavyweight concrete by making a second trial mix with a different quantity of aggregate. After one trial mix is made, however, any small adjustments in the amount of ingredients can be made as long as the proportions total 3600 kg/m^3. This process will be illustrated by the following examples.

Sand Adjustment

Assume the mix was too harsh and needed a greater proportion of sand. The adjusted mix is as follows:

Cement	364
Water	200
Sand (add 35 kg)	1249
Coarse aggregate (subtract 35 kg)	1787
Total	3600 kg/m^3

Adjustment in Slump

Assume the slump was too low (Table 5-12) (1 percent increase in water content for 1-cm increase in slump). The mix adjustment for an increase in slump of 4 cm is

Water	$(200 \times 1.04) =$	208
Cement	$\dfrac{208}{0.55} =$	378
Sand		1249
Coarse aggregate		1765
Total		3600 kg/m^3

Minor adjustments in mix proportions will not significantly affect the density of the concrete.

5-15 MANUFACTURE OF CONCRETE

Concrete as a manufactured product is unique since the various steps in manufacture are handled by different segments of the industry. Portland cement, the cementing ingredient, is manufactured by the portland cement industry. The sand

and gravel industry and the crushed-stone industry provide aggregates for concrete. Usually, the ready-mixed concrete industry combines the ingredients of concrete. The final step in manufacturing may be controlled by the purchaser or final consumer of concrete by adding water on the job. The final proportion of water to concrete is the most difficult to control and yet is critical in producing high-quality, economical concrete.

5-16 MEASURING CONCRETE INGREDIENTS

The ready-mixed concrete industry is one of the newest members of the concrete industry. Until recently it was the responsibility of contractor or consumer to purchase the various ingredients of concrete, move them to the site of construction, and proportion and mix them in a concrete mixer as needed on the project. Today concrete of any desirable proportions or quality for numerous special purposes can be ordered directly from the ready-mix concrete producer and within a few minutes be delivered to the project in the quantities desired. A modern ready-mixed concrete plant is controlled electronically. The various concrete mixes are programmed, and batches of concrete of any desired size are proportioned automatically (Fig. 5-5).

Figure 5-5 Large, ready-mixed concrete plant. *(C. S. Johnson Co.)*

5-17 MIXING CONCRETE

Mixing of concrete should be thorough so as to produce homogeneity of proportions of cement, water, and aggregate from the beginning to the end of each batch discharged. The mixing action of a concrete mixer involves the general blending of all ingredients and, in addition, the working of the cement paste into the surface of the aggregate particles. Concrete mixers must be properly designed, cleaned, and maintained in good condition in order for the mixing to be accomplished in a reasonable time (Figs. 5-6 and 5-7).

In rare cases where concrete may be mixed in the field, ingredients may be measured by weight or by volume. The aggregates are usually weighed, but water may be measured by gallons and cement by sacks.

In centralized ready-mixed concrete plants, concrete may be mixed in either transit truck mixers or stationary mixers. The batch may be placed in a transit mixer at a centralized batching plant, and the mixing takes place from the time the mixer leaves the plant until it reaches the job. Some ready-mixed concrete plants use stationary, centralized mixers. The concrete is mixed before it is placed in truck mixers or agitators. Centralized mixing has the advantage of more accurate control of the consistency and other properties of the fresh concrete.

Two types of mixers are used in central mixing plants (Figs. 5-6 and 5-7). Large tilting mixers are held approximately level during the mixing cycle and then tilted downward to discharge into the truck mixers. In recent years a new turbine-type mixer has been used. This mixer is a horizontal pan type where the in-

Figure 5-6 Tilting-type concrete mixer. *(C. S. Johnson Co.)*

Figure 5-7 Nontilting-type concrete mixer. *(C. S. Johnson Co.)*

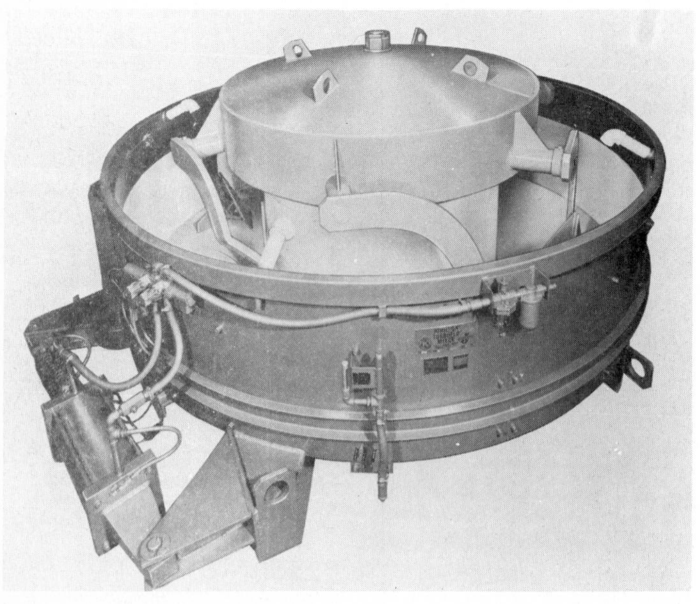

Figure 5-8 Vertical-shaft concrete mixer. *(C. S. Johnson Co.)*

gredients are fed into a revolving mixer blade and water is added around the periphery of the mixer (Fig. 5-8). Adequate mixing is accomplished in a comparatively short time.

5-18 DELIVERING CONCRETE TO THE FORM

Ready-mixed concrete is sometimes placed directly into the forms by means of chutes running directly from the back of the truck. Ready-mixed concrete trucks have a high-level discharge, permitting sufficient slope of the chute from the truck to the form. The blades in a truck mixer are designed so that when the drum rotates in an opposite direction from mixing, the concrete is lifted and discharges from the high opening of the mixer (Fig. 5-9).

When concrete is to be placed in locations inaccessible to ready-mixed trucks, concrete is first discharged into a concrete bucket, which is then lifted by a crane to the point of placement. Concrete is discharged from the bucket through a large opening in the bottom. Concrete is sometimes delivered to the form in buggies.

Figure 5-9 Delivering concrete to the forms.

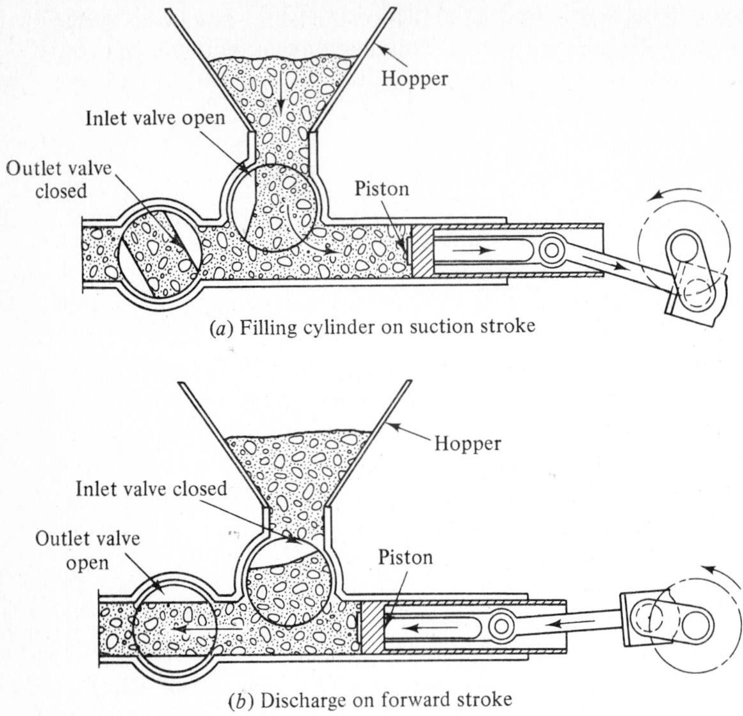

Figure 5-10 Valve-action concrete pump.

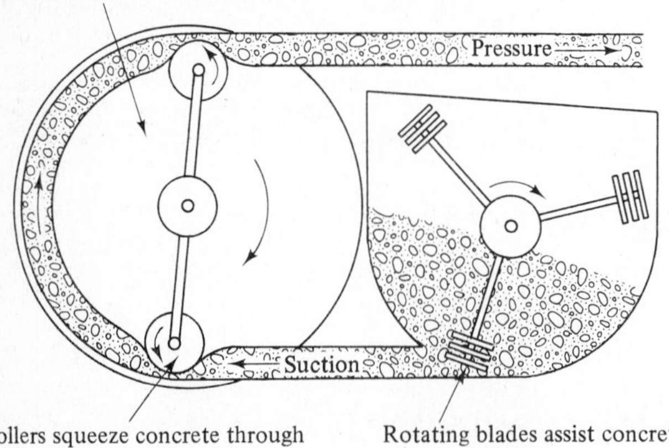

Figure 5-11 Squeeze-type, small line concrete pumping system.

In recent years, successful transportation of concrete has been accomplished by pumping. Concrete is pumped with a variety of types of concrete pumps, some using large steel pipelines and others using rubber hoses (Figs. 5-10 and 5-11). A concrete pump located at strategic locations can pump to inaccessible locations of a structure.

5-19 CONSOLIDATION OF CONCRETE

After concrete reaches the forms, proper placing and consolidation methods will produce a higher-quality structure. ACI Committee 304 recommends certain current methods under various placing conditions. Also shown in Figs. 5-12, 5-13, and 5-14 are methods which are considered incorrect.

After concrete is placed in its final location, it must be consolidated to fill all the voids, corners, and recesses of the form. It is also desirable to remove all entrapped air. Most effective compaction is accomplished with internal vibration. Concrete vibrators, consisting of rapidly turning eccentric rods encased in a flexible shaft, cause the concrete to consolidate to maximum density. One of the greatest advantages of using internal vibration is the fact that concrete of lower slump may be used. This permits the use of lower water contents; hence, a higher-quality paste is achieved with a given amount of cement.

5-20 SPECIAL PLACING METHODS

The use of slipforms has greatly increased the speed and efficiency in placing concrete in pavements and certain concrete structures. Nearly all highway and airport pavements are placed by slipform methods (Figs. 5-15 and 5-16). Slipforms are used successfully in construction of silos and walls (Fig. 5-17). Concrete is placed in the form continuously. The form moves continuously as the concrete hardens. By the time the concrete is exposed, it has set sufficiently to carry the loads.

Concrete can be placed under water if it is deposited through a pipe with the lower end buried in the fresh concrete (Fig. 5-18). Concrete is much heavier than water and, as the form is filled, the water is forced out. An extra-rich mix is usually used to compensate for possible loss of cement in the concrete exposed to water.

5-21 FINISHING CONCRETE

Concrete surfaces can be finished with different treatment and textures depending on their exposure and use. A hard, dense surface is not recommended for outdoor concrete because of the danger of its being slick in wet or freezing weather. Highway pavements, for example, are finished with a burlap drag which follows

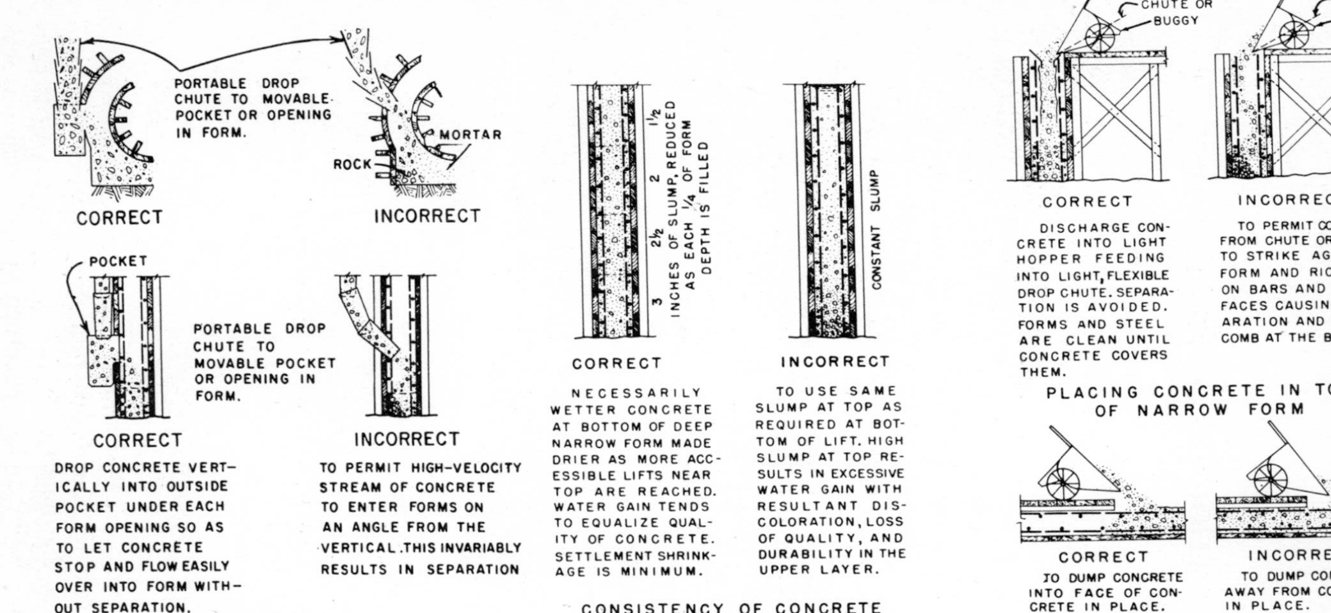

Figure 5-12 Proper introduction of concrete into forms. *(ACI 304.)*

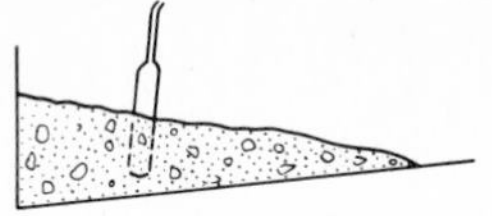

CORRECT

START PLACING AT BOTTOM OF SLOPE SO THAT COMPACTION IS INCREASED BY WEIGHT OF NEWLY ADDED CONCRETE. VIBRATION CONSOLIDATES.

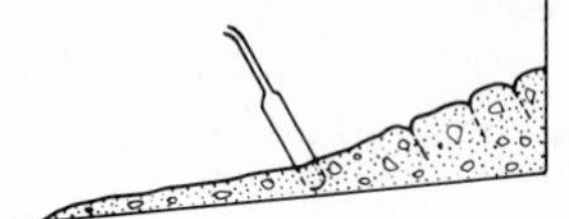

INCORRECT

TO BEGIN PLACING AT TOP OF SLOPE. UPPER CONCRETE TENDS TO PULL APART, ESPECIALLY WHEN VIBRATED BELOW, AS VIBRATION STARTS FLOW AND REMOVES SUPPORT FROM CONCRETE ABOVE.

WHEN CONCRETE MUST BE PLACED IN A SLOPING LIFT

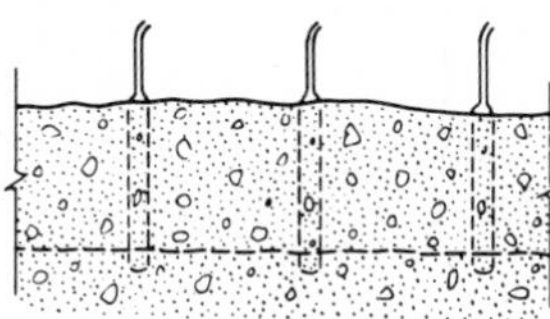

CORRECT

VERTICAL PENETRATION OF VIBRATOR A FEW INCHES INTO PREVIOUS LIFT (WHICH SHOULD NOT YET BE RIGID) AT SYSTEMATIC REGULAR INTERVALS FOUND TO GIVE ADEQUATE CONSOLIDATION.

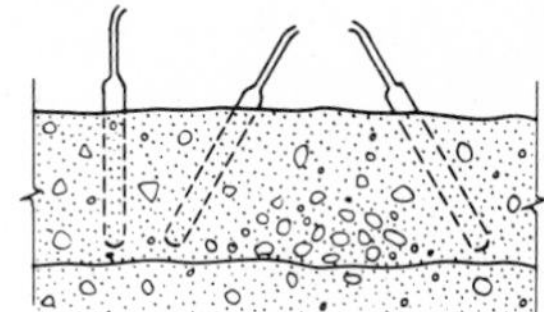

INCORRECT

HAPHAZARD RANDOM PENETRATION OF THE VIBRATOR AT ALL ANGLES AND SPACINGS WITHOUT SUFFICIENT DEPTH TO ASSURE MONOLITHIC COMBINATION OF THE TWO LAYERS.

SYSTEMATIC VIBRATION OF EACH NEW LIFT

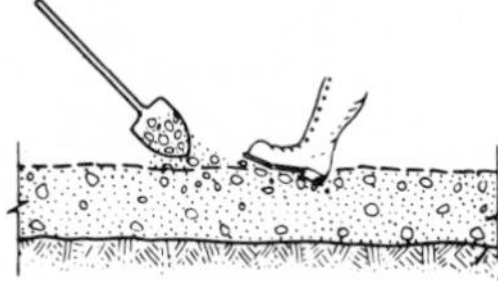

CORRECT

SHOVEL ROCKS FROM ROCK POCKET ONTO SOFTER, AMPLY SANDED AREA AND TRAMP OR VIBRATE.

INCORRECT

ATTEMPTING TO CORRECT ROCK POCKET BY SHOVELING MORTAR AND SOFT CONCRETE ON IT.

TREATMENT OF ROCK POCKET WHEN PLACING CONCRETE

Figure 5-13 Proper placement and vibration of concrete. *(ACI 304.)*

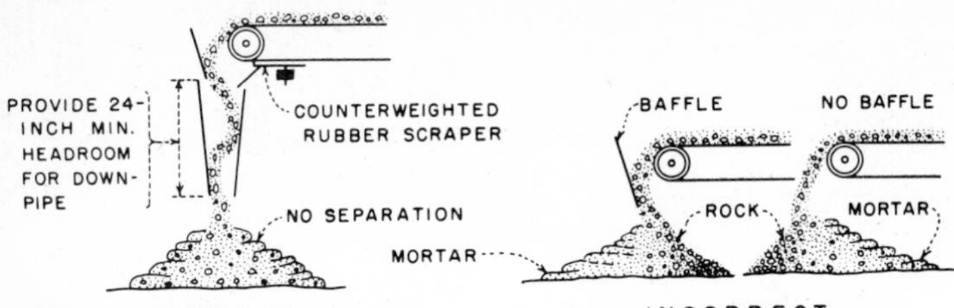

CORRECT

THE ABOVE ARRANGEMENT PREVENTS SEPARATION OF CONCRETE WHETHER IT IS BEING DISCHARGED INTO HOPPERS, BUCKETS, CARS, TRUCKS, OR FORMS.

INCORRECT

IMPROPER OR COMPLETE LACK OF CONTROL AT END OF BELT.

USUALLY A BAFFLE OR SHALLOW HOPPER MERELY CHANGES THE DIRECTION OF SEPARATION.

CONTROL OF SEPARATION OF CONCRETE AT THE END OF CONVEYOR BELT

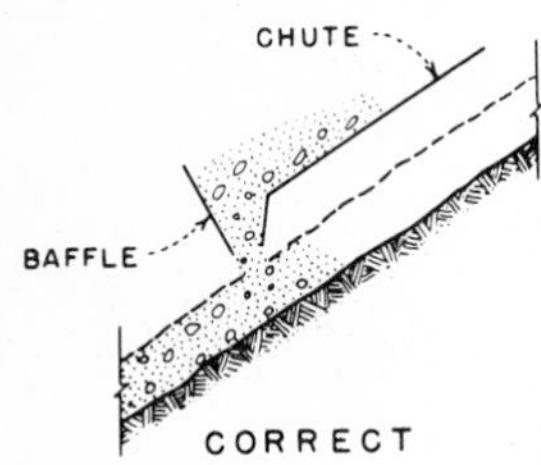

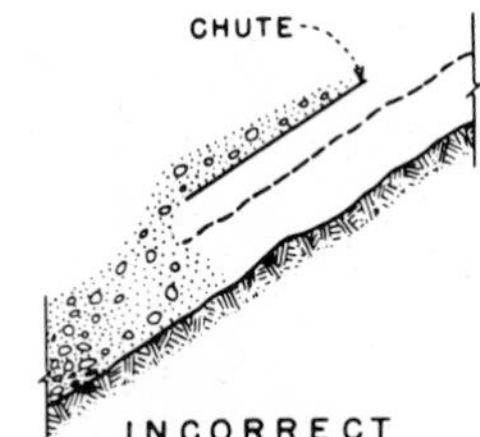

CORRECT

PLACE BAFFLE AND DROP AT END OF CHUTE SO THAT SEPARATION IS AVOIDED AND CONCRETE REMAINS ON SLOPE.

INCORRECT

TO DISCHARGE CONCRETE FROM A FREE END CHUTE ON A SLOPE TO BE PAVED. ROCK IS SEPARATED AND GOES TO BOTTOM OF SLOPE.

VELOCITY TENDS TO CARRY CONCRETE DOWN SLOPE.

PLACING CONCRETE ON A SLOPING SURFACE

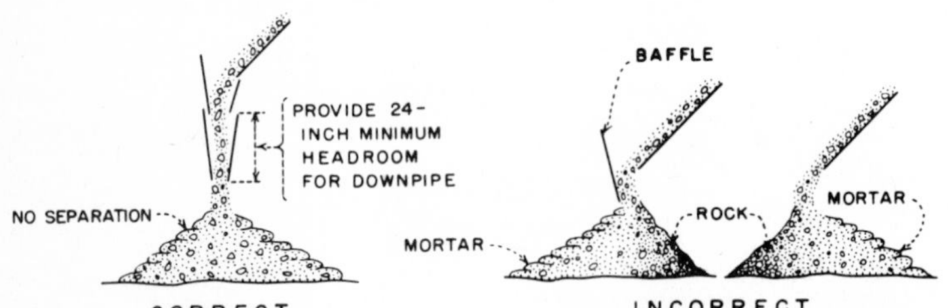

CORRECT

THE ABOVE ARRANGEMENT PREVENTS SEPARATION, NO MATTER HOW SHORT THE CHUTE, WHETHER CONCRETE IS BEING DISCHARGED INTO HOPPERS, BUCKETS, CARS, TRUCKS, OR FORMS.

INCORRECT

IMPROPER OR LACK OF CONTROL AT END OF ANY CONCRETE CHUTE, NO MATTER HOW SHORT.

USUALLY A BAFFLE MERELY CHANGES DIRECTION OF SEPARATION.

CONTROL OF SEPARATION AT THE END OF CONCRETE CHUTES

THIS APPLIES TO SLOPING DISCHARGES FROM MIXERS, TRUCK MIXERS, ETC AS WELL AS TO LONGER CHUTES, BUT NOT WHEN CONCRETE IS DISCHARGED INTO ANOTHER CHUTE OR ONTO A CONVEYOR BELT.

Figure 5-14 Correct and incorrect methods of placing concrete. *(ACI 304.)*

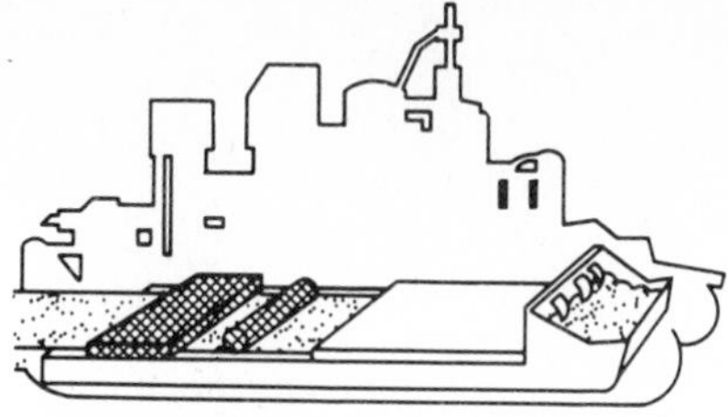

Figure 5-15 Schematic sketch of slipform for pavements.

the slipform-placing machine and leaves a rough, gritty finish with high skid resistance. This type of finishing operation does leave a high-density compact surface and allows the "bleed" water to rise to the surface before the heavier particles of concrete settle.

Concrete slabs are usually finished in the following sequence:

1. Consolidate concrete.
2. Level concrete by screeding.
3. Float concrete with a large "bull float" or "darby" to fill holes and remove ridges.
4. Let concrete set until desired finish can be applied. It is important not to compact the surface before all bleed waters have come to the surface and evaporated.

Figure 5-16 Placing concrete pavement by slipform method. (*Concrete Construction Handbook.*)

Figure 5-17 Construction of concrete cement silos by slipform method.

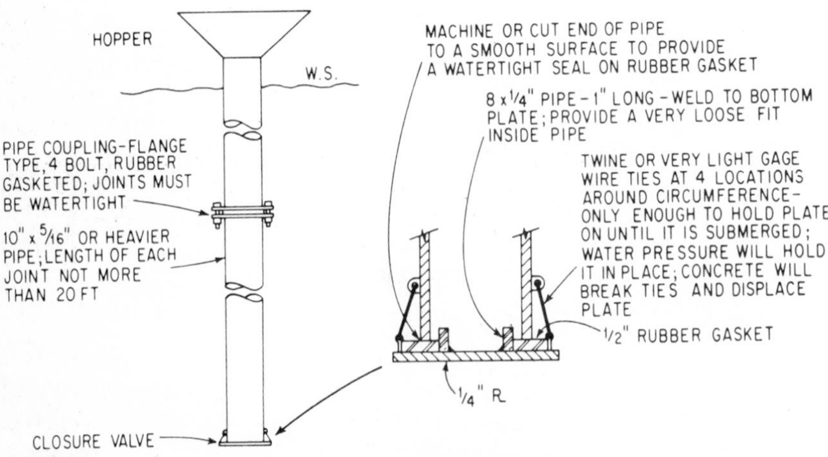

Figure 5-18 Pipe for placing concrete under water. *(Concrete Construction Handbook.)*

5. *Float finish.* Float the surface with a wooden or magnesium float as the concrete begins to set, while the surface can still be worked.
6. "*Broom*" *finish.* Use a float to work out all imperfections, and draw a broom across the surface. It is important that the concrete has set sufficiently to give the proper texture.
7. *Hard trowel finish.* Wait until the concrete is in the process of taking its initial set. Then smooth the surface with a float and follow with a slick, hard finish made with a steel trowel. Work until all wetness has disappeared.
8. *Exposed aggregate finish.* Sprinkle decorative aggregate on the surface of the concrete as soon as screeding is complete, and compact the aggregate particles into the surface. Wait until the concrete has taken its initial set; then gently remove any grout from the surface of the aggregate particles with a stiff brush and water. Wash the surface with clean water.

5-22 CURING CONCRETE

Concrete will not harden unless there is sufficient water present to hydrate the portland cement. The hydration process progresses rapidly as long as there is a large surface area of unhydrated current particles exposed to moisture. As the hydration process progresses, the only unhydrated cement remaining is in the unexposed interior of the large cement particles. It is important, therefore, that freshly placed concrete be exposed to moisture until the hydration process has progressed sufficiently to produce concrete of desired strength and durability. Common methods of curing concrete include the following:

1. *Curing compounds.* Curing compounds which prevent the escape of mixing water from concrete.
2. *Plastic or wet burlap covering.* Plastic or wet burlap covering which will prevent evaporation of water from the concrete surface.
3. *Ponding with water.* Ponding with water not only prevents evaporation but also supplies additional water which may be needed to complete the hydration of the portland cement.

5-23 SUMMARY

Concrete is one of the most versatile structural materials. Because of the abundance of the raw materials for portland cement and concrete in the earth's crust, concrete may become even more important in the future as more strategic materials are exhausted.

The important properties of fresh and hardened concrete which determine its usefulness as a structural material may be classified as follows:

1. *Quality*
   (*a*) Strength
   (*b*) Durability
   (*c*) Dimensional stability

2. *Workability*
   (*a*) Plasticity
   (*b*) Mobility
3. *Economy*

Many methods have been developed for proportioning concrete mixes. The most widely accepted method is the ACI Standard 211. The quality of concrete is based on the *w*/*c* ratio, and other proportions are based on previous experience with average materials. The final-mix proportions are established, however, by adjustment of trial mixes.

The proportioning of lightweight concrete and heavyweight concrete requires variations in the standard recommended practice. Properties peculiar to each aggregate type must be taken into consideration.

The manufacture of concrete is not complete until it is mixed, transported, placed, finished, and cured.

REFERENCES

1. ACI Standard 211.1-74: "Recommended Practice for Selecting Proportions for Normal and Heavyweight Concrete."
2. ACI Standard 211.2-69: "Recommended Practice for Selecting Proportions for Structural Lightweight Concrete."
3. ACI Standard 304: "Measuring, Mixing, Transporting and Placing Concrete."
4. Cordon, William A.: "Article on Concrete," *Encyclopedia Americana*, 1974.
5. Cordon, William A., and J. Derle Thorpe: "Proportioning and Evaluation of Concrete Mixtures," *ACI Journal*, February 1975.
6. Neville, A. M.: *Properties of Concrete*, Wiley, New York, 1963.
7. *Engineering Materials*, Pitman, New York (Committee on Engineering Materials), 1958.
8. Troxell, G. E., H. E. Davis, and J. W. Kelley: *Composition and Properties of Concrete*, 2d ed., McGraw-Hill, New York, 1968.
9. U.S. Bureau of Reclamation: *Concrete Manual*, 8th ed., 1975.
10. Withey, M. O., and G. W. Washa: *Materials of Construction*, Wiley, New York, 1954.
11. Waddell, J. J.: *Concrete Construction Handbook*, 2d ed., McGraw-Hill, New York, 1974.

QUESTIONS AND PROBLEMS

1 List all the other materials concrete may compete with in modern construction.

2 List as many uses for concrete as you can.

3 What three principal properties of fresh and hardened concrete determine its suitability as a structural material?

4 Explain the difference between plasticity and mobility.

5 What is dimensional stability?

6 How does aggregate decrease workability?

7 Why does water decrease quality?

8 Compare the cost of paste and aggregate if portland cement costs $66 per megagram and aggregate costs $6.00 per ton. The cost of water can be assumed to be zero.

9 Why is it important to use as much aggregate as possible in concrete?

10 List the factors that increase the amount of aggregate which can be used in a concrete mix.

11 Why are admixtures used in concrete?

12 Explain how a water-reducing admixture increases the amount of aggregate that can be used in a given volume of concrete.

13 What effect does entrained air have on concrete workability?

14 Why is it important to place concrete at the lowest practicable slump?

15 Is it always important to use the maximum size of aggregate practicable in concrete?

16 What is a trial mix?

17 List the steps recommended by ACI Committee 211 to proportion a trial mix.

18 Using ACI Committee 211 recommendations, estimate a trial concrete mix for structural concrete for a bridge to be built in Mississippi if the desired average strength is 30 MPa.

19 Assume you have made several laboratory mixes and have prepared the evaluation chart shown in Fig. 5-4. Make the following determinations:

(*a*) The mix proportions (kg/m^3) for mix with and without a water-reducing admixture. Estimated slump is 15 cm.

(*b*) The comparative cost of concrete per cubic meter for each mix, assuming you can purchase aggregates for $6.00 per ton and cement costs $3.00 per 100 lb.

20 Assume the sand in the stockpile contains 5.3 percent free moisture and the coarse aggregate is dry. Compute the batch weight for 1 m^3 of concrete using the field materials.

21 Explain why a centralized ready-mixed concrete plant can produce uniform concrete more efficiently and economically for a small job than a contractor can.

22 List the relative merits of a centralized mixing plant versus truck mixing.

23 What is meant by the slipform method of placing concrete?

24 Why are vibrators used in placing concrete? Do they improve the quality of the concrete?

25 How can concrete be placed in water without washing the fines out of the mix?

26 What is meant by segregation?

27 Why are ingredients batched by weight and not by volume?

CHAPTER

SIX

PROPERTIES OF HARDENED CONCRETE

The adequacy of hardened concrete is generally measured by its ability to resist stresses caused by imposed loads, its resistance to the forces of deterioration, and its dimensional stability. In Chap. 5 we referred to these properties as *concrete quality*.

6-1 STRENGTH

The strength of concrete is generally accepted as an indication of the quality of concrete in a structure. The most common measure of the strength of concrete is the ultimate axial pressure resisted by a 6 × 12 in cylinder approximately 30 cm high and 15 cm in diameter. Larger cylinders are required when large-size aggregates are used. Testing machines in use in the United States weigh in pounds, and the standard test specimen for concrete is a 6 × 12 in cylinder. This equipment will probably be used for some time in the future. The total load in pounds on a 6 × 12 in cylinder, divided by 4100, will give the compressive strength in megapascals.

A concrete cylinder may fail because of tension stresses (cohesion), shearing stresses (sliding), or by compression stresses (crushing). A material such as concrete is much weaker in tension and shear, and a cylinder will usually fail in shear with cone-shaped sections forming at one or both ends (Fig. 6-1). The theoretical angle of the cone of failure is approximately 35° with the vertical. From mechanics, it can be shown that the theoretical shear plane is equal to the angle of maximum shear (45°) minus half the angle of internal friction, or $45° - \phi/2$ (Fig. 6-2). This failure plane may vary widely depending on the end bearing, the

(*a*)

(*b*)

Figure 6-1 Large cylinder at the moment of failure in compression. The upper shear cone is clearly visible. *(U.S. Bureau of Reclamation.)*

(c)

Figure 6-1 (*Continued.*)

distribution and size of aggregate particles, and the tensile strength of the paste. When there is a tension failure, the failure plane may be vertical because of splitting.

The standard strength of concrete which is used in design formulas is designated f'_c. This is the strength of a standard cylinder moist-cured at $23 \pm 1.5°C$ for a period of 28 days.

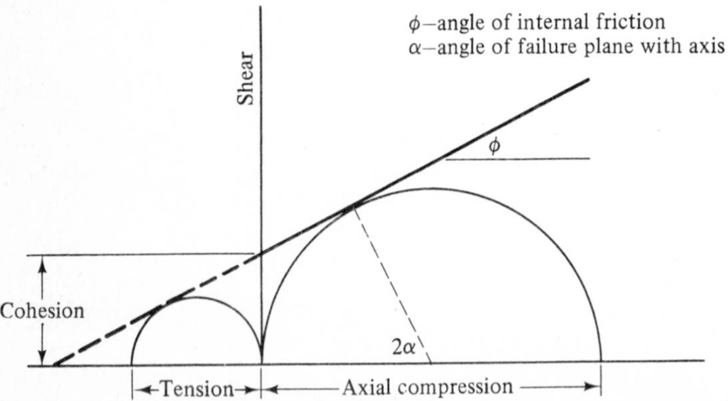

Figure 6-2 Relation between angle of rupture and angle of internal friction.

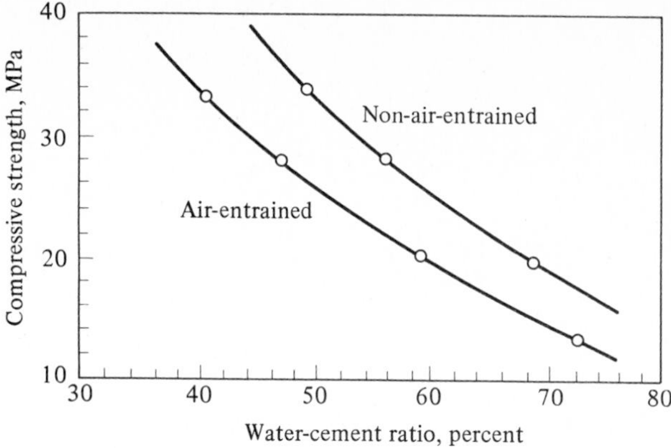

Figure 6-3 Typical *w/c* ratio–strength curves.

It has been estimated that as many as 50 factors may influence the strength of a concrete cylinder. We will discuss several of the most important of these factors.

Relationship between Water-Cement Ratio and Strength

As previously discussed (Chaps. 4 and 5), the proportion of water to cement used in concrete is the most important single factor in determining the quality of the paste. The quality of the cement-water paste, in turn, determines, to a large extent, the quality of concrete. In 1918 extensive testing by Duff Abrams at the Lewis Institute, University of Illinois, established a relationship between water-cement ratio and strength (Fig. 6-3). This relationship varies with variations in aggregates, cements, and admixtures and must be established for each combination of ingredients.

Influence of Curing on Strength

During the initial setting and hardening of concrete, only the outside layer of each cement particle has combined with water. Portland cement will continue to hydrate in the presence of moisture as long as any unhydrated cement remains. In some cases concrete has gained strength for years. Moist curing of concrete is necessary to complete the hydration process. Figure 6-4 shows a typical strength-gain curve of concrete kept moist up to 180 days and indicates how the strength gain is interrupted or stopped when curing is discontinued. The indicated increase in strength when concrete is moist-cured and then dried is due to the increase in shear strength in dry concrete when the voids are not filled with water.

Curing can be accomplished by applying and holding water on the surface of concrete or by applying membrane curing compounds. The amount of mixing water used in a concrete mix to achieve workability is more than that necessary to hydrate the portland cement (estimated to be about 30 percent of the weight of cement). The concrete can be properly cured if the mixing water is prevented from

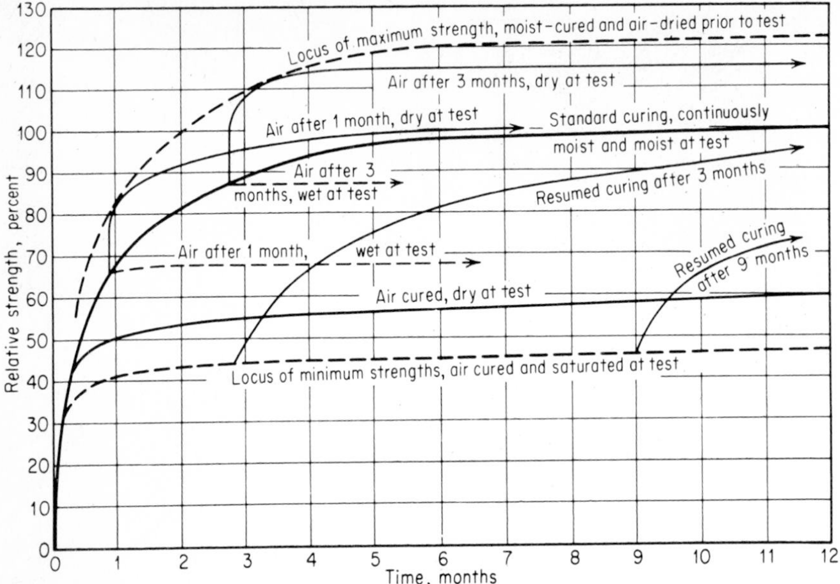

Figure 6-4 Effect of moist curing on the strength of concrete. *(U.S. Bureau of Reclamation,* Concrete Manual, *8th ed., 1975; George W. Washa,* Concrete Construction Handbook, *McGraw-Hill, New York, 1974.)*

evaporating by applying curing compounds which form a membrane over the surface of the concrete.

Figure 6-5 shows the influence of curing temperatures on concrete. Increased temperatures accelerate the hydration of portland cement. High initial curing temperatures give higher initial strength but do not increase the strength at 28 days. Decreased temperatures retard the strength gain of concrete.

Influence of Aggregates on Strength

Obviously aggregates play an important role in producing strength in concrete. The shearing strength of an aggregate particle itself may control the strength across a shear plane when the bond between the aggregate and the paste is strong enough to force the shear plane through the aggregate particles rather than around them. This is usually true in lightweight aggregate concretes.

Surface texture Angular particles and rough surface textures will generally produce higher-strength concrete with the same quality of paste (equal water-cement ratio) but require a higher paste content. The gel structure of hydrated portland cement tends to permeate a rough, porous surface of an aggregate particle and creates better bond. As explained in Chap. 9, angular aggregate particles will also create greater "aggregate interlock" and force shearing stresses through the aggregate particles.

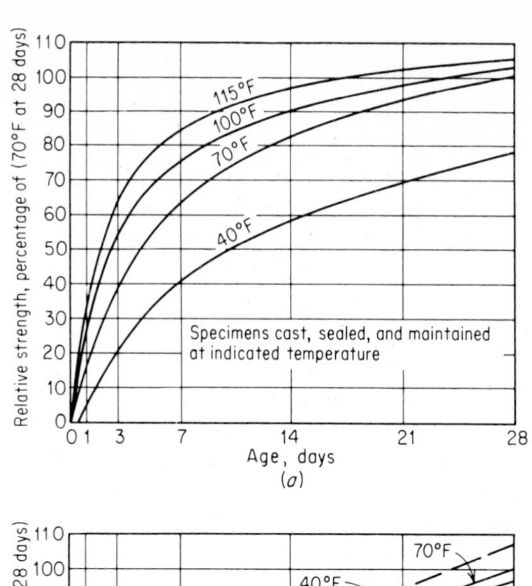

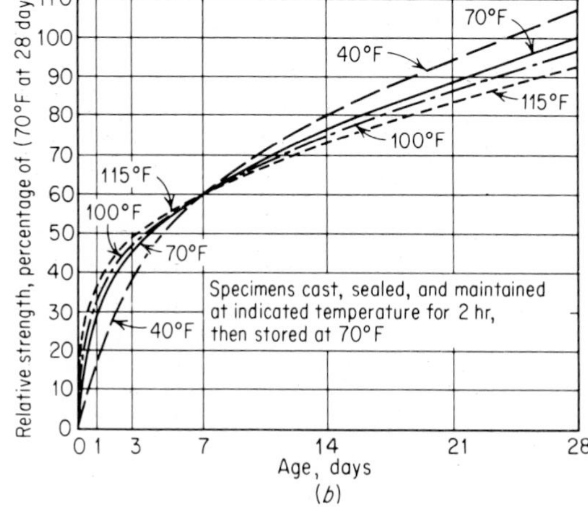

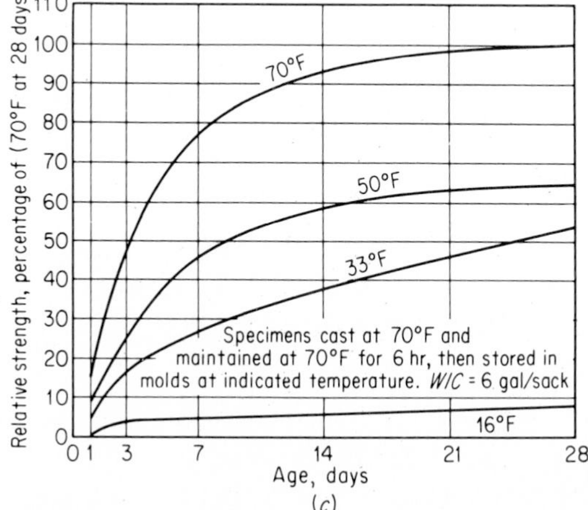

Figure 6-5 Influence of curing temperatures on the strength of concrete. (*U.S. Bureau of Reclamation,* Concrete Manual, *8th ed., 1975.)*

Particle shape In Chap. 3 we discussed why crushed aggregates are required for stability in asphaltic concrete pavements. This is not true in portland cement concrete since the hardened cement paste provides stability. Rounded aggregates have a lower void content, requiring less paste and less cement for a given water-cement ratio. Rounded aggregates also produce more workable concrete.

The advantages and disadvantages of crushed and rounded aggregates tend to balance out. It has been found that in concrete mixes containing an equal amount of cement, the strength is also nearly equal, regardless of whether crushed or rounded aggregates are used. The lower water-cement ratio obtained when rounded aggregate is used balances the better strength-producing properties achieved when crushed aggregate is used.

Maximum size of aggregate There has long been consensus that the largest size of aggregate practicable should be used to produce quality concrete. The larger the maximum size of aggregate, the fewer voids are left to fill with paste. This is important in the construction of concrete dams and other massive structures where the heat of hydration cannot readily escape and the thermal coefficient of expansion becomes a problem in dimensional stability. With large-size aggregates, a minimum amount of cement is required for high-quality, economical concrete.

Aggregate-Paste Bond

It is possible to produce concrete with higher strength when smaller maximum-size aggregates are used because of the increase in total bonding surface of the aggregate particles. For example, the surface area of an equal amount of $\frac{3}{4}$ aggregate is about double that of $1\frac{1}{2}$ aggregate, if we assume that the aggregate particles are spheres.

In a given plane of shear, therefore, the $\frac{3}{4}$ aggregate will have about 2 times as much bonding surface as the $1\frac{1}{2}$ aggregate.

The influence of the maximum size of aggregate on the strength of concrete is demonstrated in Fig. 6-6. In this case, the maximum strength that a given concrete can reach is limited by the aggregate size. Larger-size aggregates have the highest strength when the quality of paste controls. As the bond strength between the paste and the aggregate particles begins to control, the concretes having smaller maximum-size aggregate produce higher strengths.

Influence of Admixtures on Strength

Admixtures influence the strength of concrete in different ways. Air-entraining agents reduce strength; water-reducing admixtures increase strength by permitting a reduction in the water-cement ratio. Accelerating agents produce higher early strength, and retarding agents delay the initial strength gain.

Air-entraining agents As the gel structure of portland cement paste becomes more porous, its resistance to stress decreases. Air voids between the surface of aggregate and the gel structure decrease the bond. The influence of entrained air on concrete strength is shown in Fig. 6-7. This figure indicates that where the

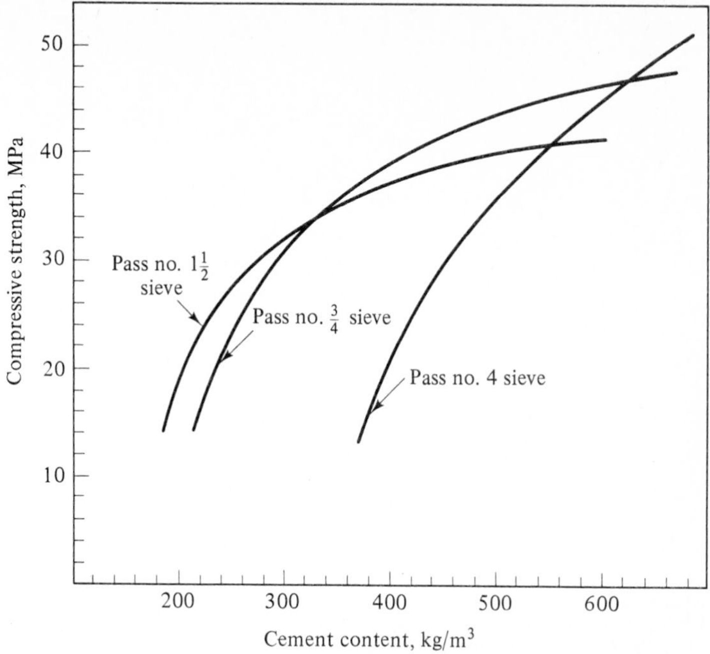

Figure 6-6 Smaller aggregates will produce greater strength in richer concrete mixtures. *(William A. Cordon and H. A. Gillespie, "Variables in Concrete Aggregates and Portland Cement Paste which Influence the Strength of Concrete,"* ACI Journal, *August 1963.)*

water-cement ratio is the same, entrained air will reduce the strength of concrete about 5 percent for each percent of entrained air.

Entrained air increases the workability of concrete, which permits a reduction in water requirement. This increases the strength for a given amount of cement.

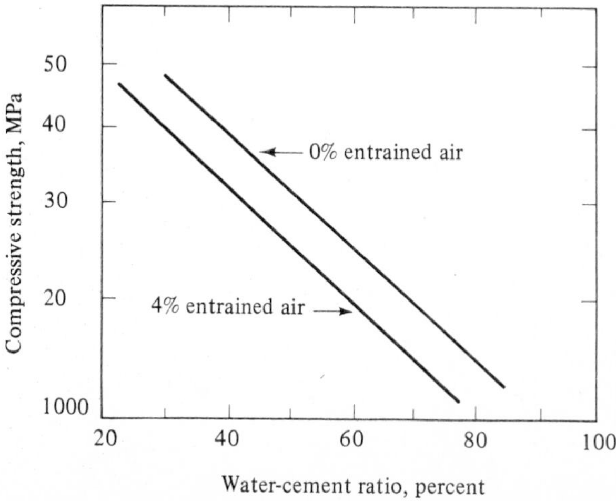

Figure 6-7 Influence of entrained air on the strength of concrete having the same *w/e* ratio. *(U.S. Bureau of Reclamation,* Concrete Manual, *8th ed., 1975.)*

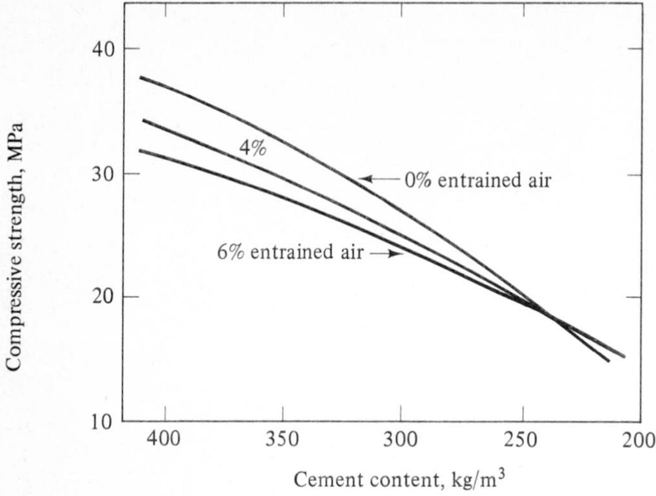

Figure 6-8 Entrained air reduces the strength of concrete in richer mixes. *(U.S. Bureau of Reclamation,* Concrete Manual, *8th ed., 1975.)*

Figure 6-8 shows the strength with and without entrained air for equal amounts of cement. For lower cement contents, entrained air actually increases the strength of concrete. For high-strength concrete, however, entrained air causes a significant loss in strength.

Water-reducing admixtures Water-reducing admixtures are widely accepted as a means of increasing slump and workability without sacrificing strength and quality. A second option is to reduce the water content and water-cement ratio without decreasing the slump or workability.

For example, assume the water content is reduced by 10 percent. In a typical mix, a 10 percent reduction in water will lower the water-cement ratio from 55 percent by weight of cement to 50 percent. From Fig. 6-3, this indicates an increase in strength of 4 MPa.

Pozzolans When pozzolans are added to a concrete mix, they add another cementing material which combines with lime and soluble alkalies (Chap. 4). When a suitable pozzolan is used as a partial replacement for portland cement, the early strength of the concrete is reduced, but the strength of concrete at later ages, when the pozzolanic action is complete, is not significantly changed.

When pozzolans are added, in addition to the regular amount of portland cement, they increase the strength of concrete; in some cases, very high strength concrete has been produced.

Accelerating and retarding admixtures As their name implies, accelerating and retarding admixtures either accelerate or retard the hydration reaction of portland cement.

Calcium chloride is the most common accelerating agent and will produce a strength gain with a type I cement similar to that obtained with a type III, high-early-strength cement. The major advantage of accelerating agents is to speed up the hydration and setting of cement in cold weather, which produces reasonable finishing times and reduces the time of protection from freezing. Calcium chloride cannot be used in prestressed concrete and should not be used in any concrete where corrosion of reinforcing steel is critical.

Retarding admixtures are useful in hot weather to keep concrete plastic and prevent setting and "cold joints" before successive layers of concrete can be placed. Retarding agents do not decrease slump loss of fresh concrete, nor do they reduce the strength gain of concrete after set has taken place. Many water-reducing admixtures are also set-retarding admixtures.

Flexural Strength

In reinforced-concrete design, the tensile strength and flexural strength of the concrete are of secondary importance since the reinforcing steel is designed to resist tensile stress. Tensile strength is of importance in plain concrete members and in pavement design.

The flexural strength of concrete is only about 10 percent of the compressive strength and is dependent to a large extent on the bond between the hardened portland cement paste and the aggregate particles. The size, surface texture, and shape of the aggregate particles, therefore, have a pronounced influence on the flexural strength of concrete.

6-2 DURABILITY

Concrete as a suitable structural material must be able to withstand the forces of deterioration. The most important of these include

1. Freezing and thawing action
2. Chemical attack
3. Abrasion
4. Alkali-aggregate reaction

In cold climates the most serious and persistent deterioration force in concrete is freezing and thawing. When water freezes into ice, it expands about 9 percent of its original volume and exerts tremendous force on any confining vessel. In concrete, water-filled voids are subject to these pressures. Hydrated portland cement gel contains voids of different sizes.

Void System in Hardened Concrete

Several types of voids occur in concrete and are classified according to size and origins (see Fig. 6-9).

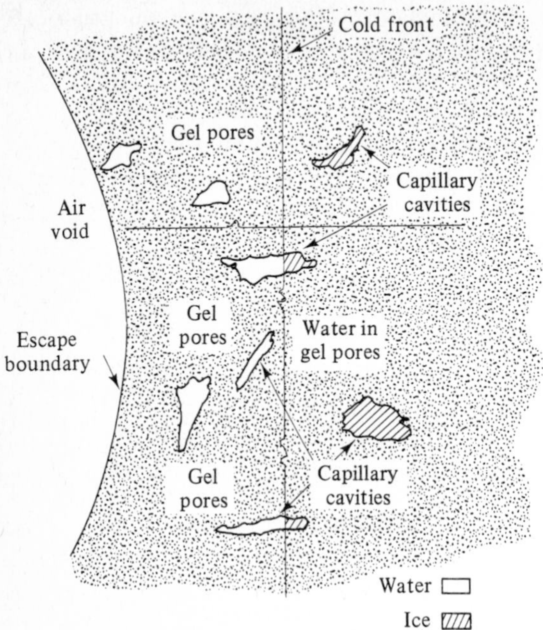

Figure 6-9 Model of void system in concrete paste. *(William A. Cordon,* Freezing and Thawing of Concrete Mechanisms and Control, *ACI Monograph, no. 3, 1966.)*

1. *Gel pores.* Gel pores are the interstitial cavities among the hydration products of portland cement. Gel pores are estimated to be about 1.5 to 2.0 nm in diameter.
2. *Capillary cavities.* Capillary cavities are estimated to average about 500 nm in diameter and are usually formed by excess uncombined water not required for hydration.
3. *Entrained air.* When air-entraining agents are used, billions of tiny spheres of air are introduced into the gel structure. These are many times larger than capillary voids and will vary from 1 μm to 1 mm or more in size.
4. *Entrapped air.* If concrete is not completely compacted, pockets of air are left among the aggregate particles. They commonly collect beneath particles of coarse aggregate and are irregular in shape. When they show on a formed surface, they are unsightly and indicate poor workmanship. If these large pockets of air are filled with water, when frozen, they exert enough force to fracture the concrete. Fortunately, large voids are seldom completely filled with water.

Porosity and Permeability

It is necessary for any of the various voids in concrete to become filled with water before any of the deteriorating mechanisms of freezing and thawing operate. Gel pores are too small to significantly contribute to permeability, and the air voids are not connected. It is the capillary voids that become filled with water and

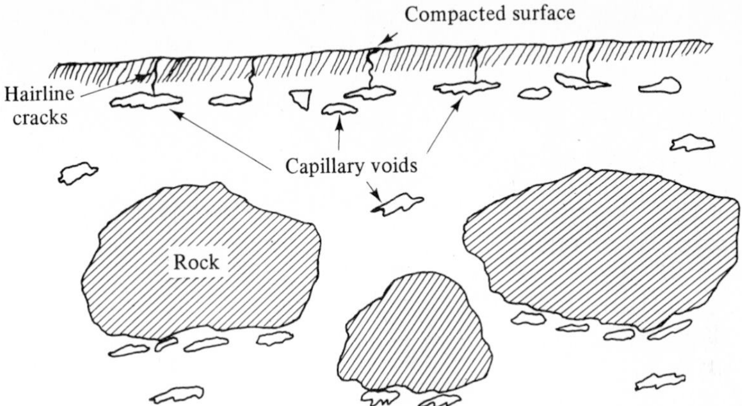

Figure 6-10 Model of capillary voids forming under rock particles and beneath a compacted surface.

permit the ingress of moisture into concrete (Fig. 6-10). They tend to rise and collect under particles of aggregate, thus providing channels for water to penetrate. The capillary porosity can be reduced by reducing the amount of uncombined water in the portland cement paste. Low *w/c* ratios and low mixing-water content will reduce permeability (Fig. 6-11). Although normal

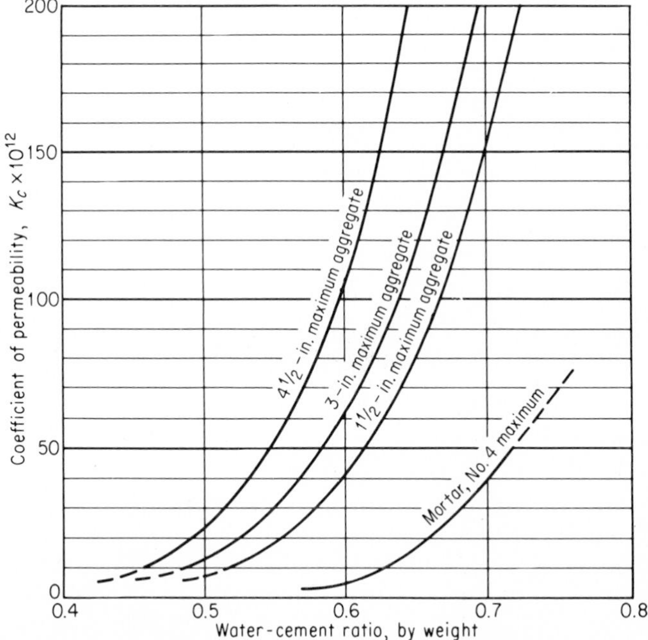

Figure 6-11 Permeability varies with the quantity of capillary voids. *(George W. Washa,* Concrete Construction Handbook, *McGraw-Hill, New York, 1974.)*

amounts of entrained-air voids increase the porosity of concrete, they do not tend to increase permeability. Being larger, spherical disconnected voids, they tend to stop capillary flow through concrete.

Freezing and Thawing Mechanisms

The following mechanisms have been suggested as being contributing factors in freezing and thawing deterioration.

Critical saturation Unless a void is filled, freezing water can expand and fill the void. The critical saturation point is above 91 percent since water will expand about 9 percent upon freezing.

Osmosis The gel structure may be considered a porous membrane, and any void containing a solution of water which has a greater concentration of alkalies and salts will draw water from the surrounding gel structure. Moisture may also be drawn from the soil or water in contact with the concrete, which increases the likelihood of critical saturation. Forces resulting from osmosis are in an opposite direction to the expansion forces of freezing water and therefore add to the pressures exerted in the gel structure.

Hydraulic pressure Water does not freeze instantaneously, but ice crystals start forming within the solution. As freezing progresses, the ice crystals grow larger until they completely fill a void. During the freezing process in capillaries of hardened cement, the frozen water expands and forces the unfrozen water into the surrounding gel structure (Fig. 6-9). Water in the gel pores will not freeze because the gel pores are so small that ice crystals cannot form and the gel-pore water exists as supercooled water. The pressure will build, unless there is flow away from the void, and the gel structure will be destroyed.

The comparatively large entrained-air voids provide an escape for the water pressure (Fig. 6-9). The pressure developed in the gel structure will depend on

1. The coefficient of permeability of the gel structure
2. The distance from the capillary void to the air void boundary
3. The rate of freezing

When the entrained-air voids in concrete are spaced sufficiently close, the hydraulic pressure mechanism does not operate.

Diffusion When water freezes in a capillary, its energy level is reduced. The surrounding gel water has a higher energy level and will migrate to the frozen ice crystal where it, too, will freeze. In soils this is referred to as "frost heave" and will continue as long as unfrozen water is available. In concrete, ice lenses will form and fracture the concrete.

Any water drawn from the gel structure by diffusion will cause shrinkage and, if near the surface, may result in fine, hairline cracks.

Diffusion is particularly damaging when it occurs near a pavement surface. If the surface of a pavement is compacted by poor, premature finishing methods or by rapid drying, any subsequent excess mixing water that bleeds to the surface will be trapped below the compacted surface and create an abundance of capillary voids (Fig. 6-10). When these voids are filled with frozen water, diffusion of the gel water is often sufficient to force the compacted surface off the pavement. This is known as "scaling." Hairline cracks which form open channels for surface moisture to flow to the ice crystals may also contribute to scaling.

Deicing salts The use of salts to melt the snow and ice on concrete pavements develops other mechanisms of concrete deterioration.

1. Lowers temperature of concrete. Snow and ice melting in a salt solution draws heat from a concrete pavement and may lower the temperature of the concrete significantly.
2. Provides a supply of water for diffusion to capillary ice.
3. Increases the concentration of salt in capillary water which increases saturation and stress through osmosis.
4. Makes eutectic expansion possible.

Eutectic expansion A second expansion in salt solutions may cause damage such as scaling and deterioration of concrete and explains some conflicting test results.

With relative dilute solutions of salt, the phase diagram of water-salt solutions (Fig. 6-12) shows the relative freezing point of solutions with various percentages

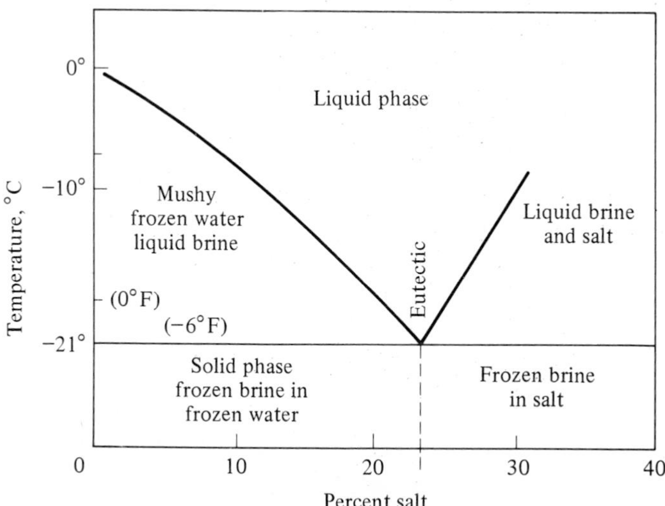

Figure 6-12 Water-salt (NaCl) phase diagram. *(Charles Hansen, unpublished test results.)*

of salt. In weak salt solutions, the water freezes first and gradually concentrates the salt solution until it reaches the eutectic concentration of about 23 percent, at which time it freezes at a temperature of about −20°C. If the eutectic concentration of salt solution freezes in a capillary, the hydraulic pressure mechanism operates and can be overcome with entrained air. In more dilute solutions, however, the water freezes solid, leaving pockets of unfrozen salt solution. When the temperature reaches −20°C, the remaining salt solution freezes. The resulting expansion occurs in solid ice, so that the capillary ice expands as a unit. This secondary expansion may cause deterioration in concrete otherwise protected, including air-entrained concrete, and will possibly explain unanswered problems in concrete scaling.

Recommendations to Avoid Freezing and Thawing Deterioration

1. Keep concrete from becoming saturated. Unless the capillary voids are filled, freezing and thawing mechanisms will not operate.
   (*a*) Good drainage.
   (*b*) Protective coatings.
2. Reduce the number of capillary voids by using a low water-cement ratio.
3. Entrain about 5 percent air in the concrete.
4. Avoid compaction of pavement surface by finishing before all bleed water has come to the surface.
5. Prevent compaction of surface by rapid drying of fresh concrete.
6. Prevent exposure to freezing and thawing action while concrete is immature and contains uncombined water.
7. Avoid the use of deicing salts.

Chemical Attack

Acids The cement paste of concrete is composed of several hydration products containing calcium. These compounds will react with any acid; as a result, the concrete will disintegrate. Common types of acid attack come from food, processing plants, and certain types of sewage. Lactic and acidic acids found in the dairy and food processing industries may show a mild attack on concrete and, over a long period of time, cause deterioration (Table 6-1).

Sewage Concrete pipe is used extensively in the conveyance of domestic sewage without appreciable deterioration. Hydrogen sulfide gas (H_2S) may be formed under certain conditions by decomposition of sulfur compounds by bacteria. If this gas combines with oxygen and condenses on the surface of exposed concrete, it will change to sulfuric acid, which will attack the concrete. Certain types of industrial sewage containing acids or sulfates will cause deterioration of concrete.

Table 6-1 Effect of commonly used chemicals on concrete (ACI 201)

Rate of attack at ambient temperature	Inorganic acids	Organic acids	Alkaline solutions	Salt solutions	Miscellaneous
Rapid	Hydrochloric Hydrofluoric Nitric Sulfuric	Acetic Formic Lactic	—	Aluminum chloride	—
Moderate	Phosphoric	Tannic	Sodium hydroxide— > 20 percent†	Ammonium nitrate Ammonium sulfate Sodium sulfate Magnesium sulfate Calcium sulfate	Bromine (gas) Sulfite liquor
Slow	Carbonic	—	Sodium hydroxide 10 to 20 percent† Sodium hypochlorite	Ammonium chloride Magnesium chloride Sodium cyanide	Chlorine (gas) Seawater Soft water
Negligible	—	Oxalic Tartaric	Sodium hydroxide < 10 percent† Sodium hypochlorite Ammonium hydroxide	Calcium chloride Sodium chloride Zinc nitrate Sodium chromate	Ammonia (liquid)

† Avoid siliceous aggregates because they are attacked by strong solutions of sodium hydroxide.

Sulfate attack Alkali soils and drainage water in certain regions and, to a lesser extent, seawater contain magnesium and sodium sulfate and other salts. These chemicals, particularly magnesium salts, will react with hydrated calcium aluminate in hardened concrete and produce calcium sulfoaluminates. This causes expansion and disintegration of the hardened cement paste.

The severity of sulfate attack depends on the percentage of tricalcium aluminate (C_3A) in the cement and the concentration of the sulfate salts. Specifications for sulfate-resisting cements limit the percentage of tricalcium aluminate (Table 6-2).

Carbonation

As explained in Chap. 4, when calcium hydroxide, $Ca(OH)_2$, is exposed to the air, it will react with CO_2 and form $CaCO_3$. Calcium hydroxide is one of the hydration products of portland cement and is available to react with CO_2 in the atmosphere. This process occurs slowly and is not usually important in hardened

Table 6-2 Recommendations for normal-weight concrete subject to sulfate attack (ACI 201)

Exposure	Water-soluble sulfate (SO_4) in soil, %	Sulfate (SO_4) in water, ppm	Cement	Water-cement ratio, maximum†
Mild	0.00–0.10	0–150	—	—
Moderate‡	0.10–0.20	150–1500	Type II, IP (MS) IS (MS)	0.50
Severe	0.20–2.00	1500–10,000	Type V	0.45
Very severe	Over 2.00	Over 10,000	Type V + Pozzolan§	0.45

† A lower water-cement ratio may be necessary to prevent corrosion of embedded items. See sec. 4.5.1.1. of ACI 201.

‡ Seawater also falls in this category.

§ Use a pozzolan which has been determined by tests to improve sulfate resistance when used in concrete containing type V cement.

concrete with the possible exception of dimensional instability of lightweight masonry units.

Carbonation can be a serious problem when freshly placed concrete floors are exposed to excessive concentrations of CO_2. This problem occurs frequently when unvented, open-flame space heaters, used to prevent freezing, exhaust the oxygen in the air and leave excessive concentrations of CO_2. This produces a soft inferior layer on the surface of the concrete.

6-3 DIMENSIONAL STABILITY

The volume and dimensions of hardened concrete will change slightly for the following reasons:

1. Elastic deformation (strain) resulting from stress
2. Creep or permanent deformation because of stress
3. Shrinkage of plastic and hardened concrete
4. Thermal volume change
5. Expansion because of chemical reactions

Elastic and Plastic Deformation

In the initial stages of applying a compression load to a concrete cylinder, it exhibits elastic properties; that is, it will deform under load and return to its original length when the load is released (Fig. 6-13). As the stress approaches the

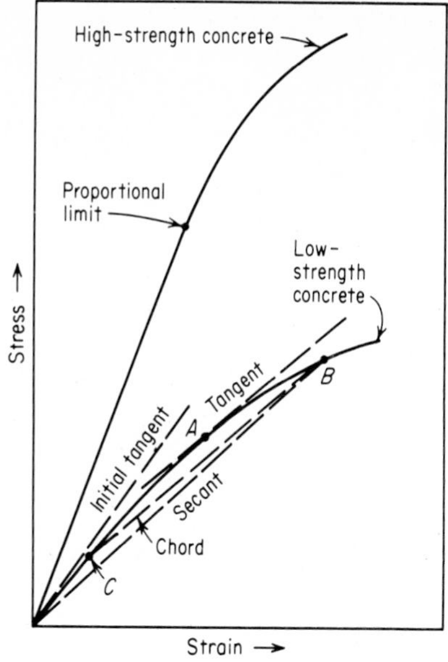

Figure 6-13 Stress-strain curve for concrete showing the various ways of determining the modulus of elasticity.

ultimate strength of the concrete, strain increases more for a given stress and the stress-strain relationship is no longer a straight line, but shows increasing curvature (Fig. 6-13). When the load is released, part of the deformation is recovered. The permanent deformation is called "creep."

Modulus of Elasticity

The "modulus of elasticity" is defined as the ratio of stress over strain, and in elastic materials it is a straight-line relationship:

$$E = \frac{\text{stress}}{\text{strain}} \tag{6-1}$$

In determining E for concrete, strain is usually measured at zero load and at some load well below the ultimate strength of the concrete. This gives the secant modulus of elasticity, which is generally used in design (Fig. 6-13). The chord will indicate a lower modulus, and the initial tangent will indicate a higher modulus.

The modulus of elasticity is important in reinforced-concrete design, since deflection of beams and floors is inversely proportional to the modulus of elasticity:

$$D = \frac{PL^3}{48EI} \tag{6-2}$$

where E = modulus of elasticity
P = applied center load
D = deflection
L = distance between simple supports
I = moment of inertia

Since deflection controls many design considerations, the modulus of elasticity is of first importance. The modulus of elasticity of normal structural concrete varies with the strength and can be estimated from the following ACI formula:

$$E_c = W^{1.5} 33 \sqrt{f'_c} \tag{6-3}$$

where E_c = modulus of elasticity of concrete
W = density of concrete (unit weight, lb/ft^3)
f'_c = strength of concrete

Creep

When concrete is loaded, elastic deformations and some nonelastic deformations take place. If the load is maintained, the nonelastic deformation or creep continues for long periods (Fig. 6-14). Creep occurs because of the shifting of the internal structure of the cement gel, movement of moisture, and possibly the adjustments in the aggregate-cement bond. Creep is desirable in some cases since it tends to relieve stress concentrations. Weaker concrete will deform, shifting stresses to stronger concrete or to reinforcing steel.

A portion of inelastic deformation is permanent and must be considered in the design of concrete structural members since all structures have a permanent dead load.

In prestressed concrete a camber, with the center of the member slightly higher than ends, is designed into the member so that when creep and elastic deformation of concrete and steel cables take place, the member will be level.

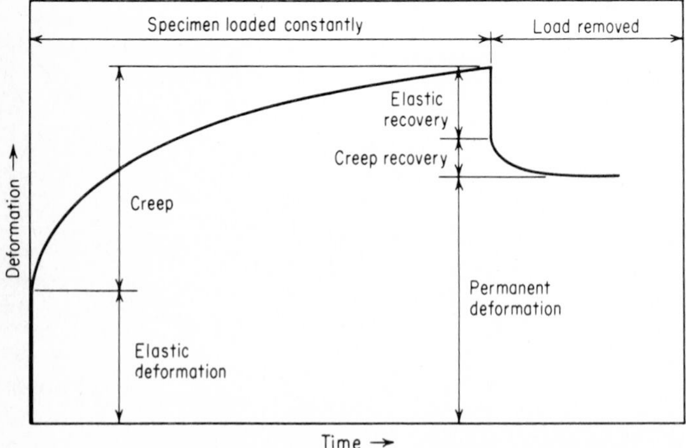

Figure 6-14 Elastic and creep deformations of mass concrete under constant load followed by load removal. *(U.S. Bureau of Reclamation,* Concrete Manual, *8th ed., 1975.)*

Figure 6-15 Plastic shrinkage cracks showing irregular pattern.

Shrinkage

Plastic shrinkage Freshly placed concrete will decrease in volume as the solid particles settle and water bleeds to the surface. When there is excessive evaporation, the surface will shrink because of loss of moisture and compaction. Plastic shrinkage cracks will develop. This usually occurs before final finishing (Fig. 6-15). These cracks can be avoided by preventing rapid evaporation by protection from sun and wind or by covering with plastic sheets or a monomolecular film.

Drying shrinkage After the concrete has hardened, drying shrinkage will take place principally by the contraction of the gel structure as moisture leaves. Concrete shrinkage takes place in the hardened paste fraction and has been found to be a function of the water content and water-cement ratio of a concrete mix (Fig. 6-16).

Since drying shrinkage is an inherent property of concrete, it must be restrained with reinforcing steel or controlled by contraction joints. A contraction joint or deep groove every 3 m will prevent intermediate cracking in concrete slabs which are relatively free to move on a subgrade.

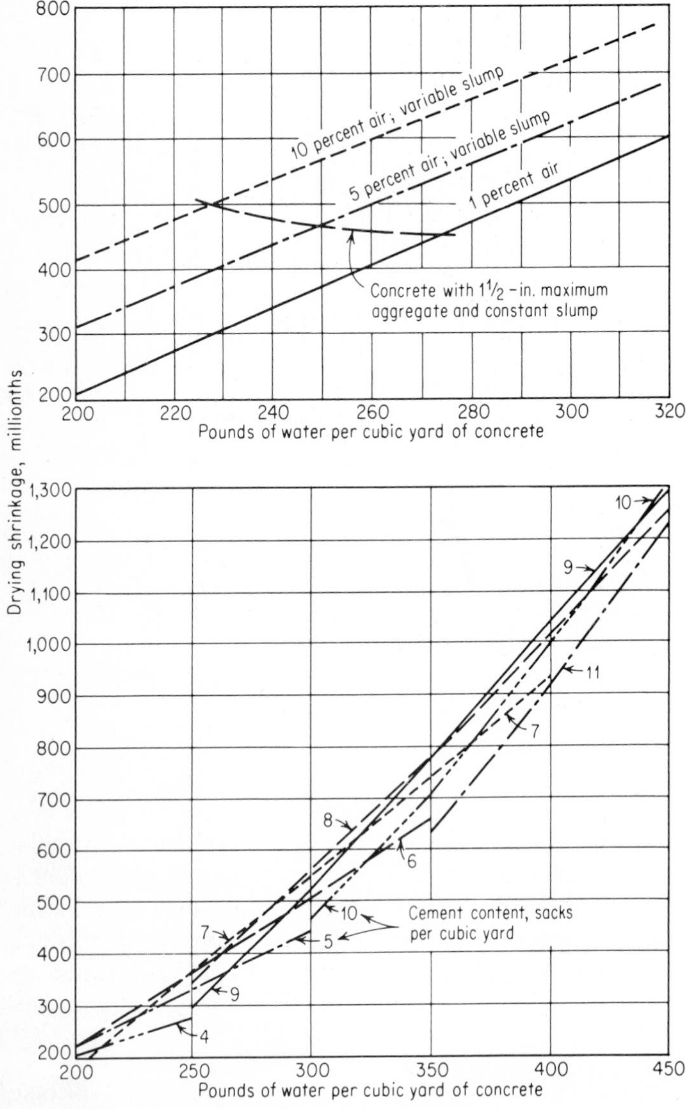

Figure 6-16 Drying shrinkage is a function of the water content of a concrete mixture which increases as the paste content increases. *(U.S. Bureau of Reclamation,* Concrete Manual, *8th ed., 1975.)*

Thermal Volume Change

The coefficient of thermal expansion averages about 14×10^{-6} cm/°C. This amount of expansion or contraction with changes in temperature is not usually significant, since it is compatible with reinforcing steel and readily dissipates in a structural member.

Severe problems develop in massive structures, however; where heat cannot be dissipated, thermal contraction on the surface without a corresponding change in the interior will cause cracking. In this type of structure, the interior temperature rise resulting from heat of hydration must be within acceptable limits from the mean ambient temperature, or the interior of the concrete block must be cooled with cooling coils to eliminate incompatible temperature differentials.

Chemical Reactions

Alkali-aggregate reaction, discussed in Chaps. 4 and 5, causes expansion in concrete because of the formation of unstable silica gel. This expansion is localized around individual aggregate particles. When the expansion stresses exceed the tensile strength of the gel structure, cracks occur and the structure is damaged. The volume of the concrete increases; but more importantly, internal stresses develop.

Certain carbonate rocks will also react with alkalies, causing damage. This type of reaction has not been as extensive or severe but can cause problems.

6-4 LIGHTWEIGHT AGGREGATE CONCRETES

Because of the wide variation of lightweight aggregate concretes, special mention should be made of their unique properties. Figure 6-17 shows the general relationship of the density and strength among all lightweight aggregate concretes.

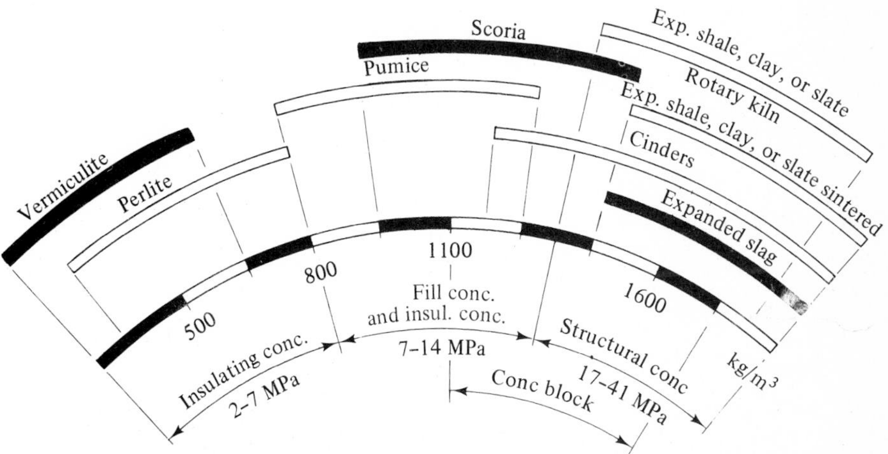

Figure 6-17 Relative strength and density of lightweight aggregate concretes. *(Shale, Clay and Slate Institute.)*

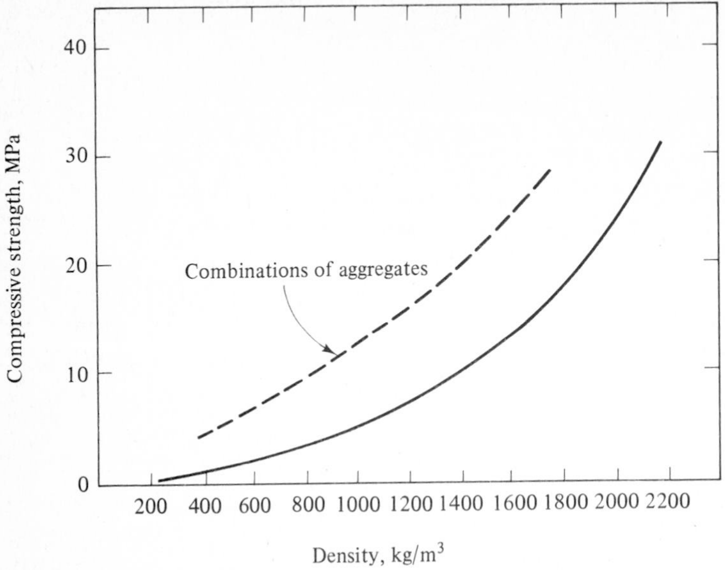

Figure 6-18 General relationships between density and strength of concretes.

Compressive Strength

The strength of concretes made with lightweight aggregates is, in general, a function of their density (Fig. 6-18). Notable exceptions to this general statement can be found in various combinations of a coarse and a fine lightweight aggregate and combinations of natural sand and structural lightweight aggregates. It is apparent that there are limitations on the amount of strength that can be produced with low-density aggregates.

Flexural Strength

In most concretes, flexural strength is about one-tenth its compressive strength. In most cases, the flexural strength of lightweight aggregate concrete is higher than that of regular concrete of the same compressive strength level. This is probably due to the porous surface texture of most lightweight aggregates.

Modulus of Elasticity

The modulus of elasticity of most lightweight concretes was found to be only about one-half as great as those of natural aggregate concretes of the same strength.

Thermal Conductivity

Concrete made with regular aggregates is a poor insulating material having a thermal conductivity, or K, value of about 10 to 12. The thermal conductivity factor K is a measure of the watts, W, transmitted through 1 m^2 of material

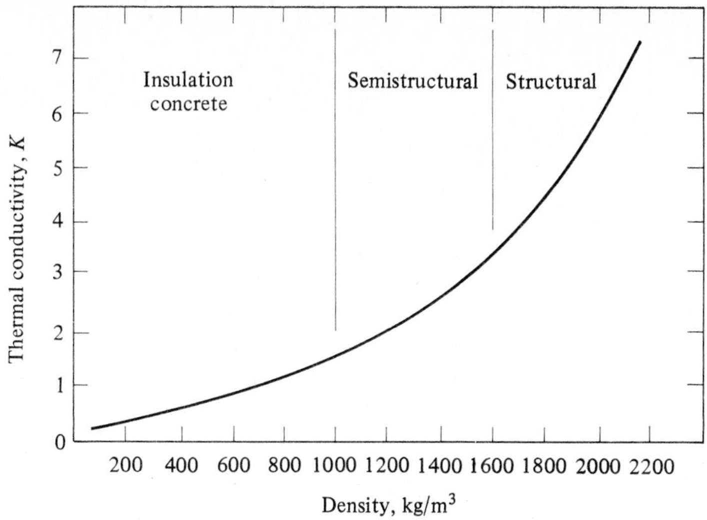

Figure 6-19 General relationship between density and thermal conductivity of all types of concrete.

1 m thick with a differential of temperature of 1°C.

$$K = \frac{\text{W}}{(\text{m})(°\text{C})} \tag{6-4}$$

The more common term for comparing insulation properties of a material is the R value, which is

$$R = \frac{1}{K} T \tag{6-5}$$

where R = insulation value
K = thermal conductivity
T = thickness, in or cm/2.54

Concrete made with certain lightweight aggregates has good insulating properties, as indicated in Fig. 6-19.

When perlite and vermiculite aggregates are used, as loose-fill insulation, the K values will be as low as 0.30, which will give an R value of 3 for each 1 in of material.

Durability

Freezing and thawing and wetting and drying tests indicate that lightweight aggregate concretes have surprisingly good resistance to these forces of deterioration. The porous structure of the concretes, especially when air-entraining agents are used, does not allow most freezing and thawing mechanisms to operate.

Drying Shrinkage

The drying shrinkage of lightweight concrete is, in general, greater than that of regular concrete, because more mixing water is used and the softer aggregates offer less resistance to shrinkage forces.

6-5 SUMMARY

The compressive strength of concrete is influenced by many variables, including the following:

1. *w/c* ratio
2. Curing
3. Aggregates
    - Grading
    - Surface texture
    - Particle shape
    - Maximum size
4. Admixtures
    - Air-entraining agents
    - Water-reducing agents
    - Pozzolans
    - Accelerating and retarding agents

The flexural strength and tensile strength of concrete vary with the compressive strength, but are much smaller. In reinforced concrete, the reinforcing steel is designed to carry these stresses.

Freezing and thawing action is the most serious cause of deterioration in cold climates. Other important causes of deterioration of concrete include chemical attack, abrasion, and alkali-aggregate reaction.

Concrete will shrink and expand as a result of stress applied to it, drying shrinkage, thermal expansion, and expansion from chemical reactions.

The properties of lightweight aggregate concretes depend on the particular aggregates used. There is wide variation in the properties of lightweight aggregates. Lightweight aggregates can produce high-strength concrete or, in the case of insulation, produce very weak concretes. Lightweight aggregates are used for the reduction of dead loads in structural concretes. Other major uses include the production of masonry units and insulation.

REFERENCES

1. U.S. Bureau of Reclamation: *Concrete Manual*, 8th ed., 1975.
2. ACI Committee 201: "Guide to Durable Concrete," December 1977.
3. Cordon, William A., and H. A. Gillespie: "Variables in Concrete Aggregates and Portland Cement Paste which Influence the Strength of Concrete," *ACI Journal*, August 1963.

4. Cordon, William A.: *Freezing and Thawing of Concrete Mechanisms and Control*, ACI Monograph, no. 3, 1966.
5. Hansen, Charles: unpublished test results.
6. Washa, George W.: *Concrete Construction Handbook*, McGraw-Hill, New York, 1974.
7. Powers, T. C.: "Resistance of Concrete to Frost at Early Ages," *RILEM Proceedings*, 1956.

QUESTIONS AND PROBLEMS

1 Why is compressive strength of concrete so important in design and construction?

2 Discuss the various things that influence the strength of concrete.

3 Does the standard compressive-strength test measure the crushing strength of concrete? Explain.

4 How do the aggregates influence the strength of concrete?

5 Explain why the w/c ratio is considered so important in concrete strength.

6 Does concrete gain strength when it dries out? Explain.

7 Do crushed aggregates produce better concrete than rounded aggregates?

8 Explain why smaller-size aggregates may produce higher-strength concrete.

9 (*a*) Explain why an air-entraining admixture may reduce the strength of concrete.
(*b*) Will air entrainment ever increase concrete strength?

10 Explain why a water-reducing admixture may increase the strength of concrete.

11 Can pozzolans be used to increase concrete strength? Explain.

12 When will accelerating and retarding admixtures be used to advantage?

13 Why is the void system in concrete important?

14 Discuss the various freezing and thawing mechanisms which may cause concrete deterioration.

15 Why is it so difficult to determine the cause of concrete deterioration?

16 How can concrete scaling be prevented?

17 What chemicals attack concrete?

18 Can concrete be made which will be immune to chemical attack?

19 Why do concentrations of CO_2 cause a freshly placed concrete floor to produce a soft, inferior surface?

20 Is concrete strictly an elastic material? How does this influence design considerations?

21 Is creep detrimental in concrete design? Explain.

22 What is the difference between plastic shrinkage and drying shrinkage in concrete?

23 Explain why thermal volume change is important in some types of construction.

24 Discuss the advantages and disadvantages of using lightweight aggregate concretes.

25 Can lightweight concrete be made as strong as normal-weight concrete?

26 Which lightweight aggregates would be used for (*a*) insulation, (*b*) structural members?

27 Is it possible to make insulating structural concrete? Explain.

CHAPTER

SEVEN

STEEL

The first use of iron, probably in Armenia, dates back to about 1500 B.C. Crude furnaces, possibly holes in the ground with natural or forced draft, produced a crude form of steel from iron ore and charcoal.

The use of steel has advanced continuously since about A.D. 1865, until it is estimated that today steel and steel alloys are used in at least a million different applications.

Three principal products of steel used on construction are

1. Structural steel
2. Reinforcing steel
3. Miscellaneous forms and pans

Because of the complex and extensive procedures involved in the manufacture of steel, the engineer and architect are required to base the design of steel structures on the standard products and shapes which are available.

Since about 1955 the steel technology has advanced rapidly. The development of the basic oxygen furnace and continuous casting and the use of computer control of production units have increased the efficiency and reduced the cost of steel production (Fig. 7-1). In the United States, the use of the latest technology has been slower than in newer plants in Japan and West Germany. The heavy investment in open-hearth furnaces in the United States has made replacement costly. Figure 7-1 indicates the relative amount of steel produced in the United States by various methods.

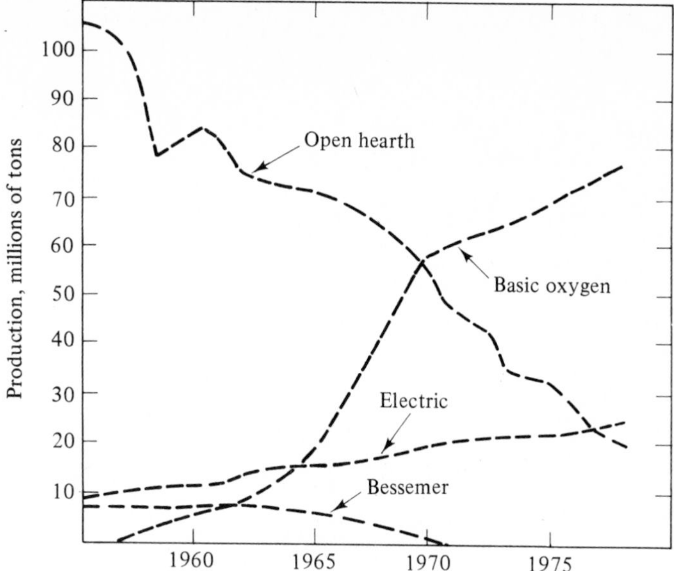

Figure 7-1 Approximate steel production by various methods in the United States.

7-1 MANUFACTURE OF PIG IRON

The first process in the manufacture of steel is the reduction of iron ore to pig iron. This is accomplished by charging alternate layers of iron ore, coke, and limestone in a continuously operating blast furnace. Blasts of hot air forced up through the charge accelerate the combustion of coke and raise the temperature sufficiently high to reduce the iron ore to molten iron (Fig. 7-2). Limestone is used as a flux and unites with impurities in iron ore to form slag. The blast furnace accomplishes the following:

1. Reduction of iron ore to metallic iron
2. Absorption of carbon into molten iron
3. Separation of impurities from iron

7-2 CONVERSION OF PIG IRON TO STEEL

As pig iron is tapped from the blast furnace, it contains an excess of carbon, silicon, manganese, sulfur, and phosphorus as impurities. Four principal methods are used to refine the pig iron and scrap metal:

1. Open-hearth furnace
2. Bessemer converter
3. Electric furnace
4. Basic oxygen furnace

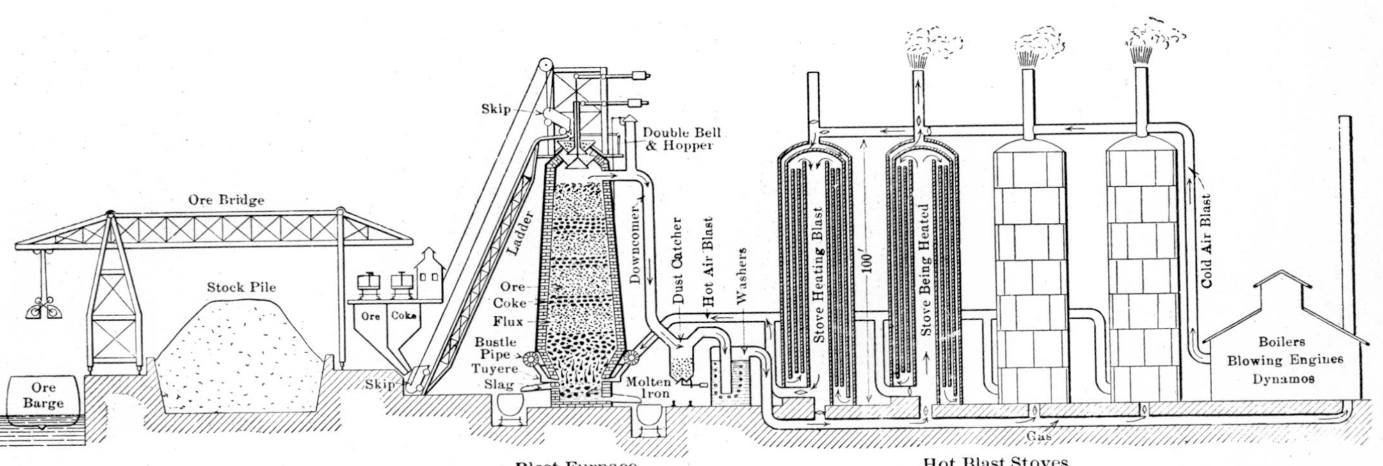

Figure 7-2 Sectional view of a blast furnace. (*O. M. Withey and G. W. Washa*, Materials of Construction, *Wiley, New York, 1954.*)

Open-Hearth Furnace

In the open-hearth furnace the charge of pig iron, limestone and miscellaneous scrap iron, steel, and alloys is exposed to overhead heat produced by a mixture of fuel and preheated air. The hearth is a rectangular, saucer-shaped basin (Fig. 7-3). Limestone is charged first, then iron ore followed by pieces of scrap iron and steel. After the solid materials are melted, pig iron is added. The impurities are removed by the oxidizing action and absorption into the slag. In recent years oxygen has been introduced through lances, resulting in greatly increased efficiency of production.

Bessemer Process

The bessemer converter is a pear-shaped, steel vessel lined with refractory brick (Fig. 7-4). The converter has a capacity of about 25 tons and can be tilted 180 degrees. The converter is tilted to receive the charge of molten pig iron and then returned to an upright position. Cold air is blown up through the charge of molten pig iron, oxidizing the impurities. This also furnishes the additional heat necessary to maintain the resulting steel in a molten state. After the impurities have been oxidized, desirable amounts of alloys, including carbon, can be added. Until about 1955 the Bessemer converter was important in steel production, but only a small amount of steel is produced by this method today.

Electric Furnace

An electric furnace uses electricity in melting a charge of scrap metal (Fig. 7-5). Pellets refined from low-grade iron ores contain 90 percent iron and can be fed directly into electric furnaces, bypassing the manufacture of pig iron.

The temperature can be closely regulated, and the addition of alloys can be accurately controlled.

The massive conversion from open-hearth furnaces to basic oxygen furnaces in recent years has increased the importance of electric furnaces. The open-hearth furnace uses about 50 percent scrap, whereas the basic oxygen furnace uses only about 30 percent scrap metal. Therefore the electric furnace has become more important in the use of scrap.

Basic Oxygen Furnace

A typical basic oxygen furnace is pear-shaped, and pure oxygen is blown through a lance onto the top of the charge (Fig. 7-6). The charge consists of molten pig iron and scrap metal. The furnace is lined with a basic refractory. In later developments the oxygen is blown into the bottom of the furnace. This technique produces greater efficiency and permits greater use of scrap.

A batch of steel can be produced in 45 min with a basic oxygen furnace. The same size batch takes from 5 to 8 h in an open-hearth furnace. The pure oxygen burns a greater percentage of impurities, and carbon is reduced by the creation of carbon monoxide gas. The basic oxygen furnace can be used to make not only low-carbon steel, but also high-carbon and alloy steels.

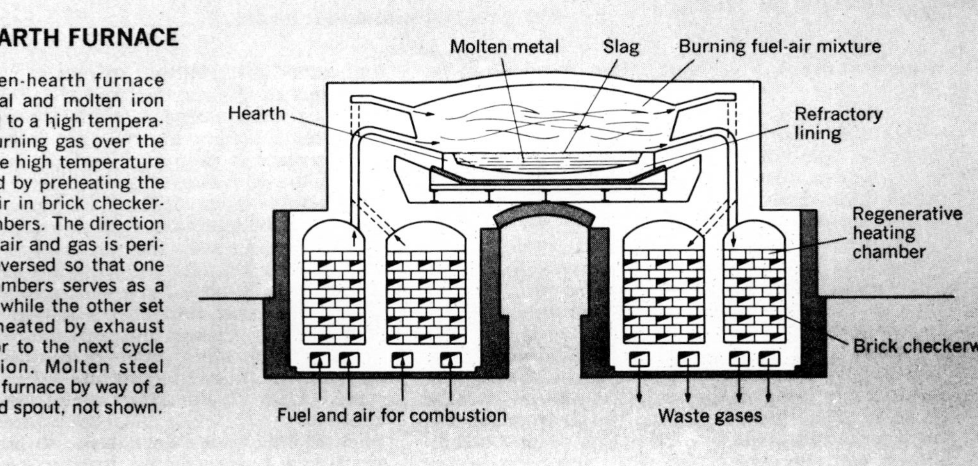

Figure 7-3 Open-hearth furnace. (*Article on steel*, Encyclopedia Americana, *1976*.)

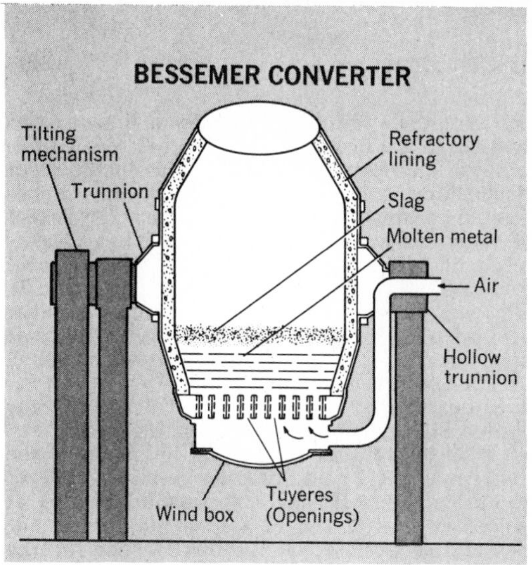

Figure 7-4 Bessemer converter. (*Article on steel*, Encyclopedia Americana, *1976*.)

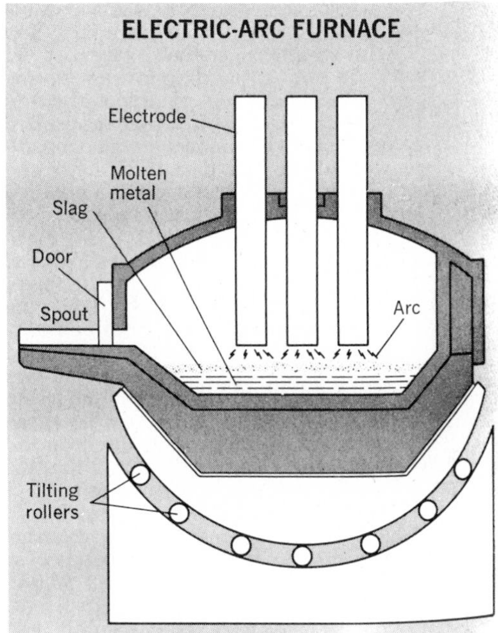

Figure 7-5 Electric-arc furnace. (*Article on steel*, Encyclopedia Americana, *1976*.)

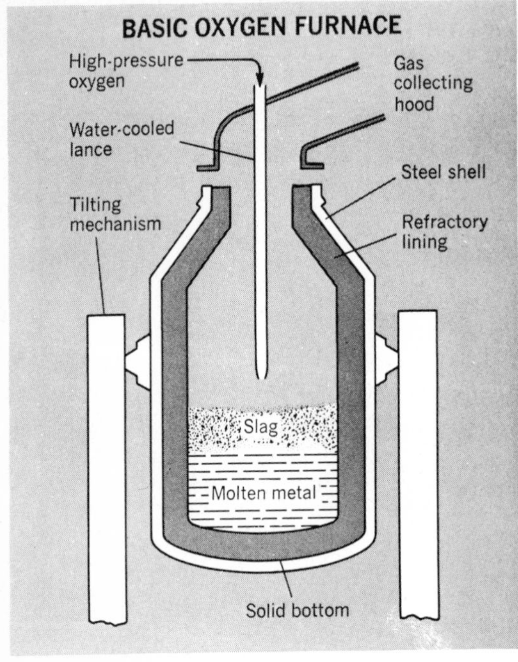

Figure 7-6 Basic oxygen furnace. (*Article on steel*, Encyclopedia Americana, *1976*.)

7-3 CARBON STEEL

Carbon steel is essentially an alloy of iron and carbon. As discussed in Chap. 2, carbon atoms replace or go into solution among the lattice structure of the iron atoms and limit the slip planes in the lattice structure. The amount of carbon determines the properties of the steel. All structural steel and reinforcing steel are low-carbon steel; and since they contain an excess of iron, they can be rolled and molded into shape. As the carbon content increases, the steel becomes increasingly hard and brittle. Cast iron contains more than 2.0 percent carbon. High-carbon steel contains less than 2 percent and more than 0.8 percent carbon. Structural steels contain less than 0.8 percent carbon. Wrought iron is a combination of iron and slag.

Phases of the Iron-Carbon Alloy

Metallurgical terms used in defining the various phases of the iron-carbon alloys are as follows:

1. *Cementite*. Cementite is a compound of iron and carbon found in high-carbon steels, often called iron carbide (FeC_3). Cementite contains 6.67 percent carbon and 93.33 percent iron and is very hard and brittle (Fig. 7-7).

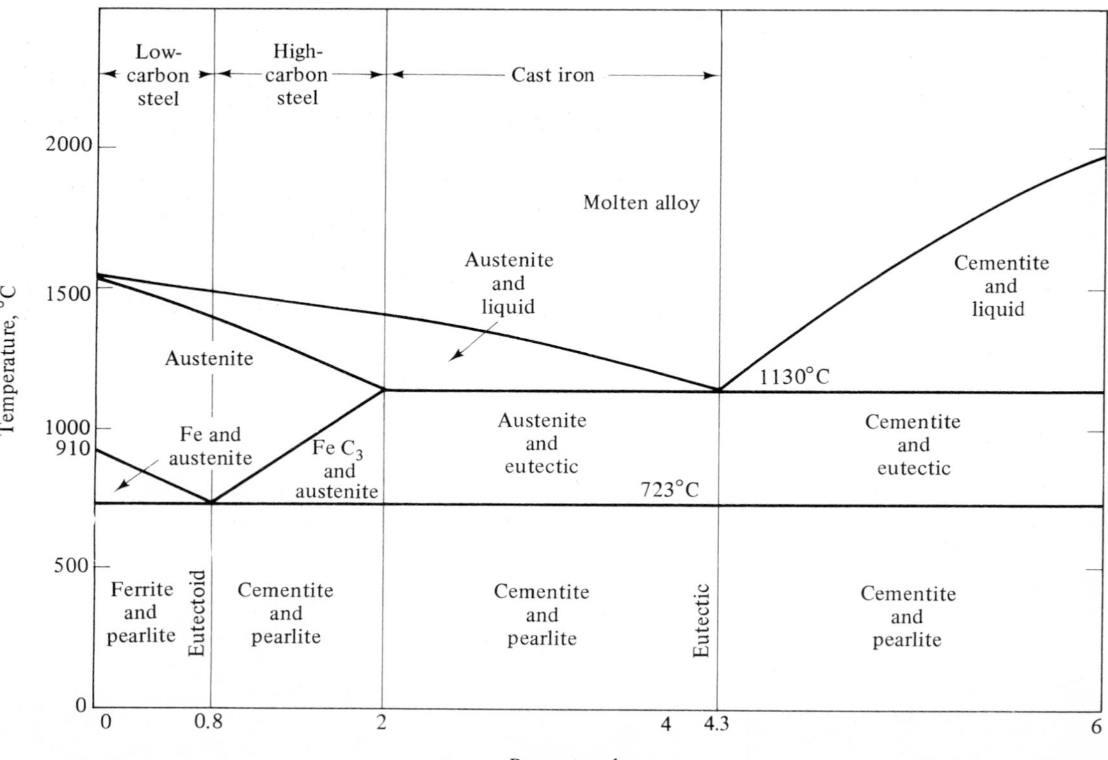

Figure 7-7 Iron-carbon equilibrium diagram.

2. *Ferrite.* Ferrite is the excess iron in low-carbon steels, and it gives the steel softness, which enables it to be cold-worked.
3. *Pearlite.* Pearlite is a mixture of ferrite and cementite in the proportion of 12 percent cementite and 88 percent ferrite.
4. *Graphite.* Graphite occurs in small flakes or nodules of carbon which become mixed with steel.
5. *Eutectic.* The eutectic of the carbon-steel alloy is the combination which freezes at the lowest temperature. The eutectic at 4.3 percent carbon freezes at 1130°C and contains solid-solution austenite and solid cementite. Below 723°C the solid-solution austenite changes to pearlite and cementite (Fig. 7-7).
6. *Eutectoid.* The eutectoid is the combination of ferrite and austenite which changes to a solid at the lowest temperature. Pearlite is the eutectoid and changes to a solid at 723°C. Excess ferrite or austenite will become solid at higher temperatures (Fig. 7-7). When the eutectic ledeburite freezes at 1130°C, all liquid is frozen; only a solid, cementite, and a solid solution, austenite, remain (Fig. 7-7).

Equilibrium Diagram

The changes that take place in slowly cooled molten iron, with various percentages of carbon, are shown in Fig. 7-7. The phase diagram shows the various materials that are formed with various combinations of iron and carbon, at each temperature from 1600 down to 0°C. For example, when steel contains 0.8 percent carbon, the eutectoid alloy begins to freeze at about 1490°C. At this stage the steel is composed of a liquid plus the solid solution of iron and carbon, austenite. At about 1380°C all the liquid freezes; and below this temperature, but above 723°C, steel can be hot-rolled and fabricated into structural members, sheet metal, wire, and reinforcing steel. At 0.8 percent carbon the alloy changes from the solid solution austenite to the solid pearlite at only one temperature, 723°C. If there is less carbon, the excess iron changes to the solid ferrite at higher temperatures. If there is more carbon, the solid cementite forms at higher temperatures. Figure 7-8

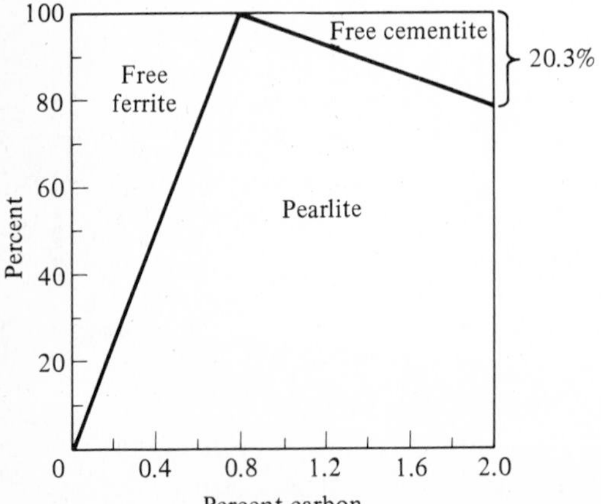

Figure 7-8 Proportions of each constituent in slowly cooled steels.

Chemical Analyses, %				
C	Mn	Si	S	P
0.19	1.00	0.12	0.027	0.023
0.49	0.75	0.22	0.026	0.014
0.64	0.66	0.15	0.037	0.032
0.90	0.41	0.18	0.028	0.022

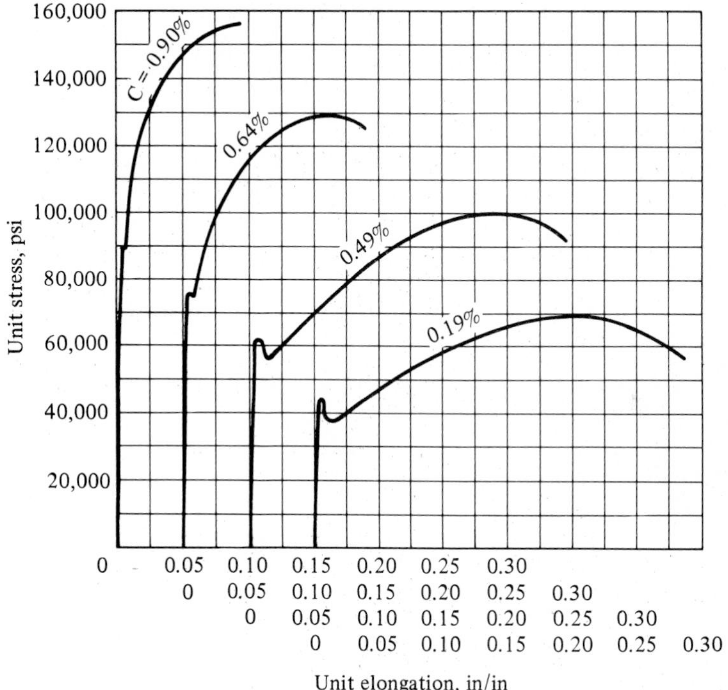

Figure 7-9 Tension stress-strain diagrams for hot-rolled steel bars. (*O. M. Withey and G. W. Washa,* Materials of Construction, *Wiley, New York, 1954.*)

shows the comparative percentage of ferrite, pearlite, and cementite in slowly cooled steel as the percentage of carbon increases from 0 to 2.0 percent. In structural steels a maximum of pearlite is desirable for strength, but sufficient ferrite is desirable to give the steel ductility and toughness to enable the steel to be molded and worked into required shapes. Figure 7-9 shows the tension stress-strain diagram for hot-rolled steel bars containing carbon from 0.9 to 0.19 percent.

7-4 IMPURITIES IN STEEL

Not all impurities can be removed from steel, but it is important that they are controlled to acceptable limits. The principal impurities in steel are (1) silicon, (2) phosphorus, (3) sulfur, and (4) manganese.

Effects of Silicon

Silicon forms a solid solution with iron. In structural steel it is generally less than 1 percent. A small amount of silicon may increase both the ultimate strength of steel and its elastic limit without decreasing its ductility. Silicon is not as effective as carbon in increasing hardness and may prevent the solution of carbon in iron.

Effects of Phosphorus

Small amounts of phosphorus in steel are in the form of iron phosphide (Fe_3P). Phosphorus causes steel to "cold-short." The toughness is decreased, particularly in high-carbon steels. Limits on the allowable amount of phosphorus are as follows:

0.1 percent—low-grade structural steel
0.05 percent—high-grade structural steel
0.02 percent—tool steel

Effects of Sulfur

Sulfur combines with iron to form iron sulfide (FeS). Iron sulfide has a low melting point and tends to segregate. Iron sulfide causes a lack of cohesion between adjacent grains in hot steel. The resulting brittleness at high temperatures is called "red shortness" and makes steel hard to roll or forge.

Effects of Manganese

Manganese has an affinity for sulfur and can be used to relieve red shortness in steel. Manganese acts as a cleanser of molten steel by combining with undesirable impurities which are then removed with the slag.

Any excess manganese in steel forms manganese carbide (MnC_3), which is similar to cementite. Manganese is used to harden steels and in high-carbon steels reduces the amount of graphite that forms.

7-5 STRUCTURAL-STEEL FABRICATION

Until recently all refined steel from the open-hearth and other furnaces was cast into ingots where it solidified. All mechanical working of steel began with the ingot. The ingots were then rolled and reduced into various sizes and shapes or shaped by forging. Common forms for initial shaping included

1. *Bloom:* Square or rectangular shape about 15 to 30 cm
2. *Billet:* Square or rectangular shape less than 15 cm minimum dimension
3. *Slab:* Width (0.6 to 1.8 m) much greater than the thickness (5 + 15 cm)

From these initial sizes, steel is rolled into structural shapes, plates, and reinforcing rods and is used in various other ways (Fig. 7-10).

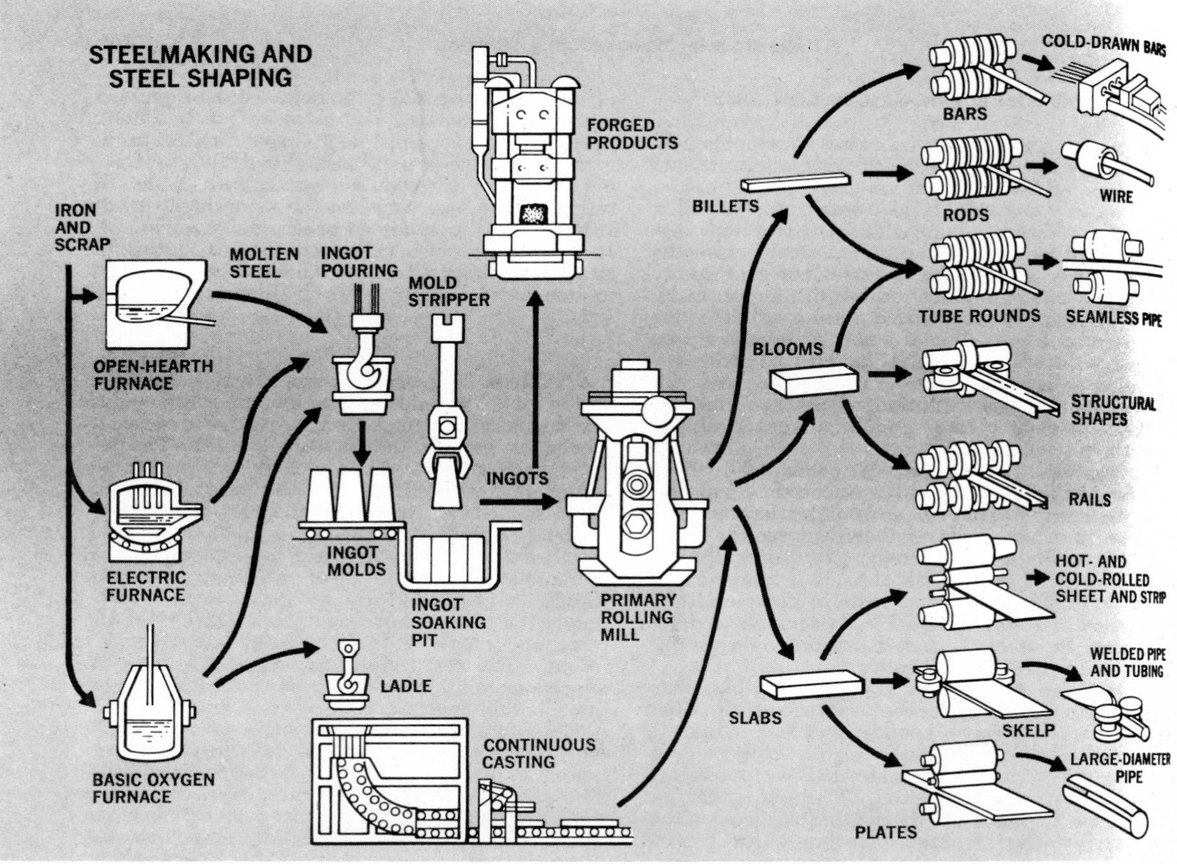

Figure 7-10 The process of making and shaping steel. (*Article on steel*, Encyclopedia Americana, *1976.*)

Continuous Casting

Continuous casting was first introduced in North America in the 1950s. This method eliminates the necessity of casting and stripping ingots, heating the ingots in a soaking pit, and rolling the ingots in primary rolls to produce blooms, billets, and slabs. The continuous casting method directly produces blooms, billets, or slabs, depending on the mold used.

Continuous casting is accomplished with a strand-casting machine, which consists of a tundish, one or more molds, a cooling chamber, and mechanisms for guiding the path of the solidified steel (Fig. 7-11).

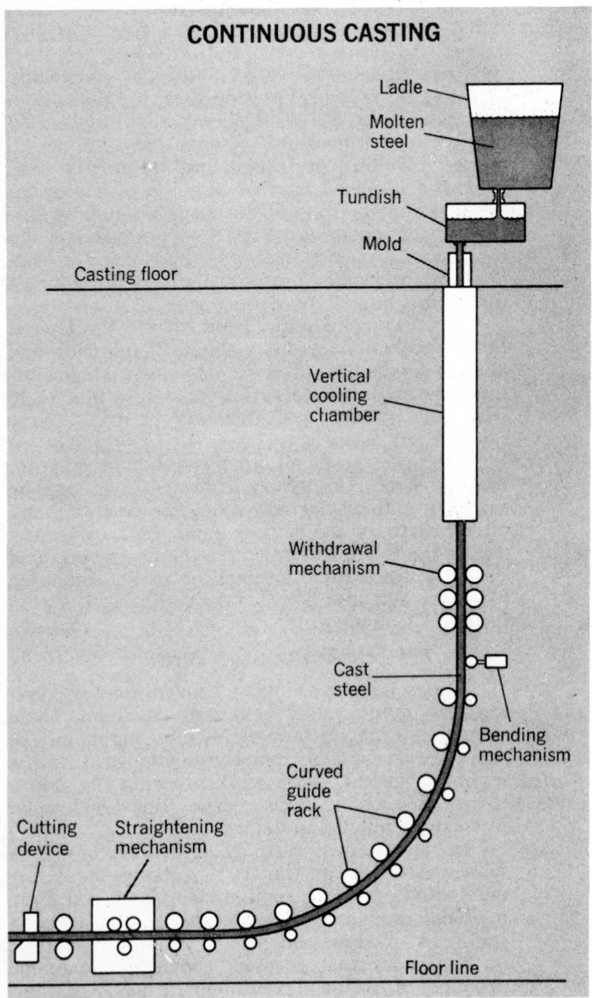

Figure 7-11 Continuous casting of steel. (*Article on steel*, Encyclopedia Americana, *1976*.)

Table 7-1 Steel for structural purposes†

ASTM designation	Product	Use
A36	Carbon-steel shapes, plates and bars	Welded, riveted, and bolted construction; bridges, buildings, towers, and general structural purposes
A53	Welded or seamless pipe, black or galvanized	Welded, riveted, and bolted construction; primary use in buildings, particularly columns and truss members
A242	High-strength, low-alloy shapes, plates, and bars	Welded, riveted, and bolted construction; bridges, buildings, and general structural purposes; atmospheric-corrosion resistance about four times that of carbon steel; a weathering steel
A245	Carbon-steel sheets, cold- or hot-rolled	Cold-formed structural members for buildings, especially standardized buildings; welded, cold-riveted, bolted, and metal-screw construction
A374	High-strength, low-alloy, cold-rolled sheets and strip	Cold-formed structural members for buildings, especially standardized buildings; welded, cold-riveted, bolted, and metal-screw construction
A440	High-strength shapes, plates, and bars	Riveted or bolted construction; bridges, buildings, towers, and other structures; atmospheric-corrosion resistance double that of carbon steel
A441	High-strength low-alloy manganese-vanadium steel shapes, plates and bars	Welded, riveted, or bolted construction but intended primarily for welded construction; bridges, buildings, and other structures; atmospheric-corrosion resistance double that of carbon steel
A446	Zinc-coated (galvanized) sheets in coils or cut lengths	Cold-formed structural members for buildings, especially standardized buildings; welded, cold-riveted, bolted, and metal-screw construction
A500	Cold-formed welded or seamless tubing in round, square, rectangular, or special shapes	Welded, riveted, or bolted construction; bridges, buildings, and general structural purposes

Table 7-1 Steel for structural purposes† (*Continued*)

ASTM designation	Product	Use
A501	Hot-formed welded or seamless tubing in round, square, rectangular, or special shapes	Welded, riveted, or bolted construction; bridges, buildings, and general structural purposes
A514	Quenched and tempered plates of high yield strength	Intended primarily for welded bridges and other structures; welding technique must not affect properties of the plate, especially in heat-affected zone
A529	Carbon-steel plates and bars to $\frac{1}{2}$ in thick	Buildings, especially standardized buildings; welded, riveted, or bolted construction
A570	Hot-rolled carbon-steel sheets and strip in coils or cut lengths	Cold-formed structural members for buildings, especially standardized buildings; welded, cold-riveted, bolted, and metal-screw construction
A572	High-strength low-alloy columbian-vanadium steel shapes, plates, sheet piling, and bars	Welded, riveted, or bolted construction of buildings in all grades; welded bridges in grades 42, 45, and 50 only
A588	High-strength low-alloy steel shapes, plates, and bars	Intended primarily for welded bridges and buildings; atmospheric-corrosion resistance about four times that of carbon steel; a weathering steel
A606	High-strength, low-alloy hot- and cold-rolled sheet and strip	Intended for structural and miscellaneous purposes where savings in weight or added durability are important

† After E. H. Gaylord, Jr., and C. N. Gaylord, *Design of Steel Structures*, McGraw-Hill, New York, 1972.

The molten steel is poured into the tundish. From there it descends through a water-cooled mold where it gradually solidifies. The mold itself is moved up and down the column of solidifying steel to prevent sticking.

After the partially solidified column of steel extends beyond the mold and is cooled with jets of water, the strand is then guided to a horizontal position and cut into proper lengths (Fig. 7-11). The entire process of continuous casting takes about 30 min.

It is essential to have large amounts of molten steel available for continuous casting, which makes the basic oxygen furnace a good choice, because of its high output and flexibility.

Table 7-2 Requirements for structural steel (ASTM)

Product	Shapes†	Plates					Bars			
Thickness, in (mm)	All	To $\frac{3}{4}$ (19), incl.	Over $\frac{3}{4}$ to $1\frac{1}{2}$ (19 to 38), incl.	Over $1\frac{1}{2}$ to $2\frac{1}{2}$ (38 to 64), incl.	Over $2\frac{1}{2}$ to 4 (64 to 102), incl.	Over 4 (102)	To $\frac{3}{4}$ (19), incl.	Over $\frac{3}{4}$ to $1\frac{1}{2}$ (19 to 38), incl.	Over $1\frac{1}{2}$ to 4 (102), incl.	Over 4 (102)
Carbon, maximum percent	0.26	0.25	0.25	0.26	0.27	0.29	0.26	0.27	0.28	0.29
Manganese, percent	—	—	0.80–1.20	0.80–1.20	0.85–1.20	0.85–1.20	—	0.60–0.90	0.60–0.90	0.60–0.90
Phosphorus, maximum percent	0.04	0.04	0.04	0.04	0.04	0.04	0.04	0.04	0.04	0.04
Sulfur, maximum percent	0.05	0.05	0.05	0.05	0.05	0.05	0.05	0.05	0.05	0.05
Silicon, percent	—	—	—	0.15–0.30	0.15–0.30	0.15–0.30	—	—	—	—
Copper, minimum percent, when copper steel is specified	0.20	0.20	0.20	0.20	0.20	0.20	0.20	0.20	0.20	0.20

Minimum tensile properties of structural steels

ASTM designation	Yield, ksi	Strength, ksi	Elongation, % (in 8 in unless noted)
Carbon steels:			
A36	36	58–80	20
A529	42	60–85	19
High-strength steels:			
A242, A440, A441:			
To $\frac{3}{4}$ in thick	50	70	18
Over $\frac{3}{4}$ in to $1\frac{1}{2}$ in	46	67	19
Over $1\frac{1}{2}$ in to 4 in	42	63	16
A572:			
Grade 42, to 4 in incl.	42	60	20
Grade 45, to $1\frac{1}{2}$ in incl.	45	60	19
Grade 50, to $1\frac{1}{2}$ in incl.	50	65	18
Grade 55, to $1\frac{1}{2}$ in incl.	55	70	17
Grade 60, to 1 in incl.	60	75	16
Grade 65, to $\frac{1}{2}$ in incl.	65	80	15
A588:			
To 4 in thick	50	70	19–21‡
Over 4 in to 5 in	46	67	19–21‡
Over 5 in to 8 in	42	63	19–21‡
Quenched and tempered steels:			
A514:			
To $2\frac{1}{2}$ in thick	100	115–135	18‡
Over $2\frac{1}{2}$ in to 4 in	90	105–135	17‡

† Manganese content of 0.85–1.35% and silicon content of 0.15–0.30% is required for shapes over 426 lb/ft.

‡ In 2 in.

Because of increased production and efficiency, these modern methods will undoubtedly dominate the steel industry in the future.

Properties of Structural Steel

Structural steel is used in all types of construction (Table 7-1). It must have a suitable combination of strength, durability, and toughness. It cannot be brittle and generally contains only about 0.2 percent carbon, which enables it to deform, yield, and withstand impact loads (Table 7-2). Additional percentages of carbon in steel increase its strength, hardness, and brittleness (Fig. 7-9).

7-6 REINFORCING STEEL

In the design of reinforced concrete in flexure the resistance of concrete to tension stresses is assumed to be negligible, and deformed bars of structural steel are embedded in the concrete to take tension stresses. In order for the tension stresses in concrete to be passed to the steel, there must be a bond between the steel and the concrete. Deformed bars have been developed which force the concrete between deformations to fail in shear before slippage occurs (Fig. 7-12). The bond strength with deformed bars is, therefore, a function of the strength of concrete. Table 7-3 lists the dimensions and weight of ASTM standard-size reinforcing bars.

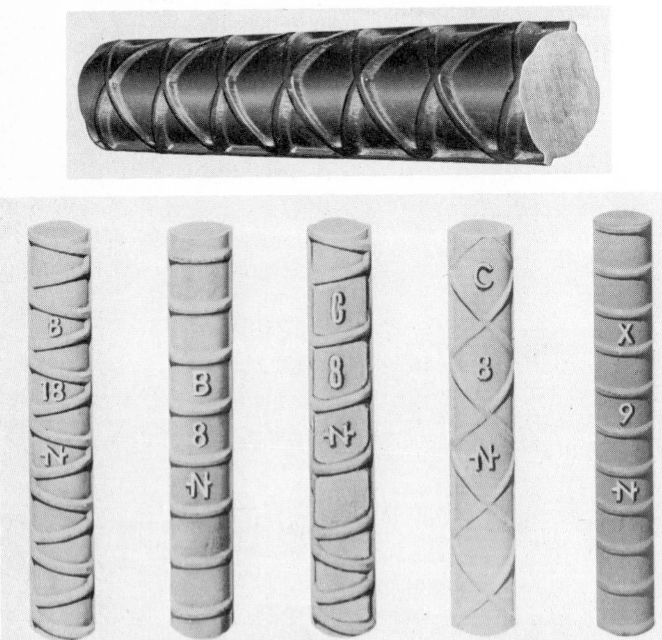

Figure 7-12 Typical deformed reinforcing bars (*Charles F. Peck, Jr., and John H. Ittel,* Concrete Construction Handbook, *McGraw-Hill, New York, 1974; Concrete Reinforcing Steel Institute, Bulletins.*)

Table 7-3 Standard reinforcing bars†

Deformed bar designation numbers, nominal weights, nominal dimensions, and deformation requirements

		Nominal dimensions‡			Deformation requirements, mm		
Bar designation number§	Nominal weight, kg/m	Diameter, mm	Cross-sectional area, cm^2	Perimeter, mm	Maximum average spacing	Minimum average height	Maximum gap (chord of $12\frac{1}{2}$ percent of nominal perimeter)
3	0.560	9.52	0.71	29.9	6.7	0.38	3.5
4	0.994	12.70	1.29	39.9	8.9	0.51	4.9
5	1.552	15.88	2.00	49.9	11.1	0.71	6.1
6	2.235	19.05	2.84	59.8	13.3	0.96	7.3
7	3.042	22.22	3.87	69.8	15.5	1.11	8.5
8	3.973	25.40	5.10	79.8	17.8	1.27	9.7
9	5.059	28.65	6.45	90.0	20.1	1.42	10.9
10	6.403	32.26	8.19	101.4	22.6	1.62	11.4
11	7.906	35.81	10.06	112.5	25.1	1.80	13.6
14¶	11.384	43.00	14.52	135.1	30.1	2.16	16.5
18¶	20.238	57.33	25.81	180.1	40.1	2.59	21.9

† Based on ASTM 6615, 6616, 6617.

‡ The nominal dimensions of a deformed bar are equivalent to those of a plain round bar having the same weight per foot as the deformed bar.

§ Bar numbers are based on the number of eighths of an inch included in the nominal diameter of the bars.

¶ Available in billet steel only.

1. *Grades of reinforcing steel.* The American Society for Testing and Materials (ASTM) has standardized reinforcing steel according to its yield point (Table 7-4). The yield point is critical in reinforced-concrete design, since there is a permanent deformation beyond that point which may cause permanent deflection in beams and floor slabs.
2. *Welded wire fabric.* Wire-fabric reinforcement is used when it is more economical and easier to place or where close spacing of bars is required because of the tension stresses caused by shrinkage and temperature changes. Many sizes of cold-drawn and deformed wires are used to fabricate wire fabric (ASTM A82 and ASTM A496).
3. *Reinforcement for prestressed concrete.* Steel for prestressed concrete reinforcement must be of high strength and low strain. Any relaxation of the resistance to tension stresses in a prestressed concrete member causes a change in design considerations. High-carbon steels and high-strength alloy steels are used in the manufacture of prestressing wire, strands, cables, and bars. Prestressing wire is generally cold-drawn. A mild annealing process is accomplished by raising the temperature to 315°C. Typical properties of prestressing wire are shown in Tables 7-5 and 7-6.

Table 7-4 Kinds and grades of reinforcing bars as specified in ASTM standards

Type of steel and ASTM specification number	Grade designation	Size numbers	Yield point minimum, MPa	Tensile strength minimum, MPa	Elongation in 203-mm minimum, %	Diameter bend test pin
Billet steel A615	40	3	276	483	11	4*d*
		4, 5			12	4*d*
		6			12	5*d*
		7			11	5*d*
		8			10	5*d*
		9			9	5*d*
		10			8	5*d*
		11			7	5*d*
		14, 18			—	None
	60	3, 4, 5	415	621	9	4*d*
		6			9	5*d*
		7, 8			8	6*d*
		9, 10, 11			7	8*d*
		14, 18			7	None
Rail steel A616	50	3	345	550	6	6*d*
		4, 5, 6			7	6*d*
		7			6	6*d*
		8			5	6*d*
		9, 10, 11†			5	8*d*
	60	3	415	620	6	6*d*
		4, 5, 6			6	6*d*
		7			5	6*d*
		8			4.5	6*d*
		9, 10, 11†			4.5	8*d*
Axle steel A617	40	3	275	480	11	4*d*
		4, 5			12	4*d*
		6			12	5*d*
		7			11	5*d*
		8			10	5*d*
		9			9	5*d*
		10			8	5*d*
		11			7	5*d*
	60	3, 4, 5			8	4*d*
		6			8	5*d*
		7			7	6*d*
		8	415	620	8	6*d*
		9, 10, 11			7	8*d*

† Number 11, 90° bend; all others 180°.
d = diameter of specimen.

Table 7-5 Tensile-strength requirements for prestress wire (ASTM)

Nominal diameter, mm	Tensile strength, minimum, MPa	
	Type BA	Type WA
4.88	†	1725
4.98	1655	1725
6.35	1655	1655
7.01	1620	1620

† This size is not commonly furnished in type BA wire.

Table 7-6 Yield-strength requirements for prestress wire (ASTM)

Nominal diameter, mm	Initial stress, MPa	Minimum stress at 1 percent extension, MPa	
		Type BA	Type WA
4.88	200	†	1380
4.98	200	1325	1380
6.35	200	1325	1325
7.01	200	1295	1295

† This size is not commonly furnished in type BA wire.
Type BA—(button anchorage) cold and deformation anchorage
Type WA—(wedge anchorage) end anchored with wedges
Maximum percent—Phosphorus, 0.040 percent
Sulfur, 0.050 percent

7-7 HEAT TREATMENT OF STEEL

Hardening

As indicated in Fig. 7-7, all combinations of iron and carbon, as well as alloy steels, go through transformations as they slowly cool from a molten state. If austenite is quenched rapidly so that the transformation takes place immediately at a temperature below 230°C, a supersaturated solution of carbon in alpha iron called "mortensite" is obtained. Mortensite has an acicular (needlelike) structure and is very hard, strong, and brittle. Steel is hardened by heat treatment; it is heated to a temperature above the transformation range (723°C) and held there until austenite is formed (Fig. 7-7). The steel is then plunged into water, brine, or oil, which cools the steel immediately. If the steel member is large, the interior may not be cooled as rapidly as the extension. This may result in a hard mortensite structure on the surface and a pearlite structure in the interior.

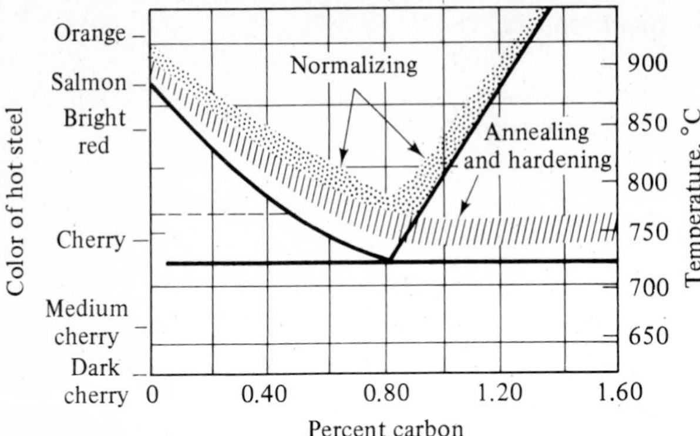

Figure 7-13 Temperatures for normalizing, annealing, and hardening carbon steels. (*American Society of Metals*, Metals Handbook, *1948*.)

Annealing

Annealing has the opposite objective to hardening. Low-carbon steels, for example, are heated above a critical temperature, depending on the carbon content, and held at that temperature long enough to allow complete solution of carbon and other alloys. The steel is then cooled slowly at room temperature to allow pearlite and ferrite and/or cementite to form. The objectives of annealing are as follows:

1. Refine the grain structure
2. Soften the metal
3. Remove internal stresses
4. Change ductility, toughness, electrical and magnetic properties
5. Remove gases

Variations in annealing temperatures and processes produce desired results with different steels and alloys (Fig. 7-13).

Normalizing

The normalizing process is similar to annealing and is used to refine the grain structure resulting from rolling, forging, or manufacturing processes. Normalizing is regarded as a corrective treatment, and not a strengthening or hardening treatment. Figure 7-13 shows the usual colors of hot steel with corresponding temperatures.

7-8 ALLOY STEELS

Alloy steels are usually made by adding one or more alloys to iron in addition to carbon. Common alloys include chromium, nickel, manganese, molybdenum, silicon, vanadium, copper, and tungsten.

Alloys are added to steel for three important reasons:

1. To increase the hardenability
2. To increase the strength
3. To add special properties such as the following:
   a. Machinability
   b. Cutting ability (tool steels)
   c. Corrosion resistance
   d. Heat and oxidation resistance
   e. Toughness, particularly at low temperature
   f. Improved magnetic and electrical properties

In considering alloys, the fact remains that carbon is the basic alloying element in steel. Other alloys are considered primarily for their effect on the amount and distribution of carbide.

Nickel

The principal effects of nickel on the mechanical properties of the pearlitic steels are as follows:

1. It increases the tensile strength and the yield strength of annealed and heat-treated steels without seriously affecting the ductility. The hardness also is increased, but not to the same extent as the strength.
2. It increases the resistance to fatigue failure most effectively in the heat-treated condition.
3. It increases the toughness of steels at both ordinary and low temperatures, particularly in the heat-treated condition. It also increases the corrosion resistance.

Chromium

Chromium is primarily a hardening agent and is utilized to impart wear and cutting ability. When the chromium content exceeds 10 percent, the resistance of steels to chemical attack under some specific conditions is greatly increased.

Nickel-Chromium

Nickel is particularly effective in combination with chromium in producing alloy steels having high elastic ratios, great hardness, and high resistance to impact and repeated applications of stress. Since nickel dissolves in the ferrite, it strengthens that constituent; and the chromium, which forms carbides, imparts hardenability. High percentages of chromium, together with nickel, produce alloy steels with high resistance to atmospheric corrosion and to oxidation at high temperatures.

Stainless steels may be made by adding other elements to the chromium-nickel compositions, including aluminum, cobalt, copper, manganese, silicon, silver, and tungsten.

Manganese

A small amount of manganese is present in practically all steels because of its presence during manufacture. The content at which the steel is considered a manganese alloy is set by some authorities at 1.0 percent.

The hardness of heat-treated manganese steel is rapidly increased by cold working, with values up to 500 Brinell hardness being easily obtained. This effect of cold working is considered responsible for the great ability of manganese steel to resist severe abrasion accompanied by heavy pressure.

Silicon

Silicon is added to carbon steels for deoxidizing purposes up to about 0.25 percent. It does not form carbides, but dissolves in the ferrite up to about 14 percent. It tends to decrease the solubility of carbon in iron, and in amounts above 14 percent it may form an iron silicide, Fe_3Si. At up to 4.5 percent it increases the tensile strength and yield point, while the ductility is not impaired up to 2.5 percent. It decreases hysteresis and eddy-current losses and hence is valuable for electrical machinery.

Vanadium

Vanadium is a deoxidizing agent, but it is not employed extensively as such because of its high cost. It forms a carbide which is very stable and requires a high temperature and considerable time to go into solution. This may partly account for its great ability to inhibit grain growth both when cooled from the molten condition and when reheated. Rarely is more than 0.10 to 0.30 percent vanadium present in the simple vanadium steels.

In comparison with carbon steels of similar composition, vanadium increases the strength slightly and the yield strength to a greater degree without sacrificing ductility. Vanadium intensifies the effects of other alloying elements and is a component of many complex alloy steels. Vanadium is used in combination with chromium, manganese, nickel, silicon, and tungsten.

Tungsten

Tungsten forms carbides and also dissolves in ferrite. Therefore, it increases the strength, hardness, and toughness of the steel. The carbides are stable and dissolve in the austenite at high temperatures after a long time, thus inhibiting grain growth. Tungsten decreases the critical cooling rate and, therefore, increases the depth of hardening. Tempering requires high temperatures, which helps explain the effect of tungsten in retaining the strength and hardness of steel at high temperatures.

Molybdenum

Molybdenum is similar to tungsten in its effect on steel, both in forming carbides and in dissolving in ferrite. It inhibits grain growth on heating as a result of its slow solubility in austenite. When in solution in the austenite, it decreases the cooling rate and, therefore, increases the depth of hardening. It is much more powerful than tungsten in increasing the hardness of steel at high temperatures.

Copper

Copper is soluble in iron up to about 0.25 percent at low temperature, and the solubility increases with higher temperatures. It forms no carbides, and its oxides are reduced by iron at high temperatures, so that the loss of copper during the melting of a heat of steel is small.

Copper increases the yield strength, tensile strength, and hardness of steel in the as-rolled condition, the increase being greater with low- and medium-carbon steels than with high-carbon steels. Ductility is decreased only slightly up to 2 percent. The effects of copper on the mechanical properties of steel in the as-rolled condition are utilized in the low-alloy, high-strength structural steels. The most important effect of copper, however, is to increase the resistance of steel to atmospheric corrosion, particularly after the first 6 to 10 months of exposure. Table 7-7 indicates how alloys affect steel.

7-9 WROUGHT IRON

Wrought iron consists of grains of ferrite more or less surrounded by filaments of slag. The carbon content is low and usually varies between 0.02 and 0.10 percent.

The properties of wrought iron are essentially those of pure iron. Its tensile strength varies between 310 and 380 MPa along the grain, with a yield strength between 160 and 275 MPa.

Wrought iron is ductile, easily welded, and has good resistance to corrosion.

7-10 SUMMARY

Steel is used extensively in many applications. The principal uses of steel in structures is for

1. Structural-steel members
2. Reinforcing steel
3. Miscellaneous forms (standard structural-steel shapes and sizes are usually available)

Table 7-7 Qualitative comparison of some steel alloys

Representative types of steel (carbon approximately 0.40%)	Index of physical properties (compared with straight carbon steel)				Distinguishing characteristic	Typical uses
	Breaking strength	Relative elasticity	Ductility	Hardness		
Straight carbon (C 0.40%)	100	100	100	100		Railroad track bolts, automobile axles, and brake levers
Medium manganese (Mn 1.75%)	145	155	58	138	Good strength and workability	Logging and road and agricultural machinery
Straight chromium (Cr 0.95%)	157	177	63	147		Springs, shear blades, wood-cutting tools
$3\frac{1}{2}$% Nickel (C 0.30, Ni 3.5%)	202	224	63	192	Toughness	Rock drill and air hammer parts, crankshafts
Carbon-vanadium (C 0.50, V 0.18%)	158	179	68	153	Resists impact	Locomotive parts
Carbon-molybdenum (C 0.20, Mo 0.68%)	149	162	53	164	Resists heat	Boiler shells; high-pressure steam equipment
High-silicon sheets (Si 4.00%)	Electrical properties are of prime importance				High electrical efficiency	Transformers, motors, generators
Silicon-manganese (Si 2.00, Mn 0.75%)	198	224	42	180	Springiness	Automobile and railroad car springs

Chromium-nickel (Cr 0.60, Ni 1.25%)	115	125	94	120	Surface easily hardened	Automobile ring gears, pinions, piston pins, transmissions
Chromium-vanadium (Cr 0.95, V 0.18%)	202	229	52	225	High strength and hardness	Automobile gears, propeller shafts, connecting rods
Chromium-molybdenum (Cr 0.95, Mo 0.20%)	130	135	94	125	Resists impact, fatigue, and heat	Aircraft forgings and fuselages
Nickel-molybdenum (Ni 1.75, Mo 0.35%)	155	177	68	153	Resists fatigue	Railroad roller bearings, automobile transmission gears
Manganese-molybdenum (Mn 1.30, Mo 0.30%)	158	177	68	151	Resists impact and fatigue	Dredge buckets, rock crushers, turbine parts
Nickel-chromium-molybdenum (Ni 1.75, Cr 0.65, Mo 0.35%)	158	203	63	161	Resists twisting	Diesel-engine crankshafts
High-speed steel (Tungsten 18, Cr 4, V 1.0%)		Cutting properties are of prime importance			Stays hard at high temperatures	High-speed metal cutting tools
Cobalt magnet steels (Co 35.0%)		Magnetic properties are of prime importance			High magnetic strength	Permanent magnets in electrical apparatus
18-8 Stainless (Cr 18, Ni 8%) (cold-worked)	207	219	53	165	Resists corrosion	Surgical instruments, food machinery, kitchenware

The efficiency in manufacture of steel has increased since about 1955 when the basic oxygen furnace and continuous casting were introduced.

The equilibrium diagram shows the types of steel formed with different proportions of carbon and iron and the changes that take place as steel cools.

The control of impurities in steel is necessary to produce steel of suitable quality and desirable properties. Alloys other than carbon are used to improve steel products.

REFERENCES

1. Article on Steel, *Encyclopedia Americana*, 1976.
2. ASTM: ASTM A-36, C1020, "Specifications for Structural Steel."
3. Peck, Charles F., Jr., and John H. Ittel: *Concrete Construction Handbook*, McGraw-Hill, New York, 1974.
4. Concrete Reinforcing Steel Institute: Bulletins.
5. American Iron and Steel Institute: *Handbook*, 1970.
6. Baker, Wilford H.: *Engineering Materials*, Pitman, New York, 1958, chap. 13.
7. Fabel, Donald C., and Raymond J. Stith: *Engineering Materials*, Pitman, New York, 1958, chap. 12.
8. Cox, Glen H., and Floyd S. Smith: *Engineering Materials*, Pitman, New York, 1958, chap. 11.
9. Withey, M. O., and G. W. Washa: *Materials of Construction*, Wiley, New York, 1954.
10. *Metals Handbook*, American Society of Metals, 1948.
11. Gaylord E. H., Jr., and C. N. Gaylord: *Design of Steel Structures*, McGraw-Hill, New York, 1972.

QUESTIONS AND PROBLEMS

1 What is pig iron? Steel?

2 Explain the eutectic and eutectoid of steel.

3 What is the range of carbon content of carbon steel?
  (*a*) Low-carbon steel?
  (*b*) High-carbon steel?

4 (*a*) What is the source of heat in the open-hearth process?
  (*b*) Explain the basic oxygen furnace.

5 Define the following: pearlite, austenite, ferrite, cementite.

6 Explain the processes of making structural-steel shapes by continuous casting.

7 What is meant by bond in reinforcing steel?

8 Explain why the ultimate strength of steel cannot be considered in reinforced-concrete design.

9 Why are alloys added to steel?

10 Which alloy steel would you select for the following?
  (*a*) High-speed tool steel
  (*b*) Teeth on a drag line or shovel
  (*c*) Plumbing fixtures

11 Why is steel harder than iron? (See Chap. 2.)

12 What major advances have been made in the last 20 years in the technology and manufacturing processes of steel making?

CHAPTER

EIGHT

WOOD

Wood has long been a common material used in construction. The workability of wood has made it a favored material for the small builder. It can be used to frame the simplest structure or in many complicated and diverse forms. Wood is a material that can be worked with a variety of tools. The log cabin became a standard for home construction in pioneer days because of its simplicity. As woodworking machinery was refined, lumber was produced in standard sizes. Plywood and laminated structural timber have added to the various uses of wood. Wood is one of the most important materials used in home construction, which may be attributed to these characteristics:

1. High strength
2. Low weight
3. Ease of working
4. Availability

The ratio of strength to weight is much higher for wood than for steel or concrete. Wooden structural members also have high shock resistance.

8-1 TREES

Most types of trees of suitable size can be used in construction, but they vary widely in the suitability and properties of lumber produced. Most deciduous trees, which shed their leaves, come under the general classification of hardwoods.

Common hardwoods include ash, oak, birch, beech, maple, and walnut. However, the wood of other broad-leaved, deciduous trees such as cottonwood, aspen, and poplar is soft, although they come under the general classification of hardwood (Table 8-1). Conifers are classified as softwoods and include the trees from which most lumber is produced such as Douglas fir, southern yellow pine, redwood, and cedar (Table 8-2).

Table 8-1 Domestic hardwoods†

Commercial names for lumber	Official common tree names
Alder:	
Red alder	Red alder
Ash:	
Black ash	Black ash
Oregon ash	Oregon ash
Pumpkin ash	Pumpkin ash
White ash	Blue ash
	Green ash
	White ash
Aspen	Bigtooth aspen
	Quaking aspen
Basswood	American basswood
	White basswood
Beech	American beech
Birch	Gray birch
	Paper birch
	River birch
	Sweet birch
	Yellow birch
Box elder	Box elder
Buckeye	Ohio buckeye
	Yellow buckeye
Butternut	Butternut
Cherry	Black cherry
Chestnut	American chestnut
Cottonwood	Balsam poplar
	Eastern cottonwood
	Plains cottonwood
	Swamp cottonwood
Cucumber	Cucumber tree
Dogwood	Flowering dogwood
	Pacific dogwood
Elder: See box elder	

Table 8-1 Domestic hardwoods (*Continued*)

Commercial names for lumber	Official common tree names
Elm:	
Rock elm	Cedar elm
	Rock elm
	September elm
	Winged elm
Soft elm	American elm
	Slippery elm
Gum	Sweet gum
Hackberry	Hackberry
	Sugarberry
Hickory	Mockernut hickory
	Pignut hickory
	Shagbark hickory
	Shellbark hickory
Holly	American holly
Ironwood	Eastern hop hornbeam
Locust	Black locust
	Honey locust
Madrone	Pacific madrone
Magnolia	Southern magnolia
	Sweet bay
Maple:	
Hard maple	Black maple
	Sugar maple
Oregon maple	Big-leaf maple
Soft maple	Red maple
	Silver maple
Mulberry	Red mulberry
Myrtle: See Oregon myrtle	
Oak:	
Red oak	Black oak
	Blackjack oak
	California black oak
	Cherrybark oak
	Laurel oak
	Northern pin oak
	Northern red oak
	Nuttall oak
	Pin oak
	Scarlet oak
	Shumard oak
	Southern red oak
	Turkey oak
	Willow oak

Table 8-1 Domestic hardwoods (*Continued*)

Commercial names for lumber	Official common tree names
White oak	Arizona white oak
	Blue oak
	Bur oak
	California white oak
	Chestnut oak
	Chinquapin oak
	Emory oak
	Gambel oak
	Mexican blue oak
	Live oak
	Oregon white oak
	Overcup oak
	Post oak
	Swamp chestnut oak
	Swamp white oak
	White oak
Oregon myrtle	California laurel
Osage orange	Osage orange
Pecan	Bitternut hickory
	Nutmeg hickory
	Water hickory
	Pecan
Persimmon	Common persimmon
Poplar	Yellow poplar
Sassafras	Sassafras
Silverbell	Carolina silverbell
Sycamore	American sycamore
Tupelo	Black tupelo
	Ogeechee tupelo
	Water tupelo
Walnut	Black walnut
Willow	Peachleaf willow

† Based on ASTM D-1165.

Table 8-2 Domestic softwoods†

Commercial names for lumber	Official common tree names
Cedar:	
Alaska cedar	Alaska cedar
Eastern red cedar	Eastern red cedar
	Southern red cedar
Incense cedar	Incense cedar
Northern white cedar	Northern white cedar
Port Orford cedar	Port Orford cedar
Southern white cedar	Atlantic white cedar
Western red cedar	Western red cedar
Cypress	Bald cypress
	Pond cypress
Fir:	
Balsam fir	Balsam fir
	Fraser fir
Douglas fir	Douglas fir
Noble fir	Noble fir
White fir	California red fir
	Grand fir
	Noble fir
	Pacific silver fir
	Subalpine fir
	White fir
Hemlock:	
Eastern hemlock	Carolina hemlock
	Eastern hemlock
Mountain hemlock	Mountain hemlock
West Coast hemlock	Western hemlock
Juniper:	
Western juniper	Aligator juniper
	Rocky Mountain juniper
	Utah juniper
	Western juniper
Larch:	
Western larch	Western larch
Pine:	
Idaho white pine	Western white pine
Jack pine	Jack pine
Lodgepole pine	Lodgepole pine
Longleaf yellow pine	Longleaf pine
	Slash pine
Northern white pine	Eastern white pine
Norway pine	Red pine
Ponderosa pine	Ponderosa pine
Redwood	Redwood

Table 8-2 Domestic softwoods (*Continued*)

Commercial names for lumber	Official common tree names
Southern yellow pine	Loblolly pine
	Longleaf pine
	Pitch pine
	Shortleaf pine
	Slash pine
	Virginia pine
Sugar pine	Sugar pine
Spruce:	
Eastern spruce	Black spruce
	Red spruce
	White spruce
Engelmann spruce	Blue spruce
	Engelmann spruce
Sitka spruce	Sitka spruce
Tamarack	Tamarack
Yew:	
Pacific yew	Pacific yew

† Based on ASTM D-1165.

8-2 LUMBER

Lumber is obtained from trunks of trees which are sawed into lengths parallel to the longitudinal surfaces. Lumber is sawed into smaller pieces planed to provide a smooth finish and crosscut into desired lengths.

Timber

Timber is classified as lumber with a minimum dimension of 2 in. It should be noted in Fig. 8-1 that all annular rings run nearly perpendicular to the diameter of a tree. They are also perpendicular to the side of a board in a rift cut, whereas the annual rings of the outside boards of a slash cut run more parallel to the side of the board. Consequently, the rift cut produces a more uniform structure in lumber, and the slash cut produces more "figure" in the board face because of irregular cutting of the annular rings.

Wood is a valuable engineering material, not only for construction, but also for form work for concrete and finished cabinets, doors, floors, and walls. The engineer is limited to the properties of lumber that are economically available and obviously does not become involved in the manufacturing process, as is the case with concrete and asphaltic concrete.

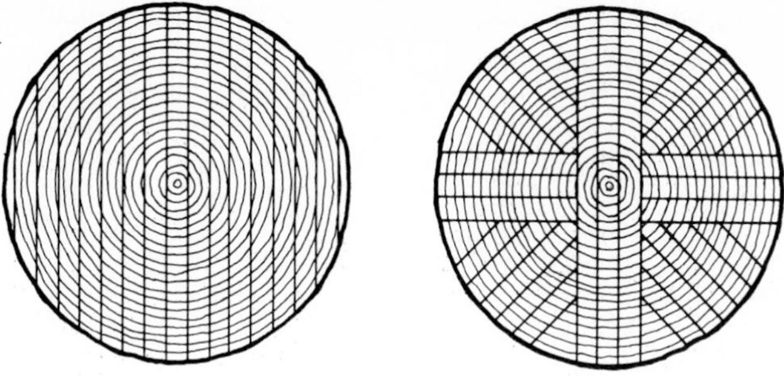

Figure 8-1 Manner of sawing logs into boards: left, slash cut; right, rift cut.

Grading of Lumber

The American Lumber Standard PS 20-70 became effective in 1970. This standard is the basis for lumber grading in the United States (Table 8-3).

Unseasoned dimension lumber must be surfaced larger than "dry lumber" (maximum 19 percent moisture content) to compensate for shrinkage. The same design values will, therefore, apply to both.

Table 8-3 Lumber grading by categories

Category	Grades	Sizes†	Comments
Light framing	1. Construction 2. Standard 3. Utility	2 to 4 in wide 2 to 4 in thick	Where high-strength values are not required such as studs, plates, sills, etc.
Studs	Stud	2 to 4 in thick 2 to 4 in wide	All-purpose stud grade, 10-ft maximum strength, and stiffness suitable for all stud uses
Structural light framing	*Select Structural* No. 1 No. 2 No. 3	2 to 4 in thick 2 to 4 in wide	For engineering applications, higher strength and bonding ratios; trusses, concrete forms, etc.
Structural joists and planks	*Select Structural* No. 1 No. 2 No. 3	2 to 4 in thick 6 in and wider	Engineering applications for lumber 6 in and wider; trusses, joists, rafters, and general framing
Appearance framing	Appearance	2 to 4 in thick 2 in and wider	For exposed framing in housing where high strength combined with finest appearance is required

† The lumber industry has not adopted metric dimensions. A standard 2 × 4 is approximately 4 × 9 cm.

Table 8-4 Average strength properties of woods commonly utilized for structural timber (results of tests of small, clear specimens)†

Commercial name of species	Moisture content of green wood, percent	Modulus of rupture, MPa		Modulus of elasticity, MPa	Compressive strength parallel to grain, MPa	Shearing strength parallel to grain, MPa
		Green	Air dry	Air dry	Air dry	Air dry
Cedar, western red	37	35	53	7,700	35	5.9
Cedar, southern white	35	32	47	6,600	32	5.5
Cypress, southern	91	46	73	9,930	44	6.9
Douglas fir	42	47	78	11,100	46	8.2
Fir, balsam	117	34	52	8,480	31	4.9
Fir, commercial white	108	40	64	10,140	37	6.4
Hemlock, eastern	111	44	61	8,200	37	7.3
Hemlock, western	74	42	70	10,270	43	8.1
Larch, western	58	52	82	11,790	52	9.4
Oak, red	80	59	99	12,480	34	12.6
Oak, white	70	56	96	11,100	49	13.0
Pine, Norway	54	44	86	12,410	51	8.5
Pine, southern yellow:						
Loblolly	81	50	88	12,400	49	9.5
Longleaf	63	60	101	13,700	58	10.3
Shortleaf	81	50	88	12,100	49	9.0
Pine, western white	54	36	66	10,400	39	
Redwood	112	52	69	9,200	42	6.5
Spruce, eastern	46	39	70	9,930	39	7.4
Spruce, Engelmann	100	29	59	8,000	32	7.0
Spruce, Sitka	42	39	70	10,800	39	7.9

† Based on U.S. Forest Products Laboratory, *Wood Handbook*, U.S. Dept. of Agriculture, U.S. Government Printing Office, Washington, D.C., 1958.

Characteristics and Imperfections of Lumber

1. *Figure.* Pattern produced in a wood surface by irregular coloration, annular rings, knots, and deviations from regular grain.
2. *Grain.* Direction, size, quality, and appearance of wood fibers.
3. *Knot.* Branch or limb embedded in a tree and exposed in sawing. Knots may seriously affect the tensile and flexural strengths of lumber.
4. *Bark pocket.* Patch of bark enclosed in the wood.
5. *Pitch.* Pocket or streak of resin accumulated in wood.
6. *Shake.* Separation of wood along the grain, usually between annual rings.
7. *Wane.* Bark or lack of wood on corners.
8. *Check.* Lengthwise separation of wood, usually across annual rings.

9. *Warp*. Any deviation from true or plane surface.
   a. *Bow*. Deviation from end to end flatwise.
   b. *Crook*. Deviation from end to end edgewise.
   c. *Cup*. Curve across width of a piece of wood.
10. *Drying shrinkage*. Shrinkage resulting from uneven drying of lumber causes warping and can cause serious problems. Shrinkage can be controlled by kiln-drying before the lumber is sold. The optimum amount of moisture in wood depends on the relative humidity of the surrounding atmosphere. When the moisture is at equilibrium, wood achieves dimensional stability.

Structural Properties of Lumber

In proportion to its weight, wood is one of the strongest structural materials available when measured in compression or in flexure along the grain (Table 8-4). Because of lack of uniformity, knots, connections, and the possibility of imperfections, working stresses in wood must be greatly reduced.

Compressive strength and tensile strength across the grain of wood are low, which limits its use in bearing and bending.

The shearing strength of wood along the grain is low and is important in short, deep beams.

The stress-strain curve for wood in bending across the grain is usually a straight line to failure. The modulus of elasticity is lower than steel or reinforced concrete, making deflection an important design consideration in beams and joists.

8-3 PLYWOOD

Plywood is made by gluing together thin layers of wood. The wood fibers in the various layers are arranged crosswise to take advantage of the maximum strength of the wood. Plywood has numerous uses from fabrication of structural members and diaphragm construction to floors and walls and for decorative interior panels. Cabinet and furniture construction makes use of a thin veneer of walnut or other hardwoods with less expensive woods used in the remaining plies.

In order to meet the needs of these various uses, the plywood industry produces many types and grades of plywood panels; they are usually 4 ft by 8 ft in dimension, but they are available in other sizes.

Types of Plywood

Plywood is manufactured in two types: exterior type with 100 percent waterproof glue used in bonding the several sheets, and interior type which may be bonded with exterior, intermediate, or interior glue. Exterior-type plywood should be used for outdoor application in locations of high humidity or where the plywood may be exposed to moisture.

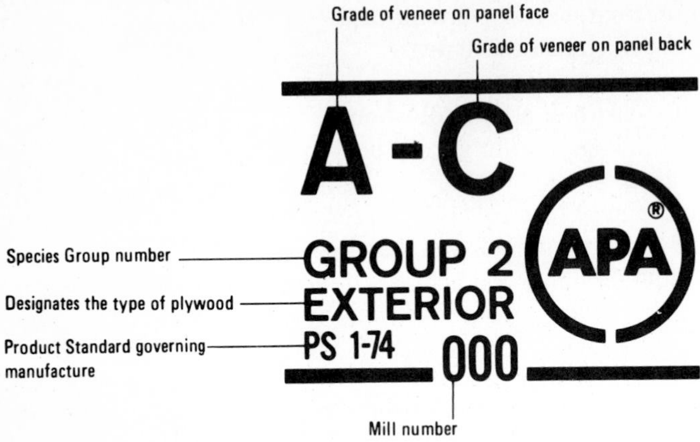

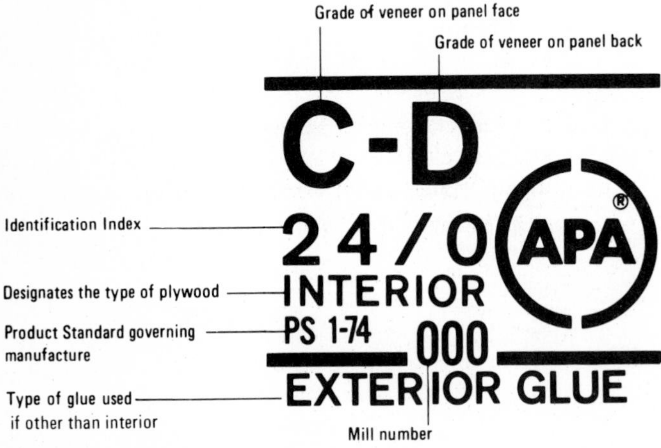

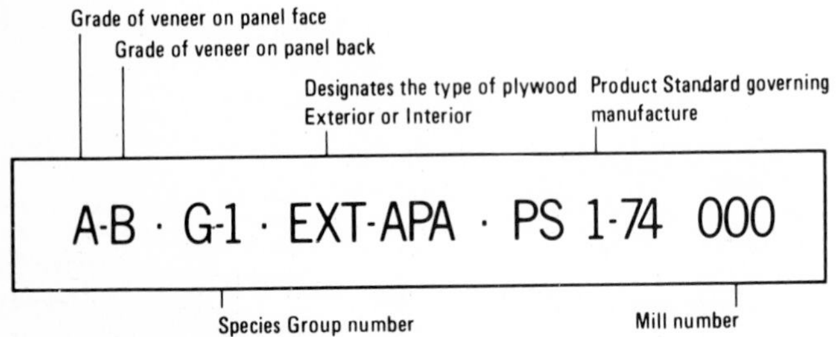

Figure 8-2 Typical grade trade marks. *(American Plywood Association)*

Groups

Wood from more than 70 species of varying strength may be used in plywood manufacture. The various species are classified in groups from 1 to 5. The stiffest and strongest woods are in group 1, and the weakest in group 5. When the group number is shown in a grade trademark (Fig. 8-2), it indicates only the weakest species used in the face and back of the panel. In decorative and sanded panels, $\frac{3}{8}$ in thick or less, the plywood is identified by the face species group PS 1.

Appearance Grades

Appearance grading applies to all types of plywood and is based on the appearance of the outside veneer. Grades N, A, B, C, and D vary from the best-looking N and A to the worst-looking D (Table 8-5).

Engineered Grades

Engineered grades of plywood are designed for structural and construction applications. Properties such as nail-bearing, shear, compression, and tension are more important than appearance. The basic unsanded grades of plywood are C-D interior (sheathing), C-C exterior, and structural I and II. The identification index shown in Table 8-6 shows two numbers, for example, 24/0 or 32/16. The left-hand number in each case refers to the recommended spacing of roof (rafters) in inches when the panel is used as roof sheathing. The right-hand number refers to maximum spacing of floor framing (joists) when the panel is used for subflooring.

Table 8-5 Veneer grades (1974 American Plywood Association)

Grade	Description
N	Smooth surface, "natural finish" veneer. Select, all heartwood or all sapwood. Free of open defects. Allows not more than six repairs, wood only, per 4 × 8 panel, made parallel to grain and well matched for grain and color.
A	Smooth, paintable. Not more than 18 neatly made repairs; boat, sled, or router type, and parallel to grain, permitted. May be used for natural finish in less demanding applications.
B	Solid surface. Shims, circular repair plugs, and tight knots to 1 in across grain permitted. Some minor splits permitted.
C Plugged	Improve C veneer with splits limited to $\frac{1}{8}$-in width and knotholes and borer holes limited to $\frac{1}{4} \times \frac{1}{2}$ in. Admits some broken grain. Synthetic repairs permitted.
C	Tight knots to $1\frac{1}{2}$ in. Knotholes to 1 in across grain and some to $1\frac{1}{2}$ in if total width of knots and knotholes is within specified limits. Synthetic or wood repairs. Discoloration and sanding defects that do not impair strength permitted. Limited splits allowed.
D	Knots and knotholes to $2\frac{1}{2}$-in width across grain and $\frac{1}{2}$ in larger within specified limits. Limited splits permitted. Limited to interior grades of plywood.

Table 8-6 Identification index on engineered grades of plywood (face grain across supports)

Thickness		C-D INT-APA C-C EXT-APA		
Common designation	cm	Group 1 and structural I	Group 2† or 3 and structural II†	Group 4‡
5/16	0.793	20/0	16/0	12/0
3/8	0.953	24/0	20/0	16/0
1/2	1.27	32/16	24/0	24/0
5/8	1.59	42/20	32/16	30/12§
3/4	1.91	48/24	42/20	36/16§
7/8	2.22	—	48/24	42/20

† Panels with group 2 outer plies and special thickness and construction requirements, or structural II panels with group I faces, may carry the identification index numbers shown for group 1 panels.

‡ Panels made with group 4 outer plies may carry the identification index numbers shown for group 3 panels when they conform to special thickness and construction requirements detailed in PS 1.

§ Check local availability.

Guides to Plywood Grades

Tables 8-7 and 8-8 give a summary list of the various types and grades of plywood as designated by the American Plywood Association. These tables will serve as a guide to the use of the most appropriate plywood panels. Obviously not all types and grades may be locally available.

Table 8-7 Guide to engineered grades of plywood

Grade designation	Description and most common use	Veneer grade Face	Back	Inner plies
	Interior			
C-D INT-APA	For wall and roof sheathing, subflooring, industrial uses such as pallets. Also available with intermediate glue or exterior glue. Specify intermediate glue for moderate construction delays; exterior glue for better durability in somewhat longer construction delays, and for treated-wood foundations.	C	D	D
Structural I C-D INT-APA and Structural II C-D INT-APA	Unsanded structural grades where plywood strength properties are of maximum importance; structural diaphragms, box beams, gusset plates; stressed-skin panels, containers, pallet bins. Made only with exterior glue.	C	D	D

Table 8-7 Guide to engineered grades of plywood (*Continued*)

Grade designation	Description and most common use	Veneer grade		
		Face	Back	Inner plies
Underlayment INT-APA	For underlayment or combination subfloor underlayment under resilient floor coverings, carpeting in homes, apartments, mobile homes. Specify exterior glue where moisture may be present, such as bathrooms, utility rooms. Touch-sanded. Also available in tongue and groove.	Plugged C	D	C and D
C-D Plugged INT-APA	For built-ins, wall and ceiling tile backing, cable reels, walkways, separator boards. Not a substitute for underlayment as it lacks underlayment's indentation resistance. Touch-sanded.	Plugged C	D	D
2·4·1 INT-APA	Combination subfloor underlayment. Quality base for resilient floor coverings, carpeting, wood strip flooring. Use 2·4·1 with exterior glue in areas subject to moisture. Unsanded or touch-sanded as specified.	Plugged C	D	C and D
	Exterior			
C-C EXT-APA	Unsanded grade with waterproof bond for subflooring and roof decking, siding on service and farm buildings, crating, pallets, pallet bins, cable reels.	C	C	C
Structural I C-C EXT-APA and Structural II C-C EXT-APA	For engineered applications in construction and industry where full exterior-type panels are required. Unsanded.	C	C	C
Underlayment C-C Plugged EXT-APA C-C Plugged EXT-APA	For underlayment or combination subfloor underlayment under resilient floor coverings where severe moisture conditions may be present, as in balcony decks. Use for tile backing where severe moisture conditions exist. For refrigerated or controlled-atmosphere rooms, pallets, fruit pallet bins, reusable cargo containers, tanks and boxcar and truck floors and linings. Touch-sanded. Also available in tongue and groove.	Plugged C	C	C
B-B Plyform class I and class II EXT-APA	Concrete-form grades with high reuse factor. Sanded both sides. Mill-oiled unless otherwise specified. Special restrictions on species. Also available in HDO.	B	B	C

Table 8-8 Guide to appearance grades of plywood

Grade designation	Description and most common uses	Veneer grade		
		Face	Back	Inner plies
Interior				
N-N, N-A, N-B INT-APA	Cabinet quality. For natural-finish furniture, cabinet doors, built-ins, etc. Special-order items.	N	N, A, or B	C
N-D-INT-APA	For natural-finish paneling. Special-order item.	N	D	D
A-A INT-APA	For applications with both sides on view. Built-ins, cabinets, furniture, and partitions. Smooth face; suitable for painting.	A	A	D
A-B INT-APA	Use where appearance of one side is less important but two smooth, solid surfaces are necessary.	A	B	D
A-D INT-APA	Use where appearance of only one side is important. Paneling, built-ins, shelving, partitions, and flow racks.	A	D	D
B-B INT-APA	Utility panel with two smooth sides. Permits circular plugs.	B	B	D
B-D INT-APA	Utility panel with one smooth side. Good for backing, sides of built-ins. Industry: shelving, slip sheets, separator boards, and bins.	B	D	D
Decorative panels—APA	Rough-sawn, brushed, grooved, or striated faces. For paneling, interior accent walls, built-ins, counter facing, displays, and exhibits.	C or better	D	D
Plyron INT-APA	Hardboard face on both sides. For counter tops, shelving, cabinet doors, flooring. Faces tempered, untempered, smooth, or screened.			C and D
Exterior				
A-A EXT-APA	Use where appearance of both sides is important. Fences, built-ins, signs, boats, cabinets, commercial, refrigerators, shipping containers, tote boxes, tanks, and ducts.	A	A	C
A-B EXT-APA	Use where appearance of one side is less important.	A	B	C
A-C EXT-APA	Use where appearance of only one side is important. Soffits, fences, structural uses, boxcar and truck lining, farm buildings. Tanks, trays, commercial refrigerators.	A	C	C

Table 8-8 Guide to appearance grades of plywood (*Continued*)

Grade designation	Description and most common uses	Veneer grade		
		Face	Back	Inner plies
	Exterior			
B-B EXT-APA	Utility panel with solid faces.	B	B	C
B-C EXT-APA	Utility panel for farm service and work buildings, boxcar and truck lining, containers, tanks, agricultural equipment. Also as base for exterior coatings for walls, roofs.	B	C	C
HDO EXT-APA	High-density overlay plywood. Has a hard, semiopaque resin-fiber overlay both faces. Abrasion-resistant. For concrete forms, cabinets, counter tops, signs, and tanks.	A or B	A or B	C or C plugged
MDO EXT-APA	Medium-density overlay with smooth, opaque, resin-fiber overlay one or both panel faces. Highly recommended for siding and other outdoor applications, built-ins, signs, and displays. Ideal base for paint.	B	B or C	C
303 Siding EXT-APA	Proprietary plywood products for exterior siding, fencing, etc. Special surface treatment such as V-groove, channel groove, striated, brushed, rough-sawn.		C	C
T 1-11 EXT-APA	Special 303 panel having grooves $\frac{1}{4}$ in deep, $\frac{3}{8}$ in wide, spaced 4 or 8 in o.c. Other spacing optional. Edges shiplapped. Available unsanded, textured, and MDO.	C or better	C	C
Plyron EXT-APA	Hardboard faces both sides, tempered, smooth, or screened.			C
Marine EXT-APA	Ideal for boat hulls. Made only with Douglas fir or western larch. Special solid jointed-core construction. Subject to special limitations on core gaps and number of face repairs. Also available with HDO or MDO faces.	A or B	A or B	B

8-4 STRUCTURAL GLUED LAMINATED TIMBER

The term "structural glued laminated timber" refers to an engineered, stress-rated product, comprising assemblies of suitably selected and prepared wood laminations securely bonded together with adhesives (Fig. 8-3).

Figure 8-3 Laminated beam. (*The American Wood Preservers Institute.*)

The grain of all laminations is approximately parallel longitudinally. The individual pieces of lumber in the laminations do not exceed 51 mm in net thickness. Laminations may be made of pieces glued end to end to form any length, of pieces glued edge to edge to make wider ones, or of pieces bent to and curved during gluing. Imperfections can be eliminated in laminated timber, something which is not always possible with natural-timber members. The production of structural timbers in a wide variety of sizes and shapes allows wide latitude in architectural expression.

1. *Shapes.* Structural glued laminated timber members may be straight or curved to meet job specifications. A wide variety of shapes can be fabricated with laminated timber, as illustrated in Fig. 8-4.
2. *Types of lumber.* Lumber used for laminating is graded in accordance with the standard grading provisions for the species used. The lumber must also meet supplementary requirements for lamination, tolerances, and moisture content. Table 8-9 shows the difference between nominal width and finished widths.
3. *Adhesives.* Waterproof adhesives are used where the members may be exposed to moisture.

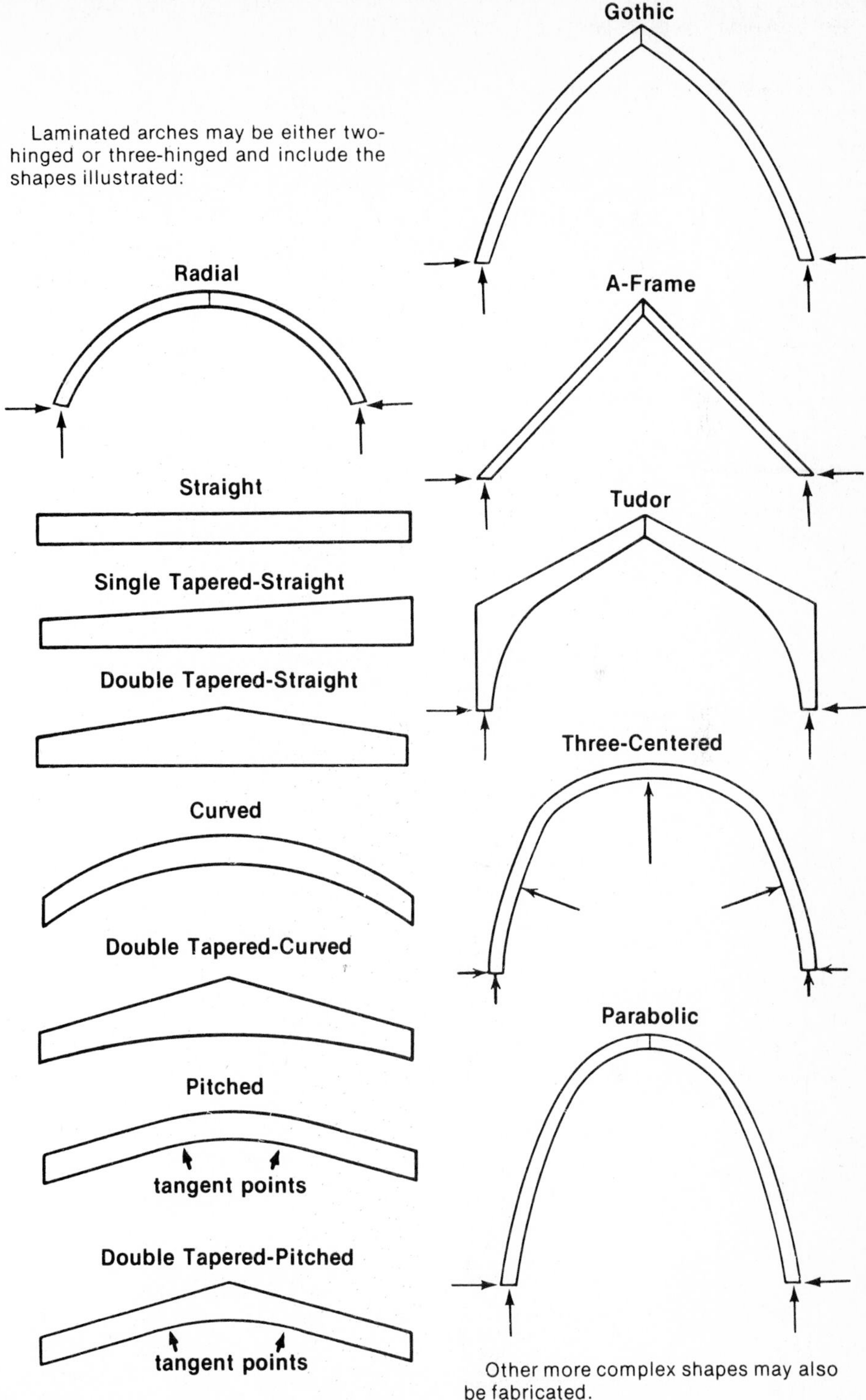

Figure 8-4 Typical shapes of structural glued laminated timbers. (*The American Wood Preservers Institute.*)

Table 8-9 Nominal and net finished widths

Nominal width, in	Net finished width	
	U.S., in	Metric, mm
3	$2\frac{1}{4}$	57
4	$3\frac{1}{8}$	79
6	$5\frac{1}{8}$	130
8	$6\frac{3}{4}$	171
10	$8\frac{3}{4}$	222
12	$10\frac{3}{4}$	273
14	$12\frac{1}{4}$	311
16	$14\frac{1}{4}$	362

4. *Appearance grades.* Laminations may possess the natural growth characteristics of the lumber grades. Other requirements of three appearance grades are shown in Table 8-10.
5. *Allowable stresses.* The strength of the wood used in laminated timber obviously does not change from the basic species used (shown in Table 8-4). The combination of laminations has a significant effect on the allowable bending and tension stresses for normal conditions of loading, as shown in Table 8-11.

Table 8-10 Appearance grades for structural glued laminated timber†

Grade	Typical use	Specification
Industrial	Industrial plants Warehouses Garages	Void filling not required Wide face free of loose knots and holes Surfaced on two sides only Misses permitted
Architectural	Where good appearance is a factor	Knotholes and voids (19 mm) replaced with clear wood inserts Exposed surfaces shall be smooth Misses not permitted
Premium	Where finest appearance is demanded	All holes and knotholes filled with selected wood similar to grain and color of adjacent wood Knots limited in size to 20 percent of net force width Reasonable care for similarity of grain and color of the laminations at edge and end joints Not over two knots in 1.8 m of length

† From Western Wood Products Association and American Lumber Standards Committee.

Table 8-11 Typical allowable unit bonding stresses (MPa) for Douglas fir under normal conditions of loading, perpendicular to the wide face of the laminations†

Combination symbol	Extreme fiber in bending	Tension parallel to grain	Compression parallel to grain	Horizontal shear	Modulus of elasticity	Compression perpendicular to grain	
						Tension face	Compression face
16F	11.0	11.0	10.3	1.14	11,000	2.66	2.66
18F	12.4	11.0	10.3	1.14	11,700	2.66	2.66
20F	13.8	11.0	10.3	1.14	11,700	2.66	2.66
20F	13.8	11.0	10.3	1.14	11,700	2.83	2.83
20F	13.8	11.0	10.3	1.14	11,700	3.10	3.10
22F	15.1	11.0	10.3	1.14	12,400	2.83	2.83
22F	15.1	11.0	10.3	1.14	12,400	3.10	2.66
24F	16.6	11.0	10.3	1.14	12,400	3.10	2.66
26F	17.9	11.0	10.3	1.14	12,400	2.83	2.66

† From Western Wood Products Association.

Table 8-12 Chemicals used for pressure treatment of wood

Type	Chemicals
Creosote	Creosote and coal-tar solutions
Oilborne	Pentachlorophenal Copper-8 Tributyl tin oxide
Waterborne	Acid copper chromate (ACC) Ammoniacal copper arsenate (ACA) Chromated copper arsenate (CCA) Chromated zinc chloride (CZC) Fluorchrome arsenate phenal (FCAP)

8-5 WOOD PRESERVATION

Wood Decay

Wood is subject to biological decay—fungi that can threaten its serviceability as lumber. Any time the moisture content of wood exceeds its fiber saturation point, and if the temperature and oxygen content of the environment are favorable, wood becomes subject to fungi attack. The wood fibers decay, and the lumber loses its strength. By the time such damage becomes visible, it is too late to save the wood.

Termites

Termites are the most common wood-eating insects. They resemble ants and live on the cellulose content of the wood. In temperate zones termites are soil dwellers that attack the wood from below. Some termites live above the ground and attack untreated wood wherever it is used. These dry-wood termites are found only in the extreme south of the United States.

Pressure Treatment

Wood is treated by impregnating the wood fiber with preservative chemicals that render it useless as food for fungi or insects. The uses of pressure-treated wood are naturally much more extensive than wood which is subject to deterioration (Table 12).

Fire Protection

Wood has been a common fuel, probably since the time fire was first discovered. Structures of lumber and timber can be destroyed by fire. In heavy timber construction, however, the timbers will char on the surface and give protection to the interior of the timber. Timber will generally perform better in a fire than unprotected steel and metal structural members which lose their strength at comparatively low temperatures.

Wood can be pressure-impregnated with chemicals in water solutions which will permanently inhibit combustion. Fire-retardant treatments do now substantially increase the fire resistance of heavy timber members.

Fire-retardant coating provides another method of protection. In general, fire-retardant coatings do not give the same amount of fire resistance as pressure-impregnated, fire-retardant treatments.

8-6 SUMMARY

Wood is the most common material used in home construction. The lumber industry has standardized sizes and grades to simplify construction.

Wood, in proportion to its weight, is one of the strongest structural materials when stresses are parallel to the grain. Imperfections in wood, such as knots and variations in grain, permit relatively small working stresses. Lumber can be made with most trees of proper size, but the structural properties and appearance vary widely.

Efficient use of most woods is possible in the manufacture of plywood and laminations. Plywood is made from more than 70 species of wood and is classified in engineering grades and appearance grades.

Structural glued laminated timber makes use of smaller pieces of lumber and eliminates imperfections in large structural members. Structural members of many different sizes and shapes can be fabricated by glued laminations.

Wood deteriorates because of (1) decay, (2) termites, and (3) fire. Various treatments of wood will help preserve it.

REFERENCES

1. ASTM Standard D-1165.
2. Davis, Jefferson D., Jr., and Carl H. Kindig: *Engineering Materials*, Pitman, New York, chap. 9.
3. American Plywood Association.
4. The American Institute of Timber Construction.
5. The American Wood Preservers Institute.
6. Western Wood Products Association.
7. American Lumber Standards Committee.

QUESTIONS AND PROBLEMS

1 What is the difference between lumber and timber?

2 In the general classification, what determines hardwood and softwood trees?

3 What trees contribute most of the lumber used in the United States?

4 List the imperfections that may be found in lumber.

5 Discuss the structural properties of lumber.

6 How do the appearance grades of plywood differ from the engineered grades?

7 To what does a designation such as 32/16 in Table 8-7 refer?

8 Is exterior glue ever used in the manufacture of interior plywood?

9 What are the major advantages of structural glued laminated timber over natural-timber members?

10 Are the dimensions of a 2 × 4 actually 2 in by 4 in? Explain.

11 Where would you use plywood which has a designation of (*a*) HDO, EXT-APA, (*b*) C-C EXT-APA?

12 Are there any special requirements of lumber used in glued laminated members?

CHAPTER

NINE

ASPHALT CEMENT AND ASPHALTIC CONCRETE

Asphalt cements fall into the broad classification of bitumens. Bitumens, by definition, are soluble in carbon disulfide. Asphalt cement made by distillation of petroleum is the most common bitumen material used for highway and airport pavements. Tars obtained from the destructive distillation of coal may also be used in pavements, but are used principally for roofing and other specialized uses.

9-1 ASPHALT CEMENT

Native asphalt occurs when petroleum rises to the surface of the earth and most of the volatile oils evaporate. One of the well-known deposits of native asphalt is the "Trinidad Lake" on the island of Trinidad off the north coast of South America.

Native asphalts were used as early as 3500 B.C. as adhesives, for caulking boats and waterproofing purposes, and in mortar for brick walls. Burning asphalt was also used by the Greeks and Romans as a weapon.

The first asphaltic pavement was built in London in 1869 and was followed one year later in the United States.

It was the invention of the automobile and the demand for smooth, all-weather roads which created the need for petroleum that led to the development of modern asphalt cement. Today asphalt cement is used in the majority of the nation's highways.

Composition

Asphalt is a complex combination of hydrocarbon compounds. The combination of carbon atoms and hydrogen atoms is the primary "building block" of many organic materials, depending on their atomic arrangement. As discussed in Chap. 2, there are an almost unlimited number of linking and crosslinking combinations of carbon, hydrogen, and other elements.

Asphalt chemistry does not fall within the training of an architect or engineer and must be left to the asphalt chemist. The physical properties of asphalt cement and its behavior in pavements are the primary concern of the engineer.

Manufacture

Asphalt cement is a hard, viscous liquid which solidifies at normal temperatures. Asphalt is that part of petroleum which remains after the gasoline, oils, and other more volatile products have been extracted by distillation.

In the early days of refining, petroleum was heated in a closed vat, and the temperature was increased in successive increments. The most volatile naphtha and gasoline evaporated first and was distilled. Kerosene and light and heavy motor oils would evaporate next in successive increments of temperature. After all the usable products were evaporated, what was left included asphalt with miscellaneous undesirable gas oils. This uncontrolled residue was used for pavements

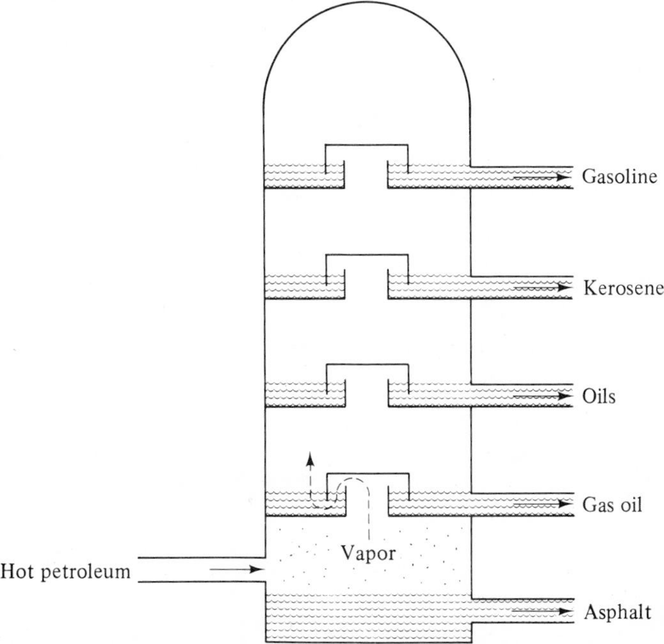

Figure 9-1 Schematic diagram of a continuous distillation tower (bubble tower). Petroleum vapors condense at various levels depending on the decreasing temperature at each higher level.

commonly called "blacktop." Many advances have been made in refining processes since that time, and today the production of asphalt is scientifically controlled to produce the most desirable product for each particular environment and temperature range.

A simplified sketch of the refining process is shown in Figs. 9-1 and 9-2. Heated petroleum under pressure is introduced into a "bubble tower." All the

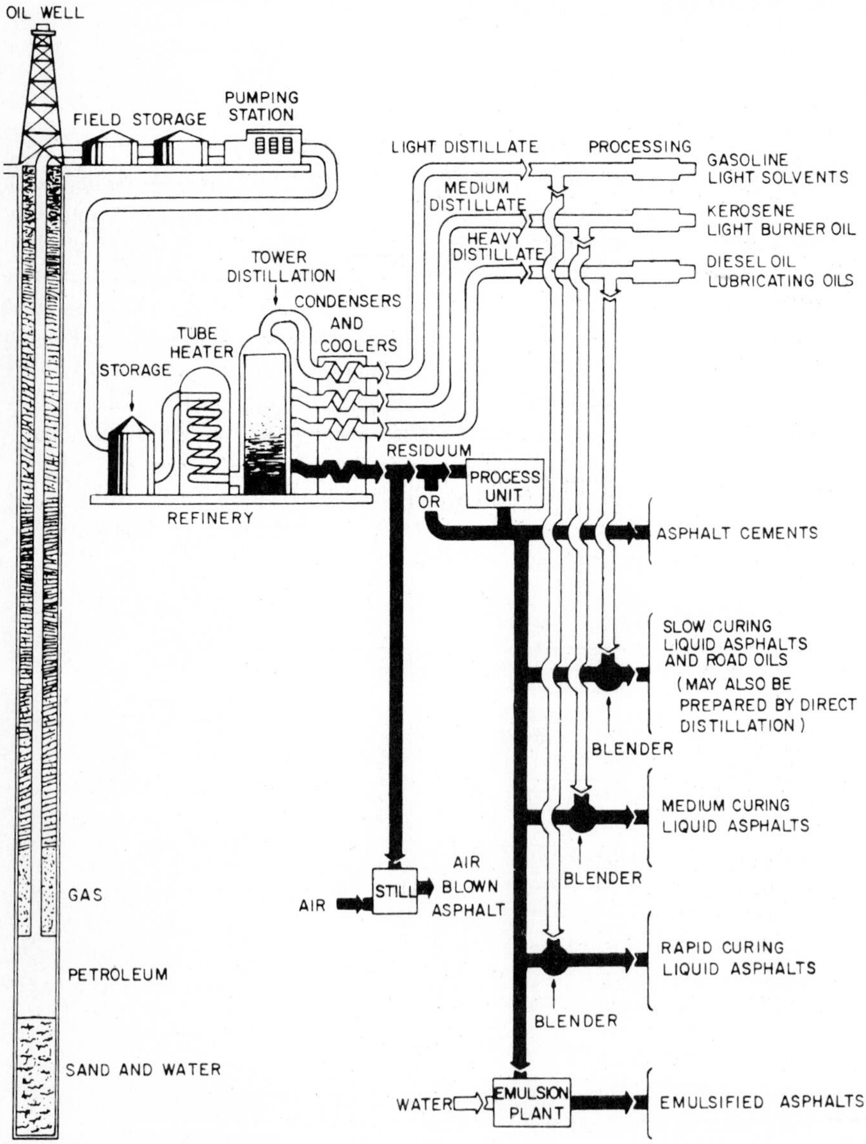

Figure 9-2 Petroleum asphalt flowchart. (*Asphalt Institute.*)

volatile oils turn to vapor, and each of the several products is distilled continuously. The heavier oils distill at successively lower levels, and the lighter oils, kerosene, and gasoline vapors keep rising (Fig. 9-1) until they liquefy at the top.

Asphalt from a modern refinery does not contain any of the miscellaneous unwanted oils from petroleum. All heavy oils not removed as usable products are known as "gas oil." Gas oil is taken through additional refining processes where the molecules are broken down and rearranged into molecules of gasoline and other usable products. The distillation process is repeated.

Modification of Asphalt Cement

Asphalt cement may be modified into several different products in order to make it easier to use. Since asphalt cement is a hard, viscous solid, it must be heated or treated before it can be mixed with aggregates to produce asphaltic concrete. Asphalt cement can be made into a liquid at lower temperatures by being mixed with volatile oils (cutback) or emulsified with water to produce liquids at normal temperatures (Fig. 9-3). When the volatile oils evaporate or when the emulsion breaks, hard, stable asphalt cement remains to cement together the aggregate particles.

1. *Rapid curing* (*RC*) (*cutback*). Gasoline is mixed with asphalt cement to produce rapid-curing cutbacks. The grades range from RC.0 to RC.5, depending on the amount of gasoline used. The percentage of the total distillate driven off at 260°C varies from 75 percent for RC.0 to 25 percent for RC.5. Consequently, the viscosity increases from RC.0 to RC.5.

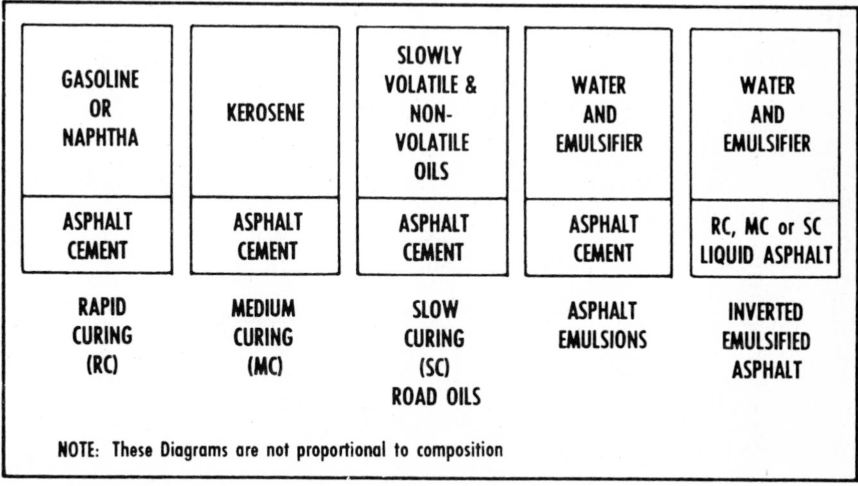

Figure 9-3 Liquid asphaltic products. (*Asphalt Institute.*)

Table 9-1 Requirements for asphalt cement use in pavement construction†

	Penetration grade										ASTM standard for each property
	40–50		60–70		85–100		120–150		200–300		
	Min	Max	Min	Max	Min	Max	Min	Max	Min	Max	
Penetration at 77°F (25°C), 100 g, 5 s	40	50	60	70	85	100	120	150	200	300	D-5
Flash point, °F (Cleveland open cup)	450	—	450	—	450	—	425	—	350	—	D-92
Ductility at 77°F (25°C), 5 cm/min, cm	100	—	100	—	100	—	100	—	100	—	D-113
Retained penetration after thin-film oven test, percent	55+	—	52+	—	47+	—	42+	—	37+	—	D-1754
Ductility at 77°F (25°C), 5 cm/min, cm after thin-film oven test	—	—	50	—	75	—	100	—	100	—	D-113
Solubility in trichloroethylene, percent	99.0	—	99.0	—	99.0	—	99.0	—	99.0	—	D-2042

† ASTM D-946.

2. *Medium curing (MC) (cutback).* The MC cutback is similar to the RC with the exception that kerosene is used rather than gasoline to liquefy the asphalt cement.
3. *Slow curing (SC) (road oils).* In the case of road oils, residual oils may be left in the asphalt cement, or it may be cut back with slowly evaporating volatile oils.
4. *Emulsified asphalt cement.* Three types of asphalt emulsions are listed by ASTM: rapid-setting (RS), medium-setting (MS), and slow-setting (SS), the setting time being determined by the breaking of the emulsion and the evaporation of water. Each type of emulsion has two grades, 1 and 2, depending on the viscosity. There is also an MS-2h grade, suitable for cold and hot plant mix. All other types are used cold.

Properties of Asphalt Cement

Heated asphalt cement and aggregates are used in nearly all the asphaltic concrete today. The concrete is "laid down" and compacted while hot, and the pavement becomes hard and usable as soon as it cools. Table 9-1 shows the ASTM requirements for the various grades of asphalt cement. The tests indicated in Table 9-1 are discussed in Chap. 13.

9-2 ASPHALTIC CONCRETE

High-type asphaltic concrete pavements for highways, airports, parking lots, and driveways use a hot asphalt cement, as it comes from the petroleum refinery. The hot cement is then mixed with hot, properly graded aggregates. The cement and aggregate are mixed in a "hot plant," delivered to the construction site, laid down, and compacted before the concrete cools.

The responsibility of the engineer and project personnel is to purchase the proper "penetration grade" asphalt cement, which is suitable for the climatic conditions involved, and to make sure that the asphalt cement is mixed in the proper proportions with properly graded, quality aggregates. Unlike portland cement paste, the quality of the asphalt cement cannot be varied after it reaches the job site.

The important properties of asphaltic concrete for pavement construction include the following:

1. Stability
2. Durability
3. Skid resistance
4. Economy

Stability

Asphalt cement, being a viscous liquid, will flow under load. The stability of asphaltic concrete pavements depends on the distribution of loads by point-to-point contact of the aggregate particles. The mechanics causing this stress distribution is referred to as "aggregate interlock," "intergranular pressure," and "internal friction." The quality and particle shape of the aggregate particles and the stiffness and proportion of the asphalt cement used are important considerations in determining the stability of asphaltic concrete.

Influence of aggregates on stability Rounded, river-worn sand and gravel produce low stability and load distribution. They tend to slide over each other with less capability of aggregate interlock and frictional resistance (Fig. 9-4). For this reason, aggregates for asphaltic concrete contain crushed particles, and the sand should be sharp and angular. Soft aggregate particles which break and wear under the impact of vehicle loads reduce concrete stability.

Aggregate grading is important in producing maximum stability at minimum cost. A maximum amount of aggregate should be compacted in a given volume. This is usually accomplished with a dense-graded aggregate where successive smaller-size particles fit into the voids of the larger-size particles. This produces maximum point-to-point contact in all sizes.

Influence of asphalt cement on stability The function of asphalt cement in producing stability is to be stiff enough to hold the aggregate particles in place. Too much asphalt cement fills all the voids among the aggregate particles and allows the aggregate particles to float in the mixture. This destroys the point-to-point framework of the rock (Fig. 9-4). The pavement will not carry appreciable loads and may result in (1) bleeding, or asphalt cement rising and covering the surface of the pavement; (2) shoving, or pavement moving laterally as vehicles accelerate or decelerate; (3) rutting, or successive ridges formed perpendicular to the direction of traffic.

There should be at least 2 percent voids among the aggregate particles after the asphalt cement has been added and the pavement compacted.

Insufficient asphalt cement, on the other hand, may not bind the aggregate particles together, and raveling and potholes can result. The penetration grade of the asphalt cement is also important to stability. If the asphalt becomes too soft in hot weather, the aggregate particles are forced down and the pavement loses its stability and may bleed. If the asphalt cement becomes too brittle in cold weather, the pavement will crack. Selection of the proper penetration grade for each climate is important.

Durability

Durable asphaltic concrete will remain smooth and serviceable during the summer heat, will not crack or ravel during winter cold, and will withstand the deterioration forces of freezing and thawing action and stripping.

Figure 9-4 Aggregate framework structure with angular and rounded aggregates, and with different amounts of asphalt cement. (*J. R. Martin and H. A. Wallace*, Design and Construction of Asphalt Pavements, *McGraw-Hill, New York, 1958.*)

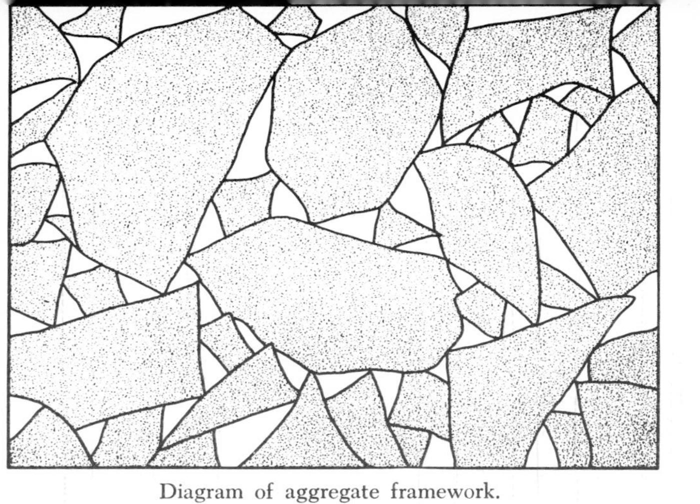

Diagram of aggregate framework.

Diagram of aggregate framework with asphalt binder.

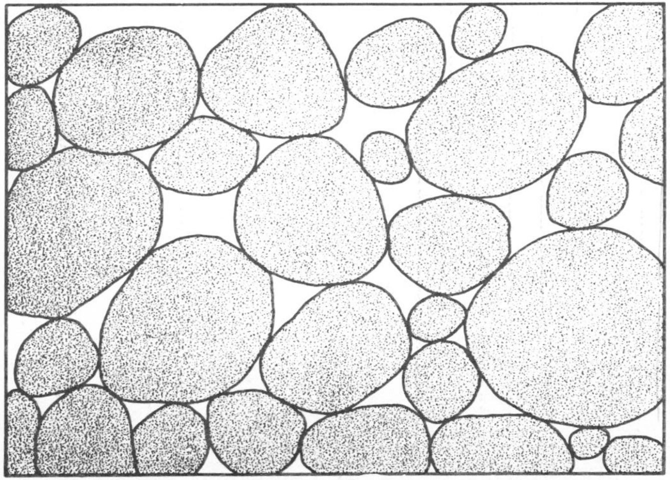

Diagram of aggregate framework with rounded aggregate.

Diagram of mix with excess asphalt binder.

Skid Resistance

Skid resistance is a form of stability. Aggregate particles must remain on the surface and give the pavement a grainy texture that will grip the tires when the pavement is wet. When too much asphalt cement is used or when the asphalt cement is too soft, the aggregate particles are forced down into the pavement, leaving only the smooth, slick asphalt cement on the surface. This process is known as "bleeding," or "flushing," and can be overcome, at least temporarily, by placing a seal coat of asphalt cement and aggregate chips on the surface.

9-3 PROPORTIONING ASPHALTIC CONCRETE MIXES

The most suitable asphaltic concrete is the one that produces a stable, durable, skid-resistant pavement at a minimum cost.

The proportions and grading of aggregates and the asphalt cement content of asphaltic concrete are usually based on the materials available and the required service of the pavement. Several organizations have developed estimates of typical gradation and asphalt requirements for various mixes. These estimated designs are generally checked for laboratory performance and adjusted to optimum proportions. In general, the following steps are recommended in a rational design.

STEP 1 *Evaluate and select aggregates:* In most government and state highway work, the contractor is allowed to select the most convenient and economical aggregate source which will meet specified requirements. These requirements usually demand the use of aggregates of the highest quality which are economically available. Crushed trap rock (dark, igneous rock types) is considered by many to be most suitable in asphaltic concrete.

STEP 2 *Select aggregate grading:* Nearly all highway departments and government agencies have specifications which define aggregate gradings for types of mixes and sizes of aggregates. Other organizations such as the Asphalt Institute also publish manuals which give recommended grading and aggregate sizes for various types of pavements.

STEP 3 *Make trial mixes with different amounts of asphalt cement:* The most important consideration in proportioning asphaltic concrete is the proportion of asphalt cement to aggregates. The optimum asphalt content can be determined from the performance of laboratory specimens. The optimum mix will produce the following: (1) maximum stability, (2) adequate film thickness on aggregate particles, and (3) sufficient voids in the mix to ensure aggregate interlock and intergranular pressure.

STEP 4 *Measure relative stability of each mix:* Several laboratory tests are in use which measure the deformation under load of compacted laboratory specimens:

1. Hubbard, ASTM D-1138
2. Marshall, ASTM D-1559
3. Unconfined Compression, ASTM D-1974
4. Hveem Stabilometer, ASTM D-1560

The Marshall test is one of the most common methods used today, and it is discussed in Chap. 13.

STEP 5 *Compute void content of the compacted specimens:* The percentage of voids in asphaltic concrete influences its stability and can be used as a specification requirement to prevent bleeding and slick pavements.

The void content can be computed by comparing the volume of the compacted asphaltic concrete with the volume occupied by each of the ingredients.

The volume of any amount of material can be computed by knowing its specific gravity or density.

$$\text{Specific gravity} = \frac{\text{density of material, kg/m}^3}{\text{density of water } (= 1000 \text{ kg/m}^3)} \tag{9-1}$$

$$\text{Solid volume of each ingredient, m}^3 = \frac{\text{kilograms of ingredient in specimen}}{\text{specific gravity of ingredient}} \tag{9-2}$$

$$\text{Percent voids} = 100\frac{V_s - V_I}{V_s} \tag{9-3}$$

where V_s = volume of specimen
V_I = combined solid volumes of all ingredients in specimen

STEP 6 *Compute voids in mineral aggregate and voids in aggregate filled with asphalt:* Asphalt cement occupies most of the total voids among the compacted aggregate particles. As previously mentioned, if these voids become completely filled, the asphalt concrete loses its stability. It is useful, therefore, to compute the voids in the mineral aggregate (VMA) and the percentage of those voids filled with asphalt.

$$\begin{aligned}\text{VMA} &= \text{volume of specimen} - \text{volume occupied by the aggregates}\\ &= V_s - V_{agg}\end{aligned} \tag{9-4}$$

$$\text{Percent VMA filled with asphalt} = 100\frac{V_a}{\text{VMA}} \tag{9-5}$$

where V_a = the volume of asphalt in the aggregate voids.

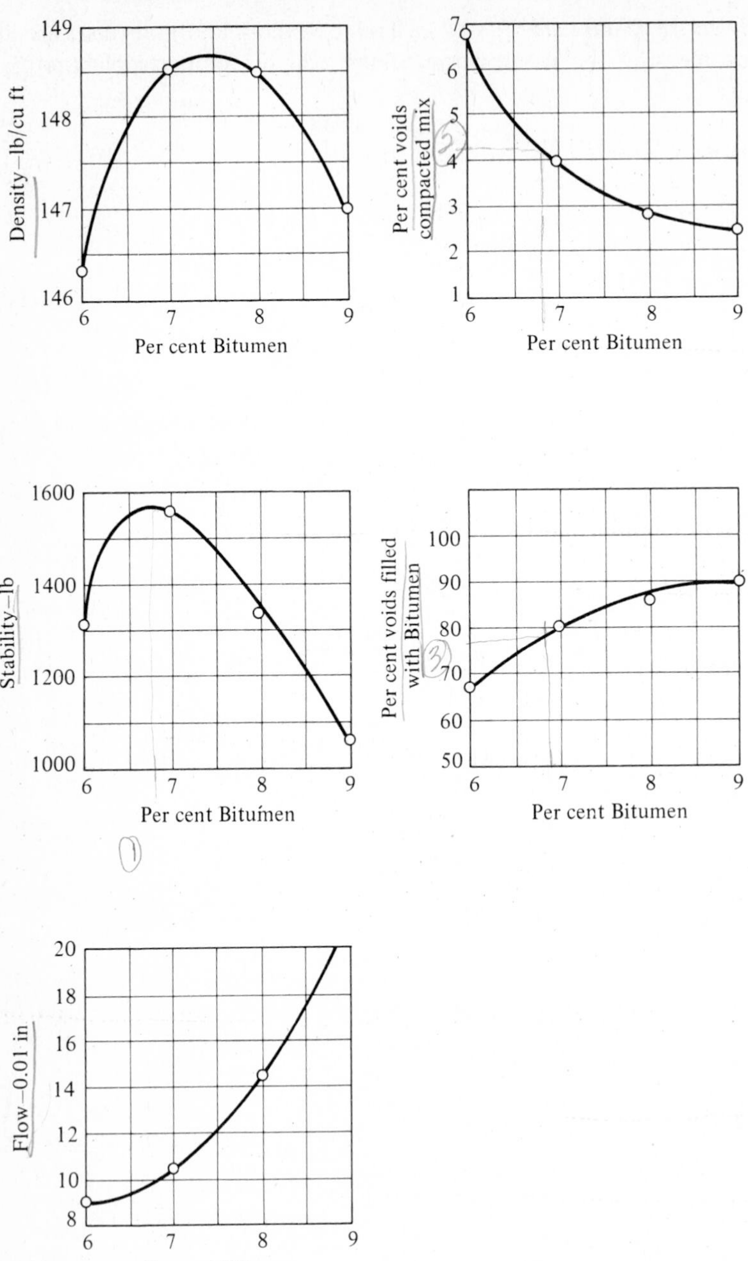

Figure 9-5 Typical Marshall test data. (*E. A. Whitehurst and W. A. Goodwin*, Bituminous Materials and Bitumen Aggregate Mixes, *Pitman, New York, 1958.*)

STEP 7 *Select optimum asphalt content:* The selection of the optimum asphalt content can best be illustrated by typical test data using the Marshall test as shown in Fig. 9-5.

1. The maximum stability occurs with 6.8 percent bitumen (asphalt cement).
2. At 6.8 percent asphalt cement, the void content of the concrete is 4.2 percent, which is within the recommended range of 2 to 5 percent.
3. The percent of the VMA filled with asphalt cement is about 78 percent, which is acceptable.

From the data 6.8 percent asphalt cement is optimum for the aggregates and grading used.

9-4 MIXING AND PLACING ASPHALTIC CONCRETE

A wide variety of methods have been used to mix and place asphalt pavements. The crudest and least satisfactory method, used in the past, was to spray cold asphalt cutback on a road to settle the dust and prevent mud. "Road mix" pavements have been used extensively. In this case cold cutback oils or asphalt emulsions are sprayed on previously placed aggregates and mixed with a grader blade.

The hot-plant asphaltic concrete in common use today produces by far the best-quality asphaltic concrete pavement and has the distinct advantage of being ready for traffic use as soon as it is laid down, compacted, and cooled. The hot asphalt cement does not contain volatile oils or water as in cold-mix asphalt cutbacks or emulsions.

Mixing Asphaltic Concrete

Asphaltic concrete is mixed in a batch-type or continuous-mix-type hot-mix asphalt plant (Fig. 9-6). The aggregates are properly graded, heated, and mixed in proper proportions with hot asphalt cement.

Placing Asphaltic Concrete

Nearly all asphaltic concrete is placed with machines such as shown in Fig. 9-7. The truck from the hot plant backs up to the machine and dumps the hot asphaltic concrete into a hopper. The "lay down" machine deposits the concrete on the previously prepared subgrade in a smooth layer at a uniform depth. Steel rollers called "breakdown rollers" (Fig. 9-8) immediately compact the concrete and smooth out irregularities.

Pneumatic rollers (Fig. 9-9) are sometimes used after steel rolling to increase the density of the concrete, particularly in the top surface. This reduces the penetration of water and solvents.

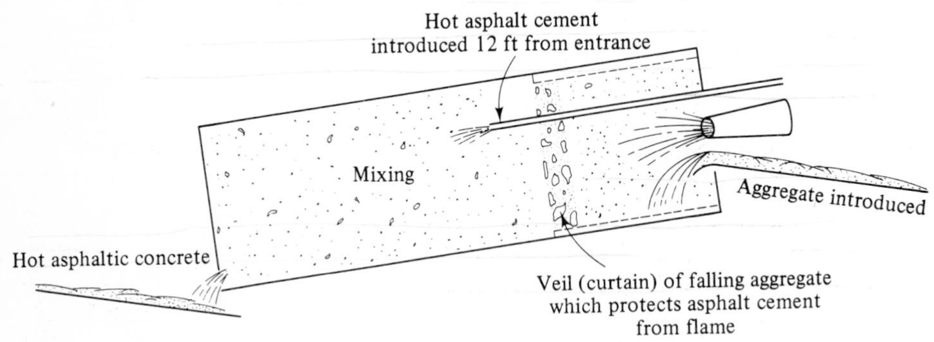

Sketch of "shear" process of drying aggregate and mixing asphaltic concrete in one operation.

Figure 9-6 Batching and mixing plants for asphaltic concrete.

Figure 9-7 Two finishing machines placing hot asphaltic concrete.

Figure 9-8 Steel wheel roller.

Figure 9-9 Pneumatic tire roller.

9-5 SUMMARY

Native asphalt has been used since about 3500 B.C. but is relatively new in its present uses. The use of asphalt cement in highway pavements dates from 1869 in London. Today asphalt is utilized in the majority of highway and airport pavements.

Asphalt cement is one of the products manufactured in the refining of petroleum and can be adjusted for cold climates (softer) or warm climates (harder) by controlling the percentage of lighter oils.

Asphalt cement can be heated and mixed with aggregates to make asphaltic concrete or can be cut back with volatile oils or emulsified with water and used cold.

The primary function of asphalt cement in asphaltic concrete is to glue together the aggregate particles. Too much asphalt cement reduces the stability of the pavement, and too little asphalt cement reduces durability.

REFERENCES

1. Martin, J. R., and H. A. Wallace: *Design and Construction of Asphalt Pavements*, McGraw-Hill, New York, 1958.
2. Asphalt Institute: *Asphalt Paving Manual*, 1962.
3. Whitehurst, E. A., and W. A. Goodwin: *Bituminous Materials and Bitumen Aggregate Mixes*, Pitman, New York, 1958.
4. Asphalt Institute: "A Brief Introduction to Asphalt," Manual MS-5, 1974.

QUESTIONS AND PROBLEMS

1 Name the important properties of asphalt cement when used in pavement construction.

2 How does a modern petroleum refinery method differ from that of early times?

3 What is the difference between an asphalt and a bitumen?

4 Can you give some reasons why the cost of gasoline (disregarding taxes) remained fairly constant from 1925 to 1970?

5 What is an asphalt cutback?

6 List three grades of asphalt cutback and give their composition.

7 What determines the quality of bituminous pavements?

8 List the important considerations in designing for flexible pavement stability.

9 What makes asphaltic concrete pavements (*a*) flush or bleed, (*b*) ravel, (*c*) crack?

10 How can skid resistance be built into bituminous pavements?

11 What are the recommended steps in proportioning asphaltic concrete mixes?

12 Assume an asphaltic concrete mix contains 2100 kg/m^3 of aggregates (specific gravity is 2.60) and 6 percent asphalt cement (specific gravity is 0.90) by mass of aggregate. Compute the percent voids in the mix and the VMA.

13 What is the difference between a batch-type and a continuous-flow-type central mix plant?

14 List some advantages in using a hot-plant asphaltic concrete rather than a cutback road mix.

15 What determines the durability of asphaltic concrete pavements?

16 How does a "bubble tower" operate?

17 What is stripping? What types of aggregate are more prone to stripping?

CHAPTER

TEN

MISCELLANEOUS MATERIALS

A number of materials, which are important in modern construction, have limited use in the structural components of structures. The following are among the most important of these.

1. *Clay products.* The use of brick, tile, pipe, and terra cotta, manufactured from clay, dates back to early history.
2. *Glass.* Windows and other glass products are as common as buildings themselves.
3. *Plastics.* Although plastics are among the newest materials, the variety of their uses has made plastic products important in modern society.
4. *Aluminum.* Aluminum is expensive and does not have the strength of steel, but its light weight, corrosion resistance, and other desirable properties have made it important for many specialized uses.

The engineer and technologist have little to do with the manufacture of these products, but should understand their properties and uses.

10-1 STRUCTURAL CLAY PRODUCTS

A variety of products are made from structural clay, including brick, building tile, terra cotta, and pipe. Brick and terra cotta have high strength and durability and give a pleasing appearance to walls. Partition and floor tile form walls and floors of high quality and fire resistance. Clay pipe are used successfully in sewers, drains, and conduits. Fire clays vitrify at high temperatures, and the resulting product has high fire resistance.

Raw Materials

The raw materials for structural clay products consist of clay or shale. The most desirable minerals for clay products are kaolinite ($2SiO_2 \cdot Al_2O_3 \cdot 2H_2O$) and other hydrated silicates of alumina. Clays consist of residual clays or sedimentary clays. Sedimentary clays have been deposited in water while the residual clays are formed by decomposition of rock. Various types of clays are discussed in Table 3-1.

Many large deposits of clay and soft shale can be mined in an open cut with heavy equipment. After mining, clays are ground with heavy rollers and then mixed with water in a pug mill.

Molding

Several processes are used to mold structural clay products. These include the soft-mud process, the stiff-mud process, and the dry-press process.

Soft-mud process A soft-mud machine for making brick consists of a pug mill mounted above gang molds. The mixed clay drops into the molds, excess clay is struck off, and the clay is compacted by jarring. This process is employed when clays are too wet to be molded by other processes.

Stiff-mud process The stiff-mud process requires less time for drying and burning. The clay and water are mixed into a stiff mud and then molded or extruded to form the desired product. Wire-cut bricks are made by passing a series of tightly drawn wires through the column of extruded clay.

Dry-press process Clay used in the dry-press process contains only about 6 percent water. The ground clay is fed into molds and compressed. A product of uniform shape is produced by this method.

Drying

Products made with the soft-mud and stiff-mud processes require drying before burning. This is usually accomplished at temperatures which do not exceed 120°C in sheds, tunnels, or "hot floor driers." Drying usually takes several days and removes excess moisture which would damage the product during burning.

Burning

Clay products require 60 to 100 h of burning, divided into four main stages:

1. *Dehydration.* During this process the temperature reaches about 700°C. All free water is gradually removed, and in the final stage the chemically combined water is driven off.

2. *Oxidation.* The oxidation period is completed by the time the temperature reaches 900°C. During this stage carbon is burned, the iron and other fluxing compounds are oxidized, and sulfur is eliminated.
3. *Vitrification.* As the temperature of clay products increases to the point of fusion, glass is formed, the pores are eliminated, and the product will have very little absorption. Firebrick, paving brick, and decorative wall tile are examples of vitrified products.
4. *Annealing.* It is necessary to cool clay products slowly from high temperatures in order to avoid checking and cracking. This usually takes from 7 to 10 days.

Glazing

Clay products can be glazed by introducing salt into the fire during burning, "salt glazing," or by spraying with "slip clays" containing lead and barium, or tin compounds which are fused to the clay during burning. Glazing produces a pleasing appearance and increases their imperviousness.

Classification of Clay Brick

Bricks are graded according to the degree of burning:

1. Hard, well burned
2. Soft, underburned
3. "Clinker brick," overburned

Other means of classifying brick depend on their quality and use.

1. *Face bricks* are more accurate and uniform in size, shape, and color. They may have smooth, rough, or textured surfaces which are exposed.
2. *Glazed bricks* are manufactured by the stiff-mud process and with the glazing coating applied before burning.
3. *Common bricks* may vary widely and consist of the kiln run not suitable for facing brick.

Structural Properties of Brick

Because of the wide variety of clays used in making brick and the variation in the degree of burning, the structural properties vary widely.

Well-burned, hard brick will generally have a compressive strength from 20.7 to 62.1 MPa and a modulus of elasticity from 9660 to 35,000 MPa. Table 10-1 shows typical properties of brick from various locations throughout the United States. The harder the brick is burned, the more voids are closed, and hence the absorption values decrease. Brick with a higher compressive strength and lower absorption values is more resistant to freezing and thawing action. The modulus of rupture will range from 3.5 to 10.5 MPa.

Table 10-1 shows average strength and absorption values for hard-burned

Table 10-1 Properties of typical brick†

Location	Average compressive strength, MPa	Average modulus of rupture, MPa	Average water absorption, %	
			48-h cold	5-h boiling
Maine, New Hampshire, and Vermont	71.2	10.38	6.3	8.7
Massachusetts	40.9	7.59	10.3	13.2
Connecticut	49.7	7.96	13.5	16.2
New York	32.9	6.93	15.4	18.3
New Jersey	37.3	6.20	10.0	13.6
Washington, D.C., and Maryland	45.2	9.93	11.9	13.8
Alabama, Tennessee, and North Carolina	30.6	6.62	9.2	13.4
Pennsylvania	32.4	10.86	7.9	10.6
	55.7	9.75	8.7	11.8
West Virginia	79.0	12.72	5.6	8.0
Virginia	65.3	18.51	7.5	10.0
Ohio	83.5	11.86	7.9	10.4
Wisconsin	36.8	7.66	16.6	20.3
Illinois	90.0	10.89	6.2	8.0
Indiana	112.3	16.27	2.3	5.4
Missouri	101.1	13.93	3.8	5.7
Kentucky	53.7	8.66	11.2	15.5
Nebraska	57.2	7.07	9.7	13.3
Kansas	109.3	13.20	3.8	5.1
Colorado	50.6	7.90	11.1	13.3
Utah	51.3	9.00	4.2	16.6
Wyoming	43.5	9.72	8.1	12.1
Washington and Oregon	52.4	8.58	10.5	14.1
California	31.7	5.07	12.7	15.2

† From M. O. Withey and G. W. Washa *Materials of Construction*, Wiley, New York, 1959.

brick from various states of the United States. This table indicates a wide variation in the quality of clays of various states with the best clays apparently found in the Midwest.

10-2 GLASS

When SiO_2 is heated to 1700°C, it melts to a clear liquid. Commercial glass is formed by cooling this liquid before crystallization takes place. The melting point of SiO_2 can be lowered by adding oxides of various metals. Those most commonly used are sodium, calcium, aluminum, lead, and iron.

Manufacture of Glass

Impurities in raw materials will cloud and color glass; hence pure SiO_2 is required. The raw material most often used is quartz. Silica sands composed primarily of quartz particles may also be suitable.

The quartz is melted in large, continuous furnaces. These furnaces hold up to 2000 tons and discharge the molten glass continuously. Molten glass is formed into commercial shapes by different processes.

1. *Pressing.* Molten glass is placed in a mold and pressed to the desired shape and cooled before ejecting.
2. *Blowing.* Air is introduced into molten glass, and the air pressure forces the glass against the sides of the mold. Glass blowing is also used to make articles without the benefit of molds.
3. *Drawing.* Molten glass is passed through rolls in a continuous stream, while it cools.

Properties of Glass

Glass is very strong in tension and compression, but is brittle and is easily broken. This is due to its noncrystalline, amorphous atomic structure, which was discussed in Chap. 2.

1. *Tensile strength.* The tensile strength of glass may be as high as 6200 MPa in glass fibers and small rods drawn in a vacuum. Polished plate glass may have a tensile strength as high as 173 MPa, but sand-blasted glass will show a strength of only 14 MPa.
2. *Modulus of elasticity.* The modulus of elasticity of glass is high and can be expected to be in the neighborhood of 65,500 MPa.

Commercial Glass

Several different types of glass are made for commercial use. These vary, depending on the additives used in the melt.

1. *Silica glass.* Silica glass contains primarily SiO_2 without additives. It is valuable for high-temperature applications because of its high softening temperature. Silica glass is viscous, hard to form, and costly, which restricts its use.
2. *Soda lime glass.* When sodium and potassium oxides are added to SiO_2, they reduce the melting point and viscosity. The first glasses made were soda lime glasses which are used extensively today for window panes, plate glass, bottles, jars, and electric light bulbs.

3. *Lead glass.* If lead is added with potassium oxide to the silica, the softening point is lowered. The glass has a higher refracture index, which gives it unusual brilliance. Lead glass is used for neon signs, for some optical glass, and as shielding against radiation.
4. *Borosilica glass.* If boron oxide is used as an additive to glass, a higher melting point and a lower coefficient of expansion result. This glass resists thermal shock and is used for glass piping, telescopes, laboratory glassware, and cookware.
5. *Glass fibers.* Fibers of glass are made by blasting a thin stream of molten glass with air or steam. They can also be made by drawing molten glass into a thin, continuous thread. Glass fibers are used for reinforcing in plastics, resins, and concrete and for insulation.

10-3 PLASTICS

The name "plastic" implies something pliable and soft. This is not necessarily true, since most plastics are hard and rigid. Most plastics are made synthetically although natural chain molecules are found in rayon, celluloid, and rubber.

Synthetic plastics fall into two important groups:

1. *Thermoplastic* resins, which soften as they are heated
2. *Thermosetting* resins, which harden and remain hard when heated

Plastics are made from long-chain polymers, which behave like an amorphous substance rather than a crystalline substance. Unless the molecules are crosslinked to one another chemically, they are held together with only weak secondary bonds. The difference in the atomic bonding between crosslinked polymers (primary bonds) and between chain polymers (secondary bonds) leads to the difference between thermoplastic and thermosetting plastics.

Properties of Plastics

Table 10-2 lists the properties of several common types of plastics. It can be seen from this table that the properties of each individual plastic vary widely, and there is also wide variation among different plastics. This is expected, since the amount of polymerization and crosslinking depends not only on the formulations but also on time, temperatures, and pressures used in manufacture.

Manufacture of Plastic Products

The versatility and simplicity of manufacturing processes make it possible to create intricate shapes in large quantities. Table 10-3 shows various methods of processing plastics into usable products.

Table 10-2 Properties of common plastics†

Property	Phenol-formaldehyde	Polyester	Polyethylene	Vinyl chloride	Polystyrene	Methyl methacrylate	Nylon	Cellulose acetate
Thermosetting or thermoplastic	Setting	Setting	Plastic	Plastic	Plastic	Plastic	Plastic	Plastic
Modulus of elasticity, MPa	2759–6207	$<$ 3448	138–414	2414–4138	2759–4138	2414–3448	1793–2759	551–2759
Specific gravity	1.2–1.3	1.0–1.5	0.93	1.16–1.45	1.05	1.18–1.19	1.09–1.14	1.24–1.34
Tensile strength, MPa	27–62	5.5–69	10–34	10–62	34–62	48–69	48–76	14–55
Hardness, Rockwell	70–120	to 115	60–90	55–65	65–90	80–105	115	50–125
Color possibilities	Opaque, limited	Transparent, unlimited	Translucent, unlimited	Transparent, unlimited	Transparent, unlimited	Transparent, unlimited	Translucent, unlimited	Transparent, unlimited
Uses	Radio cabinets, electrical parts	With glass and other fillers as structural parts	Squeeze bottles, packaging	Hoses, insulating wire	Boxes, toys, insulators	Decorative, transparent, molded items	Mechanical uses, fibers, bristles	Toys, packaging, photographic film

† From Committee on Materials, *Engineering Materials*, Pitman, New York, 1958.

Table 10-3 Manufacturing processes for plastics†

Method	Manufacturing process
Casting	Liquid or melted powder poured into mold and cured.
Slush molding	Liquid thermoplastic poured into heated mold and cooled in thin, uniform film of the mold shape.
Film casting	Liquid plastic cools on a smooth outside surface of a rotating cylinder.
Calendering	Soft plastic rolled between several pairs of rolls. Fabric inserted with plastic into last roll. Softened plastic forced through an extrusion die. Used to make rods, tubes, coated wire as well as sheet, film, and profile shapes.
Compression molding	Softened plastic forced into mold cavity to fill it completely. Mold can be heated with thermosetting resins to harden the plastic.
Transfer molding	Similar to compression molding, but heat and pressure applied in a chamber outside mold.
Injection molding	Most common method of producing thermoplastic articles of intricate patterns. Liquid plastic is forced through an orifice into a cold mold.
Laminates and reinforced plastic	The reinforcing material is molded into required shape or form. The liquid plastic is then incorporated into the reinforcing.
Sheet forming	A sheet of thermoplastic material is softened with heat and then forced against a cold mold.
Blowing	Bubbles of molten plastic are blown inside a cavity of desired shape.
Joining	Thermoplastic articles can be joined by welding with heat or by putting a solvent on the joint.

† Committee on Materials, *Engineering Materials*, Pitman, New York, 1958.

10-4 ALUMINUM

Aluminum is a soft, white, light metal. It has a specific gravity of about 2.71, which is comparable with concrete aggregates, but which is about one-third the specific gravity of steel (7.85). Aluminum is extremely malleable, can readily be extruded, and can be rolled to a thickness of only 0.00127 cm. Aluminum is strong for its weight and is used extensively in aircraft construction where weight is critical. Aluminum and its alloys are resistant to corrosion and are used extensively for window frames, partitions, and doors.

Manufacture

Aluminum is derived from bauxite, whose principal constituents are hydrated oxides of aluminum and iron.

The first step in the manufacture of aluminum is obtaining aluminum oxide from bauxite. The bauxite is first heated sufficiently to release the combined water. The oxide is then ground and heated in a solution of sodium hydrate. Aluminum oxide hydrate is then separated by precipitation and calcined at a temperature of about 1000°C.

The metal aluminum is produced in an electric furnace in a molten bath of cryolite (aluminum and sodium fluoride). The cryolite is melted in the furnace first, and the aluminum oxide is thrown into the bath where aluminum settles to the cathode bottom of the furnace with the oxygen forming on the carbon anodes, which are inserted in the bath. Aluminum usually has less than 2 percent impurities, which consist of iron and silicon.

Properties of Aluminum

The properties of aluminum vary with the amount of cold working. The strength and modulus of elasticity and hardness increase significantly as the amount of working increases from 0 to H18, which is classified as fully cold-worked (hard) (Table 10-4). Typical properties of commercial aluminum are shown in Table 10-4.

Table 10-4 Properties of commercial aluminum†

	Tension				Hardness	Shear	Fatigue
			Elongation in 2 in, percent				
Alloy and temper‡	Yield strength at 0.2 percent offset, MPa	Ultimate strength, MPa	Sheet $\frac{1}{16}$ in thick	Round $\frac{1}{2}$-in diameter	Brinell 500-kg, 10-mm ball	Shearing strength, MPa	Endurance limit,§ MPa
2S-0	34.5	89.7	35	45	23	65.5	34.5
2S-H12	89.7	103.4	12	25	28	69.0	41.4
2S-H14	96.6	117.2	9	20	32	75.9	48.3
2S-H16	117.2	137.9	6	17	38	81.8	58.6
2S-H18	144.8	165.7	5	15	44	89.7	58.6

† M. O. Withey and G. W. Washa, *Materials of Construction*, Wiley, New York, 1959.

‡ Temper designation: 0, annealed; H18, fully cold-worked (hard); H12, H14, H16, intermediate degrees of cold work between 0 and H18.

§ Based on 500 million cycles, using R. R. Moore type of rotating-beam machine.

10-5 SUMMARY

Several materials, although not included among major structural materials, have widespread use in the world today. Some of the most important include

1. Structural clay products
2. Glass
3. Plastics
4. Aluminum

It is not within the scope of this book to include a detailed discussion of the raw materials used, the manufacturing process, and the properties of each material presented.

REFERENCES

1. American Ceramics Society.
2. American Society of Metals.
3. Aluminum Company of America.
4. Withey, M. O., and G. W. Washa: *Materials of Construction*, Wiley, New York, 1959.
5. Committee on Materials: *Engineering Materials*, Pitman, New York, 1958.

QUESTIONS AND PROBLEMS

1 Where are the best clays for making brick found in the United States?

2 What is kaolinite?

3 Discuss the three processes of molding clay products.

4 Explain what happens when brick is burned.

5 What types of clay products are glazed?

6 What is meant by "clinker brick"?

7 How does the strength of brick compare with that of concrete?

8 From the discussion of atomic bonding in Chap. 2, explain why some plastics are thermosetting

9 What is the difference between commercial glass and obsidian, discussed in Chap. 3? Quartz?

10 Why is lead glass used in optical work?

11 What is a polymer?

12 Explain how articles of intricate shapes and small size can be made with plastic.

13 Can plastics be "welded" together?

14 Explain the difference between film casting and calendering.

15 Why is aluminum preferred to steel in some structural members?

16 How does the density of aluminum compare with that of concrete (kg/m^3)?

17 Why is aluminum not used in large structural members of bridges and buildings?

CHAPTER

ELEVEN

STATISTICAL EVALUATION AND SPECIFICATIONS

11-1 VARIATIONS IN THE PROPERTIES OF MATERIALS

There are variations in all materials and processes involved in engineering. In steel, the strength and ductility will vary depending on the chemical composition and uniformity of manufacture. The properties of asphaltic concrete will vary according to the quality, grade, and amount of asphalt cement used and the quality and grading of aggregates. The thickness of pavement will vary from the specified thickness.

Portland cement concrete is subject to numerous variables. Separate industries are responsible for the production of each ingredient and the proportioning and mixing of the ingredients. As mentioned in Chap. 5, project personnel are responsible for the final step in concrete manufacture, which occurs on the job. Concrete quality is the responsibility of the practicing engineer and architect. For this reason, we will discuss statistical quality evaluation and control of concrete in detail. However, the same statistical methods explained here can be applied to variations in any material or process which fall into a "normal" distribution pattern.

11-2 NORMAL DISTRIBUTION

The normal distribution curve applies to data where the variations are symmetrical about the mean of the group with fewer values occurring as the distance from the mean increases. In other words, there is an equal likelihood of variations

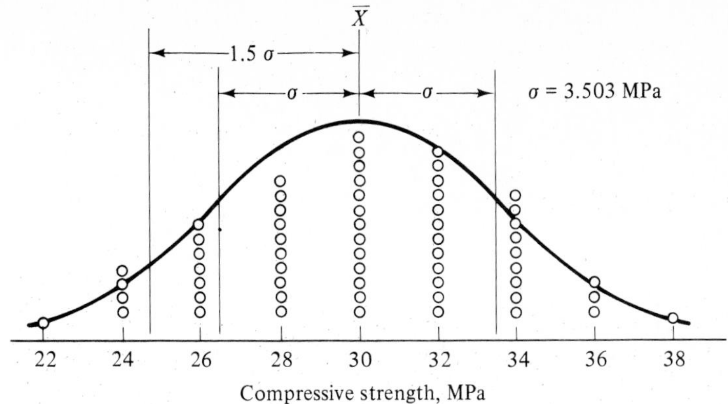

Figure 11-1 Normal frequency distribution of test results. (*William A. Cordon, "Concrete Quality," ACI Echiridion E704-4, 1973.*)

occurring above or below average. Figure 11-1 shows a typical normal frequency distribution curve for concrete strength where all strengths within a cell of 2.0 MPa are plotted at the midpoint of the cell.

11-3 MEAN STRENGTH $\bar{X}$

In statistics the value of an individual test result is given the symbol x. The mean is designated as $\bar{X}$ and is equal to

$$\bar{X} = \frac{\text{sum of all strength test values}}{\text{number of tests}} = \frac{\sum x}{n} \tag{11-1}$$

11-4 STANDARD DEVIATION σ

The standard deviation gives an indication of how closely individual test values are bunched around the average. If the standard deviation is large, the test results are widely scattered. A smaller value of σ indicates more uniformity.

The "standard deviation" is that deviation from average, where all tests greater than average can be considered concentrated and all tests less than average can be considered concentrated, and it will give the same moment (rotational effect) as all the combined individual tests. Mathematically, it is the root mean square of the deviations about the average:

$$\sigma = \sqrt{\frac{(x - \bar{x})^2 + (x_1 - \bar{x})^2 + (x_2 - \bar{x})^2 + \cdots + (x_n - \bar{x})^2}{n - 1}} \tag{11-2}$$

The use of $n - 1$ rather than n will increase σ as samples become smaller. For large samples (over 30 tests), the difference is negligible.

The computation of σ can be long and tedious when a large number of tests are involved. This may help explain why the use of statistical methods had previously been avoided. Many modern pocket calculators compute σ directly, which greatly simplifies the use of statistical methods. Shortcut methods can be used with adequate accuracy when a calculator is not available.

11-5 SHORTCUT METHOD OF COMPUTING σ

1. Compute $\bar{X}$ to the nearest whole megapascal.
2. Plot individual strength tests in cells with midpoints of cells in even multiples of 2.0-MPa deviations from $\bar{X}$.
3. Multiply the number of tests in each cell of equal deviations by the deviation squared.
4. Add the sum of the products of step 3.
5. Compute the standard deviation with Eq. (11-2).

Example: Using Fig. 11-1, we have

$$\sigma = \sqrt{\frac{13 \times 0^2 + 22 \times 2^2 + 16 \times 4^2 + 7 \times 6^2 + 2 \times 8^2}{59}}$$

$$= \sqrt{\frac{724}{59}} = 3.5 \text{ MPa}$$

11-6 STANDARD DEVIATION AND PROBABILITY

Regardless of the shape of the normal frequency curve, the standard deviation is a mathematical function of the distribution, and the area under the curve is known between any two points on the curve. Figure 11-2 shows that 34.1 percent of the area of any normal curve falls between $\bar{X}$ and $\bar{X} - \sigma$ and 15.9 percent falls below $\bar{X} - \sigma$. The theoretical curve applies to number of tests as well as to the area.

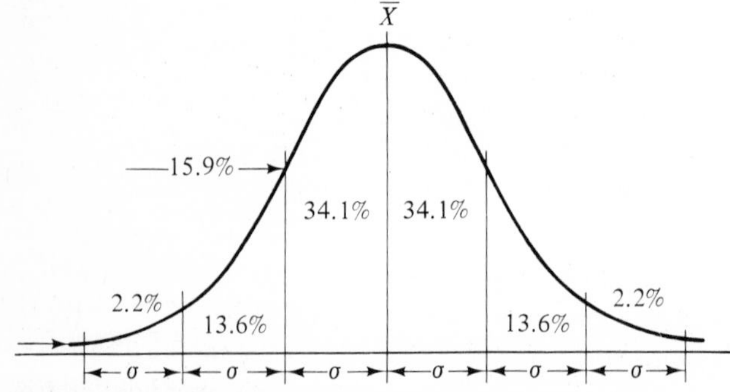

Figure 11-2 Division of the area under the normal frequency distribution curve based on deviations from $\bar{X}$ in multiples of σ. (*William A. Cordon, "Concrete Quality," ACI Echiridion E704-4, 1973.*)

Table 11-1 Expected percentages of tests lower than f'_c†

Average strength required $\bar{X}_r$	Percentage of low tests	Average strength required $\bar{X}_r$	Percentage of low tests
$f'_c + 0.10\sigma$	46.0	$f'_c + 1.6\sigma$	5.5
$f'_c + 0.20\sigma$	42.1	$f'_c + 1.7\sigma$	4.5
$f'_c + 0.30\sigma$	38.2	$f'_c + 1.8\sigma$	3.6
$f'_c + 0.40\sigma$	34.5	$f'_c + 1.9\sigma$	2.9
$f'_c + 0.50\sigma$	30.9	$f'_c + 2\sigma$	2.3
$f'_c + 0.60\sigma$	27.4	$f'_c + 2.1\sigma$	1.8
$f'_c + 0.70\sigma$	24.2	$f'_c + 2.2\sigma$	1.4
$f'_c + 0.80\sigma$	21.2	$f'_c + 2.3\sigma$	1.1
$f'_c + 0.90\sigma$	18.2	$f'_c + 2.4\sigma$	0.8
$f'_c + \sigma$	15.9	$f'_c + 2.5\sigma$	0.6
$f'_c + 1.1\sigma$	13.6	$f'_c + 2.6\sigma$	0.45
$f'_c + 1.2\sigma$	11.5	$f'_c + 2.7\sigma$	0.35
$f'_c + 1.3\sigma$	9.7	$f'_c + 2.8\sigma$	0.25
$f'_c + 1.4\sigma$	8.1	$f'_c + 2.9\sigma$	0.19
$f'_c + 1.5\sigma$	6.7	$f'_c + 3\sigma$	0.13

† William A. Cordon, "Concrete Quality," ACI Echiridion E704-4, 1973.

Values listed in Table 11-1 are computed from the theoretical curve and show the percentage of tests falling below increments of σ that are lower than $\bar{X}$.

11-7 APPLICATION OF STANDARD DEVIATION TO THE CONTROL OF CONCRETE

Since the major concern in design is the occurrence of inferior materials, the control of materials which fall outside acceptable limits is of primary importance. It becomes readily apparent from Fig. 11-2 that the use of the standard deviation offers a realistic approach to materials control based on probability. For example, it is theoretically impossible to eliminate all tests which fall below any given strength value (Fig. 11-2). However, it is possible to limit the probability of the occurrence of low tests to any realistic level by making the average strength $\bar{X}$ sufficiently greater than the strength specified in design f'_c.

Table 11-1 is an adaptation of the table of values of the normal probability integral and shows the average strength required as a function of the strength used in design f'_c plus some factor of σ corresponding to the percentage of allowable low tests. The basic equation for the control of concrete strength is

$$\bar{X}_r = f'_c + p\sigma \tag{11-3}$$

where $\bar{X}_r$ = average strength required
f'_c = strength used in design formulas
p = probability factor of σ which establishes the allowable percentage of low tests (Table 11-1)
σ = standard deviation

Required Average Strength $\bar{X}_r$

Once the value of $\bar{X}_r$ is established, it gives the mean level of strength the contractor must produce. If $\bar{X}_r$ is maintained throughout the job, there is assurance, based on previous performance, that the structure contains quality concrete.

The Strength Used in Design f'_c

The value of f'_c used in design formulas should be shown on construction drawings and specified in the specifications. The designer should be realistic in specifying f'_c. If it is too high, it may not be possible to obtain the required average strength $\bar{X}_r$ with local materials available. If f'_c is too low, it may result in structural members of uneconomical size.

Allowable Probability of Low Strength Tests

In the selection of the allowable probability of low tests, the designer should consider the following:

1. Is low strength critical to the safety of a structure? In some structural members, such as columns and brackets, low-strength concrete may cause failure.
2. In some structural concrete members such as beams and slabs, the reinforcing steel controls the load-carrying capacity of the member, and lower-strength concrete would not be serious.
3. In unreinforced concrete such as irrigation structures and foundations, strength is of minor importance for structural safety.
4. In some cases where there is freezing and thawing action or abrasion such as on highway pavements, low strength tests may indicate sections of concrete containing higher water-cement ratios and less durable concrete.

Table 11-2 gives the required average strength $\bar{X}_r$ for various structural members including recommendations of ACI Committees 214 and 318. The recommendations are based on whether strength is critical to structural safety. Figure 11-3 shows graphically the various overdesign requirements.

Number of Tests Required to Compute σ

When too few tests are available in the computation of σ, the computed value of $\bar{X}_r$ may not be reliable. For this reason, ACI Committee 318 requires the evaluation of a minimum of 30 tests to determine σ.

When 30 tests are not available, say for small jobs or at the beginning of a job, the values of p can be adjusted for the unreliability of small samples. Table 11-3 is based on the increase in student's t for small samples. It shows that if the value of p is increased by 15 percent, it will compensate for the unreliability of σ computed on only five samples.

Table 11-2 Recommendations for overdesign in computing the required average strength $\bar{X}_r$ in structural concrete

Type of structural member	Probability of a low test	Recommended values for $p\sigma$ for computing required average strength ($\bar{X}_r = f'_c + p\sigma$)
Where concrete strength below f'_c cannot be tolerated (minimum strength specification)	1.3 in 1000	3σ
Where strength is critical	1 in 100	2.32σ
Where strength below f'_c is not critical but a test below $f'_c - 500$ is critical. This requirement applies only where σ is above 500 psi (ACI 318)	Variable	$2.32\sigma - 500$
Where strength of concrete is not critical (ACI 214) (ACI 318)	1 in 10	1.282σ
Where the average of three consecutive test does not fall below f'_c (ACI 318)	1 Test: 9 in 100 Average of three tests: 1 in 100	1.343σ
Where the strength of concrete is of minor consequence in design	1 in 5	0.85σ

Table 11-3 Adjustment in values of p and required average strength $\bar{X}_r$ for small samples

Number of tests	t† (adjusted value of p)	Percentage increase in p for small samples
∞	1.282	100
30	1.310	102
20	1.325	103
15	1.341	105
10	1.372	107
5	1.476	115

† Student's t.

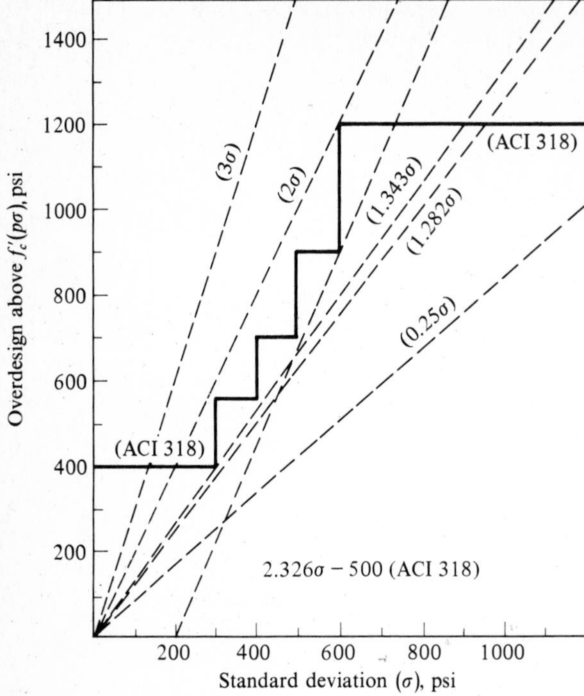

Figure 11-3 Overdesign requirements for various values of $p\sigma$.

11-8 SPECIFICATIONS FOR CONCRETE QUALITY

Objectives

The objective of specifications is to produce quality concrete in accordance with design requirements with the lowest cost to the owner and the contractor.

1. Outline in clear, concise statements exactly what the contractor is required to do.
2. Establish the contractor as a legal "independent contractor" and not an employee of the owner. This is accomplished by specifying *what* (performance of concrete) rather than *how* (mix proportions).
3. Provide a clear, unambiguous record of contract requirements.

Specifications for Overall Quality

As previously discussed, the overall quality of concrete based on previous strength tests can be obtained by requiring that the average strength be equal to

$$\bar{X}_r = f'_c + p\sigma$$

This automatically penalizes the contractor who has poor control and poor uniformity since $\bar{X}_r$ increases with an increase in σ. For general construction where strength is not critical, a requirement for $\bar{X}_r$ may be sufficient. When it is desirable to place a limitation on low strengths, additional specification requirements are needed.

Minimum Strength Specifications

The theoretical normal probability curve (Fig. 11-2) indicates that it is not possible to build a concrete structure having a previously established minimum strength. If $\bar{X}_r = f'_c + 3\sigma$, however, the probability of a test falling below f'_c is only 1.3 in 1000, and for all practical purposes f'_c can be considered the minimum strength.

Specifications for Individual Tests

Many specification writers are not comfortable with specifications for overall quality based on previous performance, and they place limitations on individual low tests. This is similar to using the tail of the curve to "wag the dog." Individual tests have a probability of failure depending on the selected value of p. Such specifications have a built-in probability of failure and invariably lead to controversy.

Specifications for Groups of Consecutive Tests

Some specification writers require that the averages of groups of consecutive tests fall above an established minimum of f'_c. When groups of tests are averaged, any variations within the group are eliminated in the computation of σ. The standard deviation is consequently smaller:

$$\sigma_3 = \frac{\sigma}{\sqrt{3}} \tag{11-4}$$

where σ_3 = standard deviation of the averages of groups of three consecutive tests
σ = standard deviation of individual tests

Assume, for example, that the probability of individual low tests is 1 in 15. Then $\bar{X}_r = f'_c + 1.5\sigma$.

The probability factor p for the averages of three tests falling below f'_c is computed as follows:

$$p = \frac{\bar{X}_r - f'_c}{\sigma} = 1.5$$

$$p = \frac{\bar{X}_r - f'_c}{\sigma_3\sqrt{3}} = 1.5$$

$$p = \frac{\bar{X}_r - f'_c}{\sigma_3} = 1.5\sqrt{3} = 2.6$$

From Table 11-1 the probability of the averages of three tests falling below f'_c is only 1 in 222. Therefore, specification for a minimum strength for the average of any three consecutive tests is much more realistic than a specification requiring a minimum strength for individual tests.

Accelerated Strength Tests

In recent years accelerated strength tests have been used on several important structures where it was necessary to check for low-strength concrete in one level before construction continued. Types of accelerated strength tests are discussed in Chap. 13.

There is always the possibility that something will happen which is not part of the normal variations. For example, an overdose of air-entraining admixture will have a disastrous effect on strength. A malfunction of batching mechanisms may reduce the cement content to dangerously low levels. An excess of water may be added on the job. When such things happen, the job is said to be "out of control," and statistical probability of the normal population no longer applies.

When strength is critical or when given structural members support additional members which will be poured before standard strength tests are available, it is advisable to cast companion accelerated strength specimens in addition to the standard 28-day tests. These tests will be tested in 24 h and will gain about 50 to 60 percent of the strength of 28-day tests. Accelerated tests will indicate any unusual low-strength concrete, and corrections can be made immediately before construction continues.

11-9 CONTROL CHARTS

Several types of control charts are used to present graphically the uniformity of control.

Control Chart of Individual Test Results

Table 11-4 shows individual random test results. Each new test is plotted, as received, and can be compared with all previous tests (Fig. 11-4). The control limit of $\bar{X} - 1.5\sigma$ shows that when sufficient tests are made, approximately 1 in 15 tests is expected to be low. It should be noted that no low tests occurred in the first 15 tests, and the first three tests of the third set of 15 were all low. This demonstrates the meaning of probability. The chances of any test being low is 1 in 15, which will average 1 low test in 15 when sufficient samples are tested. It does not mean that each set of 15 tests will contain 1 low test.

The chart shown in Fig. 11-4 indicates that the job started out with more strength than required, but after test no. 13 the strength started to decline. This trend will occur as construction moves from cool winter and spring weather to hot summer weather. In this particular job, corrections were not made in time to adjust for lower strengths. Consequently, the concrete represented by tests 30 to 32 falls below the established control limit.

Table 11-4 Test results selected from random numbers

Test number	Strength, MPa	Test number	Strength, MPa	Test number	Strength, MPa
1	30.60	21	25.90	41	30.80
2	30.00	22	35.00	42	33.50
3	36.00	23	29.70	43	27.70
4	33.60	24	24.40	44	23.20
5	32.00	25	26.60	45	30.00
6	32.00	26	27.90	46	23.00
7	30.20	27	28.10	47	26.40
8	29.40	28	26.00	48	24.00
9	30.60	29	23.80	49	29.10
10	30.20	30	22.00	50	24.00
11	35.50	31	23.50	51	27.90
12	36.50	32	21.90	52	30.80
13	38.90	33	25.00	53	29.00
14	30.10	34	31.90	54	32.20
15	32.00	35	34.10	55	36.10
16	34.10	36	35.80	56	29.20
17	33.70	37	29.20	57	26.90
18	28.20	38	30.10	58	31.90
19	30.10	39	35.00	59	33.80
20	33.80	40	26.80	60	37.20

$\bar{X} = 29.95$
$\sigma = 4.168$

Note: This table indicates only one cylinder for each test. When two or three cylinders are used for each test, the cylinders should not be averaged. All cylinder strengths should be included and shown on the control chart. Otherwise, the within-batch variations would be eliminated.

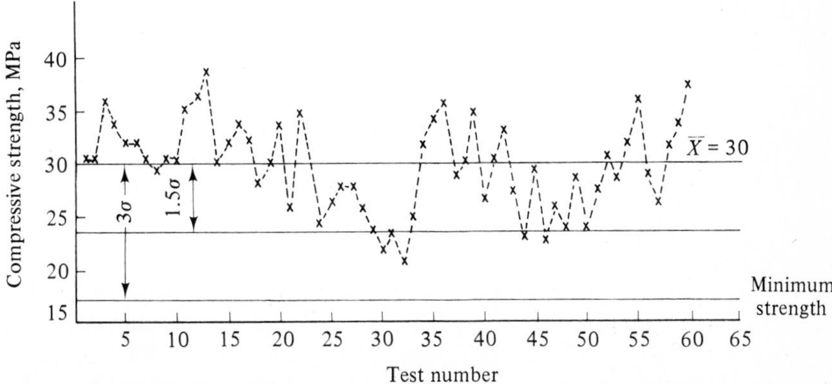

Figure 11-4 Quality control chart for individual tests.

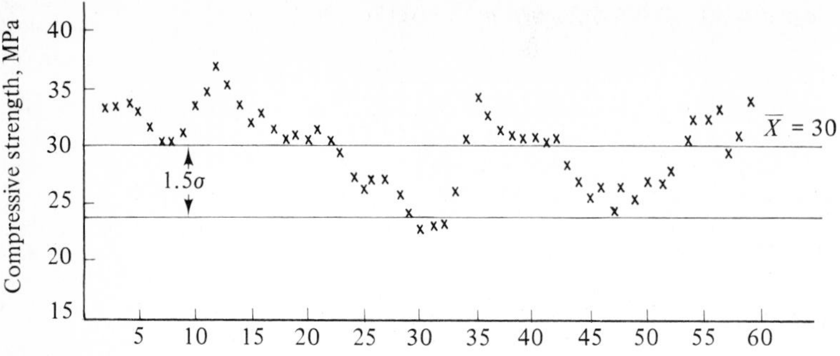

Figure 11-5 Control chart for moving average of any three consecutive tests.

Control Chart for the Moving Average of Three Tests

Figure 11-5 shows a control chart for the moving average of any three consecutive tests from Table 11-4. The first three tests are averaged for the first point. For the next point, the fourth test is included in the average and the first test is deleted. For the third point, the fifth is added, the second deleted, and so on, which gives values for any three consecutive tests. Assume that the specifications require that the strength of any three consecutive tests not fall below f'_c and $\bar{X}_r$ be equal to $f'_c + 1.5\sigma$. The control chart shows that occasional low tests will not cause the concrete to fail these specifications—tests 44 to 50 (Figs. 11-3 and 11-4). When low tests occur consecutively, however (tests 30 to 32), this is not normal variation and the concrete fails to meet specifications.

Use of Control Charts

Control charts such as shown in Figs. 11-4 and 11-5 are useful in showing the job uniformity at a glance, and also indicate trends to lower and higher strength. This is useful, particularly for accelerated tests, so that adjustments and corrections can be made before the concrete fails specification requirements.

11-10 ADJUSTMENTS IN REQUIRED AVERAGE STRENGTH $\bar{X}_r$

The required average strength $\bar{X}_r$ should be established, at the beginning of the project, from previous test results by using project materials and estimated values of σ. The value of $\bar{X}_r$ should be adjusted periodically during the job as additional test results become available. Adjustments should be based on the most recent 30 tests. The test results in Table 11-4 were checked for adjustment as each additional 10 tests were accumulated, assuming $f'_c = 24.00$ MPa (Table 11-5).

Table 11-5 Adjustment of required strength, MPa, for the moving average of 30 tests ($f'_c = 24.00$)

Test results	Average $\bar{X}$	Standard deviation σ	Required average $\bar{X}_r$ ($f'_c + 1.5\sigma$)
1–30	30.90	4.207	30.31
11–40	29.85	4.688	31.03
21–50	27.81	4.110	30.17
31–60	29.33	4.302	30.45

Analysis of Table 11-5 shows that the average strength for the project should have been maintained at about 31.00 MPa in order to meet specification requirements and should have been increased after 40 tests. It is usually advisable to start a project with $\bar{X}_r$ higher than anticipated. When the job settles down and the contractor and producer prove the reliability of their operation, adjustments can be made for more economical concrete.

11-11 CONTROL OF TESTING

Within-Test Variations

Variations in testing may significantly influence the evaluation of concrete quality. We can assume, for example, that cylinders cast from the same sample of concrete should have the same strength. Any variation among these cylinders can be attributed to testing procedures. The standard deviation for within-test variations can be estimated quite accurately if there are at least 10 tests having two or three cylinders per test:

$$\sigma_{wt} = \frac{\bar{R}}{d_2} \tag{11-5}$$

where σ_{wt} = within-test standard deviation
$\bar{R}$ = average range of at least 10 sets of strength tests (Range is the difference between the highest and lowest strength within the test group.)
d_2 = a factor from ASTM Special Technical Publication 15-c
= 1.128 for two specimens per test
= 1.693 for three specimens per test

Use of Within-Test Standard Deviation

In any controversy regarding failure of specification requirements, each organization that may have contributed to that failure becomes suspect. It is natural for a contractor or supplier to question the validity of the tests. When within-test variations are excessive, such concern may be justified. Testing variations are usually small, however, and do not significantly add to the total. The influence of testing variations can easily be checked by using the following approximation:

$$\sigma_{BB} = \sqrt{\sigma^2 - \sigma_{wt}^2} \tag{11-6}$$

where σ_{BB} = batch-to-batch standard deviations
σ = overall standard deviation
σ_{wt} = within-test standard deviation

11-12 SUMMARY

Statistical methods provide valuable tools for specifications of materials or processes when variations cannot be avoided. The variations in the strength of concrete will fall into a symmetrical distribution pattern called a "normal" distribution. The following statistical tools can be applied to specifications based on the theoretical distribution.

1. The mean or average strength $\bar{X}$
2. The standard deviation σ
   (*a*) Overall on batch-to-batch standard deviation
   (*b*) The within-batch standard deviation
3. The probability of tests falling below some established standard deviation
4. The required average strength $\bar{X}_r$ which limits the probability of low tests to an acceptable specification based on probability and provides a realistic assurance of acceptable quality or compliance for any material or process which falls into the "normal" distribution pattern

REFERENCES

1. ACI Committee 318: "Building Code Requirements for Reinforced Concrete," ACI 318–71.
2. ACI Committee 214: "Recommended Practice for Evaluation of Compression Test Results of Field Concrete," ACI 214–65.
3. Cordon, William A.: "Concrete Quality," ACI Echiridion E704–4, 1973.
4. ASTM E-380.
5. Cordon, William A.: "Minimum Strength Specifications Can Be Practical," *ACI Journal*, July 1969.
6. Paradine, C. G., and B. H. P. Rivett: *Statistical Methods for Technologists*, Van Nostrand, Princeton, N.J., 1960.
7. Cordon, William A.: "Size and Number of Samples and Statistical Considerations in Sampling," ASTM STP 169-A.

QUESTIONS AND PROBLEMS

1 (*a*) What is the standard deviation?
(*b*) Why is it valuable in preparing specifications?

2 What is meant by normal distribution?

3 What is a cell on a distribution chart?

4 Determine the probability of tests falling below $\bar{X} - 2.15\sigma$.

5 Assume $\bar{X} = \bar{X}_r$. Does this mean there will be no low tests?

6 Determine the probability of low tests if $f'_c = 30$ MPa, $\bar{X} = 36.4$, and $\sigma = 4$ MPa.

7 Write a specification for concrete in a concrete building for (*a*) columns, (*b*) floors and beams, (*c*) foundations.

8 Why are specifications for a minimum strength of any three consecutive tests more realistic than for a minimum strength of individual tests?

9 Why are accelerated tests important?

10 What is a moving average?

11 When should adjustments in $\bar{X}_r$ be made?

12 Does a testing laboratory share any responsibility for uniformity of concrete? Explain.

PART TWO

MATERIALS EVALUATION

Part Two of this text gives an overview of materials testing and evaluation. These chapters can be used not only for class instruction and correlation with previous chapters but also as a guide to standard laboratory testing procedures and specifications. The purpose and significance of each test are discussed.

A common dilemma that faces most engineers and architects is what action to take when laboratory test results fail to meet standard specification requirements. Standard specifications are based on a consensus of committee members rather than a precise measure of quality. The quality of materials, in some cases, may not be sensitive to variations from standard requirements. Properly trained engineers or architects will, therefore, not let precise conformance to laboratory test results dictate their decisions, but will use the results as a valuable tool in making sound engineering judgments.

The American Society for Testing and Materials† (ASTM) is recognized as a leading authority in the testing and evaluation of materials. ASTM publishes 48 volumes of standards for testing procedures and specifications which are revised each year. It would be impractical for each student to purchase copies of appropriate standards for laboratory exercises. This is particularly true since changes in

† 1916 Race Street, Philadelphia, Pa., 19106.

standards are continually being made by the various committees. Copies of appropriate current ASTM standards should be available for student reference.

A general outline of testing procedures is presented in this text but the student is urged to become familiar with current ASTM and other standards as used in testing and specifications.

References for Part Two include the current *ASTM* book of standards, *The Testing and Inspection of Engineering Materials*, by Davis, Troxell, and Wiscocil (McGraw-Hill, 1964) and the 8th edition of the U.S. Bureau of Reclamation *Concrete Manual.*

CHAPTER

TWELVE

TESTING AND EVALUATION OF AGGREGATES FOR CONCRETE AND ASPHALTIC CONCRETE

Aggregate comprises about 55 percent of the volume of concrete mortar that contains aggregate graded up to 4.75-mm maximum size and about 85 percent of the volume of mass concrete that contains aggregate graded up to 152-mm maximum size. Aggregates occupy about 95 percent of the volume of dense, graded, compacted asphaltic concrete. Aggregates are important in all concretes, and because of variability in properties each source must be tested and evaluated.

The following standard ASTM tests are used in evaluation and specifications for aggregates for concrete and asphaltic concrete:

C-125 Definitions of terms relating to concrete and concrete aggregates
D-75 Sampling aggregates

Physical Properties of Aggregates

C-136 Test for sieve or screen analysis of fine and coarse aggregates
C-40 Test for organic impurities in sands for concrete
C-87 Test for effect of organic impurities in fine aggregate on strength of mortar
C-142 Test for clay lumps and friable particles in aggregates
C-117 Test for materials finer than no. 200 (75-μm) sieve in mineral aggregates by washing

C-123 Test for lightweight pieces in aggregate
C-535 Test for resistance to abrasion of large-size coarse aggregate by use of the Los Angeles machine
C-127 Specific gravity and absorption of coarse aggregate
C-128 Specific gravity and absorption of fine aggregate
C-131 Test for resistance to abrasion of small-size coarse aggregate by use of the Los Angeles machine
C-88 Test for soundness of aggregates by use of sodium sulfate or magnesium sulfate

Influence of Aggregates on the Properties of Concrete and Mortar

C-29 Test for unit weight of aggregate
C-39 Test for compressive strength of cylindrical concrete specimens
C-78 Test for flexural strength of concrete (using simple beam with third-point loading)
C-227 Test for potential alkali reactivity of cement-aggregate combinations (mortar-bar method)
C-289 Test for potential reactivity of aggregates (chemical method)
C-295 Recommended practice for petrographic examination of aggregates for concrete
C-342 Test for potential volume change of cement-aggregate combinations
C-586 Test for potential alkali reactivity of carbonate rocks for concrete aggregates (rock cylinder method)
C-666 Test for resistance of concrete to freezing and thawing

12-1 SAMPLING AGGREGATES

Purpose

Aggregates are usually sampled for the following purposes:

1. Preliminary investigation of the potential source of supply
2. Control of the product at the source of supply
3. Control of the operations at the site of use
4. Acceptance or rejection of the materials

Procedures for Sampling Aggregates

Aggregate samples from conveyor belts or chutes To secure a representative sample of aggregate from a belt or chute, a complete cross section of the stream should be taken over a short period, rather than just a portion of the stream over a longer period. Samples should be taken at regular intervals until the whole supply has been sampled. The number and size of such samples will depend on the quantity and uniformity of the aggregate.

Aggregate samples from railroad cars Samples from a railroad car are best taken at points equally spaced on straight lines along the sides and center of the car. The size of samples will depend on the size of the car, the number of points from which samples are taken, and the maximum size of aggregate particles. At each point the sampler should obtain aggregate well beneath the surface. A standard tube sampler should be used for sand and, when possible, for coarse aggregate. The tube sampler is usually a steel pipe about 2 in in diameter and 6 ft long, pointed at the lower end and having a handle at the top. A series of openings is punched along the pipe in such a way that a line of "ears" projects from one side of the openings. The tube is forced into the aggregate as far as possible, turned until the ears have scooped sufficient material into the tube for a sample, and then withdrawn, with the openings being kept on top.

Since it is sometimes difficult to obtain a representative sample from a railroad car by the above method, especially with large coarse aggregate, samples should be taken so far as practicable while the material is being loaded or unloaded. While a car is being unloaded, a fairly representative sample may be obtained by taking a shovelful at regular intervals, provided care is taken that the larger pieces do not roll off the shovel. Whatever method is used to obtain the sample, it should be one which will ensure representative material.

Aggregate samples from stockpiles The entire sand stockpile from top to bottom should be sampled. Sampling should start at equally spaced points along the bottom of the pile and proceed upward, at equal intervals, over the sides and top. If only part of the pile is to be used for a portion of the job, just the part to be used should be sampled.

Where practicable, samples are taken with a standard tube sampler. If this cannot be done, samples should be obtained with a shovel and consist of material from well beneath the surface. By holding a short piece of board against the pile just above the point of sampling, the inclusion of unwanted surface material may be avoided.

Sampling from roadway bases and subbases Sample units are selected by a random method from the construction. At least three approximately equal samples are selected at random from the unit being sampled and are combined to form a field sample. All samples are taken from the roadway for the full depth of the material, with care being taken to exclude any underlying material. Clearly mark the specific areas from which each increment is to be removed; a metal template placed over the area is a definite aid in securing approximately equal increment weights.

Significance of Proper Sampling

One of the most important aspects of materials testing is obtaining samples which accurately represent the whole of the materials being tested. Accurate testing procedures made with nonrepresentative samples are useless in making proper evaluation of the materials and may give false information which could lead to erroneous conclusions. Aggregates tend to segregate in handling, which makes sampling procedures particularly important.

12-2 REDUCING SAMPLE SIZES FOR TESTS

Purpose

Several identical small samples may be required for different tests. It is important, therefore, that each sample of the same material be a duplicate of all other samples.

Samples should be reduced to test size by the quartering method or use of a sample splitter.

Procedures

Quartering method The sample is placed on a hard, clean surface where there will be neither loss of material nor accidental addition of foreign matter. The sample is mixed thoroughly by turning the entire lot over three times with a shovel. This can best be accomplished by two people, one on each side of the sample, beginning at one end and taking alternate shovels of the material as they advance the length of the pile. With the third or last turning, the entire sample is shoveled into a conical pile by depositing each shovelful on top of the preceding one. The conical pile is carefully flattened to a uniform thickness and diameter so that the material will not be transposed from one quarter to another. The flattened mass is then marked into quarters by two lines that intersect at right angles at the center of the pile. Two diagonally opposite quarters are removed, and the cleared spaces brushed clean. The remaining material is mixed and quartered successively until the sample is reduced to the desired size (Fig. 12-1).

Sample splitter The entire sample is passed through the splitter, one-half set aside and the other half split again. The procedure is repeated until the sample is reduced to the desired size (Fig. 12-2).

With large-size aggregates, it may be more desirable or convenient to hand-pick the sample. When this is done, extreme care should be taken to obtain a representative sample.

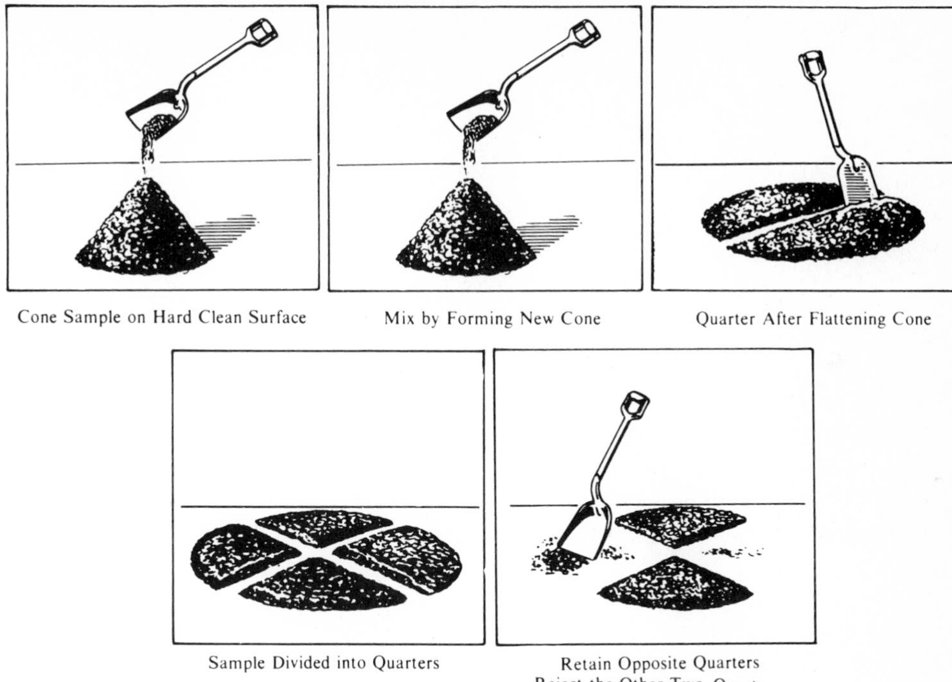

Figure 12-1 Reducing size of sample by quartering. (*ASTM D-75*.)

Figure 12-2 Riffle sample splitter. (*ASTM D-75*.)

Significance of Properly Reducing Large Aggregate Samples to Small Test Samples

Large and fine aggregate particles readily segregate from each other in handling, and unless proper precautions are taken to properly reduce the size of samples, small samples which are not representative of the whole will be obtained.

12-3 AGGREGATE GRADING (PARTICLE-SIZE DISTRIBUTION)

Purpose

The particle-size distribution of fine and coarse aggregates influences the total surface area and void content of the combined aggregate particles. This, in turn, will influence various properties of concrete and asphaltic concrete. Consequently, grading is important in the evaluation of aggregate samples. More importantly, variations in grading of aggregates cause variations in the properties of the resulting concrete and asphaltic concrete. In large laboratories, all coarse aggregate and sand sizes are separated and then recombined to ensure uniform grading (Fig. 12-3).

Figure 12-3 Equipment for separating large samples of sand into standard sizes. (*U.S. Bureau of Reclamation.*)

Table 12-1 Typical sand grading computations

Sieve number	Cumulative weight retained	Cumulative percentages retained	Individual percentages retained	Percent passing
4	4	1	1	99
8	76	19	18	81
16	157	39	20	61
30	233	58	19	42
50	306	76	18	24
100	370	92	16	8
Pan	402	—	8	—
Total		285	100	

Fineness modulus = 285 ÷ 100 = 2.85.

Testing Procedures

Fine aggregate (smaller than no. 4 sieve) Approximately 500 g of dry sand which accurately represents the material being tested is sieved through standard sieves nested from the largest (no. 4) to the smallest (no. 100) (Table 12-1). Sieving should be continued until not more than 1 percent of the residue passes any sieve during 1 min.

The cumulative grams of sand retained on each sieve is measured by starting with the no. 4 sieve, as indicated in Table 12-1.

Computation of the *fineness modulus* is made by adding the cumulative percentage of material retained on each sieve and dividing by 100 (see Table 12-1). The percentage passing each sieve is then computed and compared with ASTM limits (Table 12-2).

Table 12-2 ASTM grading requirements for fine aggregates

Sieve number	Percent passing			
		Bituminous paving		
	Concrete	Grading 1	Grading 2	Grading 3
$\frac{3}{8}$	100	100	—	100
No. 4	95–100	95–100	100	80–100
No. 8	80–100	70–100	95–100	65–100
No. 16	50–85	40–80	85–100	40–80
No. 30	25–60	20–65	65–90	20–65
No. 50	10–30	7–40	30–60	7–40
No. 100	2–10	2–20	5–25	2–10
No. 200	Silt	0–10	0–5	0–10

Table 12-3 Minimum size of samples for coarse aggregates

Maximum sieve number	Minimum size of sample, kg
$\frac{3}{8}$	2
$\frac{1}{2}$	4
$\frac{3}{4}$	8
1	12
$1\frac{1}{2}$	16
2	20
$2\frac{1}{2}$	25
3	45
$3\frac{1}{2}$	70

Coarse aggregate (larger than no. 4 sieve) The size of the sample required for the grading test of coarse aggregate will depend on the size of the aggregate particles, as indicated in Table 12-3.

Coarse-aggregate sieves are selected corresponding to the appropriate standard number (Table 12-4) and nested from coarse to fine in a sieve shaker. After sufficient shaking, the total percentage of the sample passing each sieve is recorded and compared with ASTM standard limits (Table 12-4).

Significance of Tests for Aggregate Grading

The influence of aggregate grading on the properties of concrete and asphaltic concrete has been studied extensively, and standard grading specifications have been produced. None of these have been completely accepted, because variations of particle shape and surface texture influence the most desirable grading for a particular aggregate. Standard grading specifications, on the average, will produce a concrete of satisfactory properties.

The grading of fine aggregate (sand) has significant influence on workability of concrete. If the mortar is workable, it is usually possible to secure workable concrete by using enough mortar to fill the voids and separate the coarse-aggregate particles. It is necessary to leave room for movement without particle interference. Experience has shown that very coarse sand or very fine sand is unsatisfactory for concrete mixtures. The coarse sand results in harshness, bleeding, and segregation; and the fine sand requires a larger amount of paste to cover the surface of the sand particles and produce the necessary workability.

Investigations should be made into the quality and economy of concrete produced by alternative grading requirements. For example, gap-graded aggregates where certain size fractions are eliminated have been used successfully. Successful concrete is produced in the Great Plains region with "sand-gravel" aggregates which are graded to smaller sizes of gravel and sand. This is necessary because of a shortage of coarser sizes. Quality concrete has been produced by the

Table 12-4 Grading requirements for coarse aggregate of various maximum and minimum sizes for concrete and bituminous paving or crushed aggregate for base and surface courses

		Amounts finer than each laboratory sieve, percent by mass (kg)													
	Sieve number	4	$3\frac{1}{2}$	3	$2\frac{1}{2}$	2	$1\frac{1}{2}$	1	$\frac{3}{4}$	$\frac{1}{2}$	$\frac{3}{8}$	No. 4	No. 8	No. 16	No. 50
Grading number	Size range \ Square opening, mm	100	90	75	63	50	37.5	25	19	12.5	9.5	4.75	2.36	1.18	0.3
1	$3\frac{1}{2}$–$1\frac{1}{2}$	100	90–100		25–60		0–15		0–5						
2	$2\frac{1}{2}$–$1\frac{1}{2}$			100	90–100	35–70	0–15		0–5						
3	2–1				100	90–100	35–70	0–15		0–5					
357	2–no. 4				100	95–100		35–70		10–30		0–5			
4	$1\frac{1}{2}$–$\frac{3}{4}$					100	90–100	20–55	0–15		0–5				
467	$1\frac{1}{2}$–no. 4					100	95–100		35–70		10–30	0–5			
5	1–$\frac{1}{2}$						100	90–100	20–55	0–10	0–5				
56	1–$\frac{3}{8}$						100	90–100	40–75	15–35	0–5	0–5			
57	1–no. 4						100	95–100		25–60		0–10	0–5		
6	$\frac{3}{4}$–$\frac{3}{8}$							100	90–100	20–55	0–15	0–5			
67	$\frac{3}{4}$–no. 4							100	90–100		20–55	0–10	0–5		
68	$\frac{3}{4}$–no. 8							100	90–100		30–65	5–25	0–10	0–5	
7	$\frac{1}{2}$–no. 4								100	90–100	40–70	0–15	0–5		
78	$\frac{1}{2}$–no. 8								100	90–100	40–75	5–25	0–10	0–5	
8	$\frac{3}{8}$–no. 8									100	85–100	10–30	0–10	0–5	
9	No. 4–no. 16										100	85–100	10–40	0–10	0–5

U.S. Bureau of Reclamation with wide departures from standard grading specifications. For example, in one case, the sand contained practically none of the finest or coarsest sizes. In another case, the sand contained practically none of the intermediate-size fractions.

Fine aggregates having gradings outside standard specifications have produced satisfactory concrete in some instances. But where the behavior of an available sand having a grading falling outside accepted limits is unknown and where the size of the job does not warrant the expense of trial concrete mixes, a standard specification such as ASTM C-33 should be used. On large jobs involving many thousands of cubic meters of concrete, evaluation of concrete mixes should be made to determine the most economical aggregate grading commensurate with available aggregate sources. It is emphasized, however, that regardless of the grading selected, variations from this grading cannot be tolerated during construction if uniform concrete is to be produced.

Voids among aggregate particles The particle-size distribution of aggregates naturally determines, to a large extent, the size and volume of voids among the particles of aggregate. This is important in concrete, because the smaller the volume of voids, the less water-cement paste is used. Paste increases cost, shrinkage, and other undesirable properties of concrete. It is desirable, therefore, to keep the void content to a minimum.

In asphaltic concrete, on the other hand, it is desirable to control the volume of voids. There must be sufficient voids among the aggregate particles when coated with asphalt cement to ensure point-to-point contact of the aggregate particles.

Void content in compacted aggregate becomes an important property in proportioning concrete and asphaltic concrete mixes. Table 12-5 shows the approximate void content of various sizes and grading of aggregates. The void content of crushed aggregate is greater than that of rounded aggregate.

Table 12-5 Void content in typical dry-rodded aggregates

	Voids, percent	
Size of sieve number	Natural	Crushed
Sand:		
Nos. 100 to 4	38	
Gravel:		
Nos. 4 to $\frac{3}{4}$	35	37
Nos. 4 to $1\frac{1}{2}$	32	35
Nos. 4 to 6	26	
Sand and gravel:		
Nos. 100 to $1\frac{1}{2}$	25	

Surface area of aggregates The surface area of aggregate particles is important because in concrete a film of cement-water paste must cover the surface area of each particle. Therefore, the greater the surface area of aggregate particles, the more cement-water paste is required.

In asphaltic concrete a film of asphalt cement of sufficient thickness must cover each aggregate particle to produce durable pavements. The greater the surface area, the greater the amount of asphalt cement required for durability.

The surface area of aggregate particles can be approximated for rounded aggregate by assuming the particles to be spheres. The area of a sphere equals $4\pi R^2$. The volume of a sphere equals $\frac{4}{3}\pi R^3$.

The number of particles in 1 g of aggregate with a specific gravity of 2.65 is

$$\frac{1}{2.65(\frac{4}{3}\pi R^3)} \tag{12-1}$$

The surface area of each particle equals $4\pi R^2$. Multiplying the number of particles by the surface area of each particle gives

$$\text{Surface area} = 4\pi R^2 \frac{1}{2.65(\frac{4}{3}\pi R^3)} = \frac{1.132}{R} = \frac{2.264}{D} \text{ per gram} \tag{12-2}$$

Table 12-6 shows the approximate surface area of 1 kg of aggregates of various sizes.

The surface area of a given mass of aggregate particles increases significantly as the particles become smaller. This illustrates why the water and cement requirement of concrete increases when finer aggregates are used. This also explains the increase in total bond strength between portland cement paste and the increased surface area of smaller-size aggregates.

Table 12-6 Comparative surface area of 1 kg of aggregate particles having a diameter equal to standard sieve numbers

Sieve number	Diameter of particle, cm	Surface area, cm^2/kg
3	7.5	301.9
$1\frac{1}{2}$	3.81	594.2
$\frac{3}{4}$	1.90	1,191.6
$\frac{3}{8}$	0.95	2,275.4
No. 4	0.475	4,766.3
No. 8	0.236	9,593.2
No. 16	0.118	19,186.4
No. 30	0.06	37,733.3
No. 50	0.03	75,466.7
No. 100	0.015	150,933.3
No. 200	0.0075	301,866.7

Figure 12-4 Placing gap-graded aggregate (Tignes Dam, France).

Gap-graded aggregate When one or more standard sizes of aggregate are eliminated, leaving a gap in the continuous grading curve, the aggregate is said to be "gap-graded." The theory for using gap-graded aggregate is that in continuous grading the largest aggregate particles are held apart by the next particle size and do not allow the large particles to fit closely together. Gap-graded aggregates have been used successfully in construction of large dams (Figs. 12-4 and 12-5).

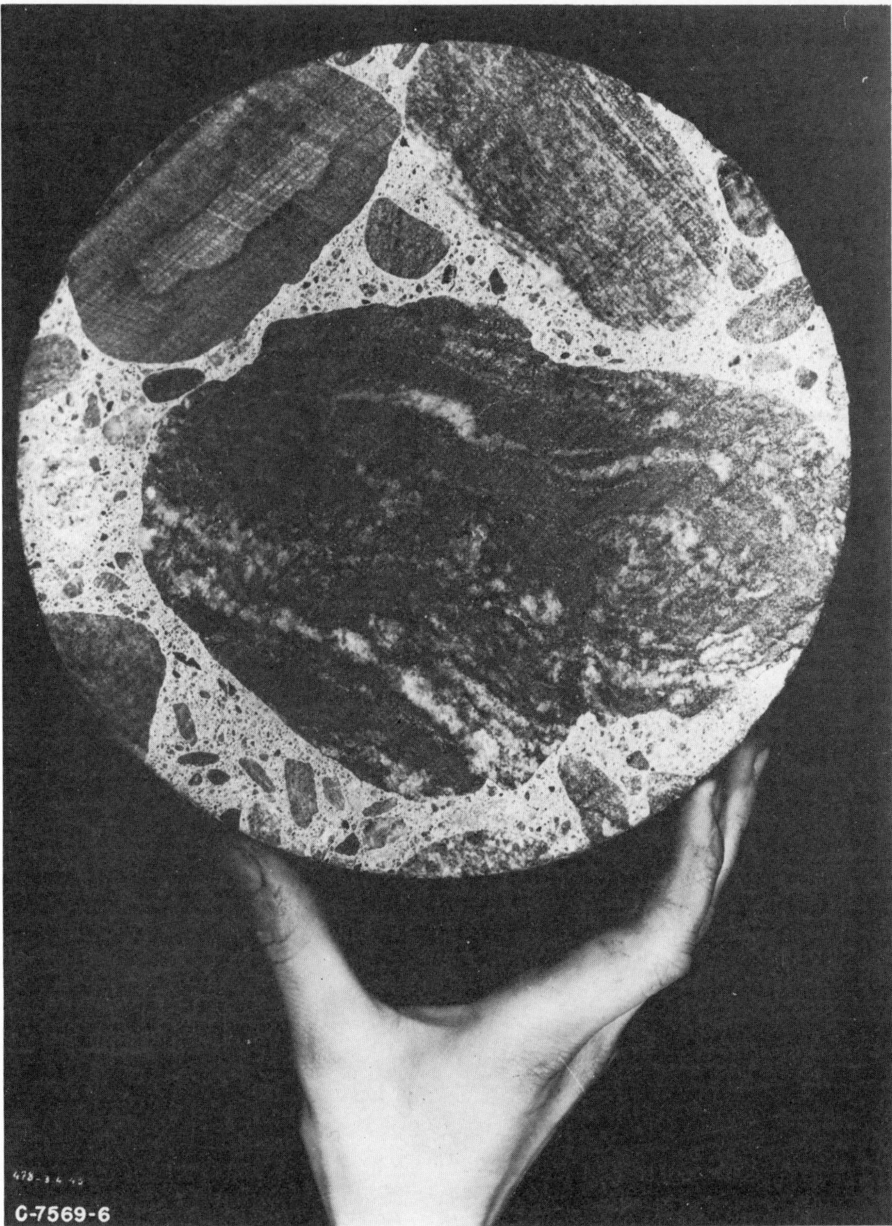

Figure 12-5 Section through a core of gap-graded aggregate concrete showing how large pieces of aggregate fit closely together.

Table 12-7 Limits for deleterious substances in fine aggregate for concrete†

Item	Maximum percentage of total sample, g
Clay lumps and friable particles	3.0
Material finer than no. 200 (75-μm) sieve:	
Concrete subject to abrasion	3.0‡
All other concrete	5.0‡
Coal and lignite:	
Where surface appearance of concrete is of importance	0.5
All other concrete	0.1

† From ASTM C-73.

‡ In the case of manufactured sand, if the material finer than the no. 200 (75-μm) sieve consists of the dust of fracture, essentially free from clay or shale, these limits may be increased to 5 and 7 percent, respectively.

12-4 DELETERIOUS MATERIALS IN AGGREGATES

Certain materials found in some aggregate samples may be harmful to concrete. These types of materials are shown in Tables 12-7 and 12-8, and limitations are placed on their use.

Materials Finer than 75 μm

Purpose of test Limitation of the amount of very fine material in concrete aggregate will ensure that harmful amounts of silt and clay are not mixed in concrete.

Testing procedure Approximately 500 g of dry sand is placed in a large bowl, covered with water, and vigorously agitated. The water is then gently poured over a 200-mesh sieve, which allows material finer than 75 μm to pass through the sieve. This process is repeated until the water becomes clear. The material retained on the 200-mesh sieve is then washed back into the bowl, and the sample is dried. The percentage of material passing the 200-mesh sieve is computed as follows:

$$P = \frac{A - B}{A} 100 \tag{12-3}$$

where P = percentage of material finer than 75 μm
A = grams of original, dry sand
B = grams of washed, dry sand

Significance of the presence of material finer than 75 μm in concrete Extremely fine fractions of concrete aggregates are commonly classed as silt or clay. These materials are not permitted in large amounts, because they tend to increase the water requirement of a concrete mixture. This contributes to drying shrinkage and decreased strength and durability of portland cement concrete. In asphaltic concrete these materials, sometimes used as filler materials, tend to give asphalt cement more stiffness. Certain fine-grained, siliceous materials, such as ground pumice or diatomaceous earth, are sometimes used to increase workability and increase strength and durability of portland cement concrete through pozzolanic action. Small amounts of fine materials which result from crushing and rolling operations or from glacial action may be beneficial in portland cement concrete. On the other hand, montmorillonite-type clays which are of a flat, platy shape will absorb large quantities of water and are harmful to the gel structure of hydrated portland cement.

When economically justified, aggregates which fail to meet standard tests for material passing a no. 200 sieve can be investigated to ascertain the characteristics of the very fine material involved and to evaluate its effect in producing quality concrete. The limitation on the allowable percentage of material finer than 75 μm serves as a conservative restriction when information regarding characteristics of the fine material is not available.

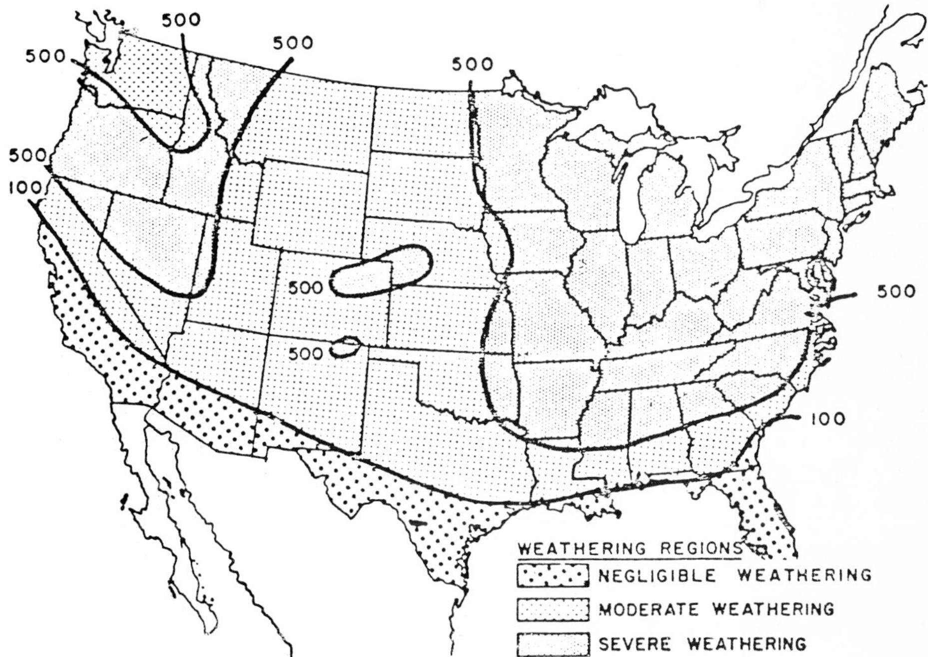

Figure 12-6 Location of weathering regions. (*ASTM C-33.*)

Table 12-8 ASTM limits for deleterious substances and physical property requirements of coarse aggregate for concrete

Class designation	Type or location of concrete construction	Maximum allowable, percent						
		Clay lumps and friable particles	Chert (less than 2.40 specific gravity *SSD*)†	Sum of clay lumps, friable particles and chert (less than 2.40 specific gravity *SSD*)†	Material finer than no. 200 (75-μm) sieve	Coal and lignite	Abrasion‡	Magnesium sulfate soundness (5 cycles)§
		Severe weathering regions						
1S	Footings, foundations, columns, and beams not exposed to the weather, interior floor slabs to be given coverings	10.0	—	—	1.0¶	1.0	50	—
2S	Interior floors without coverings	5.0	—	—	1.0¶	0.5	50	—
3S	Foundation walls above grade, retaining walls, abutments, piers, girders, and beams exposed to the weather	5.0	5.0	7.0	1.0¶	0.5	50	18
4S	Pavements, bridge decks, driveways and curbs, walks, patios, garage floors, exposed floors and porches, or waterfront structures subject to frequent wetting	3.0	5.0	5.0	1.0¶	0.5	50	18
5S	Exposed architectural concrete	2.0	3.0	3.0	1.0¶	0.5	50	18

				Moderate weathering regions				
1M	Footings, foundations, columns, and beams not exposed to the weather, interior floor slabs to be given coverings	10.0	—	—	1.0¶	1.0	50	—
2M	Interior floors without coverings	5.0	—	—	1.0¶	0.5	50	—
3M	Foundation walls above grade, retaining walls, abutments, piers, girders, and beams exposed to the weather††	5.0	8.0	10.0	1.0¶	0.5	50	18
4M	Pavements, bridge decks, driveways and curbs, walks, patios, garage floors, exposed floors and porches, or waterfront structures subject to frequent wetting††	5.0	5.0	7.0	1.0¶	0.5	50	18
5M	Exposed architectural concrete††	3.0	3.0	5.0	1.0¶	0.5	50	18
				Negligible weathering regions				
1N	Slabs subject to traffic abrasion, bridge decks, floors, sidewalks, pavements††	5.0	—	—	1.0¶	0.5	50	—
2N	All other classes of concrete††	10.0	—	—	1.0¶	1.0	50	—

† These limitations apply only to aggregates in which chert appears as an impurity. They are not applicable to gravels that are predominantly chert. Limitations on soundness of such aggregates must be based on service records in the environment in which they are used.

‡ *Note:* See Fig. 12-6 for location of weathering regions.

§ The allowable limits for soundness shall be 12% if sodium sulfate is used.

¶ In the case of crushed aggregates, if the material finer than the no. 200 (75-μm) sieve consists of the dust of fracture, essentially free of clay or shale, this percentage may be increased to 1.5.

†† For construction at altitudes exceeding 5000 ft above sea level, the requirements of the "Severe Weathering Region" shall apply.

Test for Organic Impurities

Purpose of test Some sands, particularly if they are not washed, may contain bits of roots or other organic material which may be harmful to concrete. It is important to determine the presence of such materials.

Testing procedures A small glass bottle is filled about half full of sand representative of the deposit. A 3 percent solution of sodium hydroxide is added to the bottle, covering the sand. Sufficient solution is added to fill the bottle about three-fourths full. The bottle is stoppered, shaken, and then allowed to stand 24 h. The sodium hydroxide solution will react with any organic material and color the solution. A color darker than a standard light straw color may indicate harmful amounts of organic material.

This test will also show the presence of silt and clay, since the coarser materials will settle first, leaving the finer materials on top.

Significance of organic impurities in concrete Certain types of organic matter, principally tannic acid and its compounds which come from the decay of vegetable matter, interfere with the hardening and strength development of portland cement. The color tests for organic matter detects such materials, but unfortunately also reacts with other organics such as bits of wood, which are not significantly harmful to strength. A negative test, therefore, which indicates no organic matter, is conclusive evidence of freedom from harmful organic matter. If organic matter is indicated, however, it is not conclusive evidence of deleterious organic material.

The test for organic impurities in sand was originally devised to exclude unwashed, pit-run material which contained an excessive amount of roots and decayed organic material. In a modern processing plant, where the overburden of the deposit has been carefully removed and the aggregate is thoroughly washed, it would be very unusual to find samples which failed the test for organic impurities.

A dark color, obtained in the test, is not necessarily conclusive evidence that the sand is unfit for use, since certain relatively harmless organic and even inorganic substances produce such a color. Some coals and manganese minerals are examples.

The principal value of the test is to indicate whether further tests should be made to determine the durability and strength of concrete in which the sand is to be used.

Clay Lumps, Friable Particles, Coal, and Lignite in Aggregates

Purpose Clay lumps which do not break down during the mixing of concrete will absorb a high percentage of water. When the concrete is frozen, the water expands. Clay lumps and other friable particles decrease the strength and durability of concrete or asphaltic concrete.

Testing procedures The presence of clay lumps and friable particles can be determined by careful inspection of samples of coarse aggregate and coarse sand retained on the no. 16 sieves. Clay lumps will break down if the sample is soaked for 24 h. Friable particles can often be broken by applying pressure. Coal and lignite can be recognized by color and density. The percentage of these potentially deleterious materials can be computed as follows:

$$P = \frac{A - B}{A} 100 \tag{12-4}$$

where P = percentage of deleterious particles
A = grams of sample before removal of deleterious particles
B = grams of sample after removal

Significance of test for clay lumps, friable particles, coal, and lignite Even a small percentage of clay lumps, or for that matter any aggregate particle with small voids and high absorption, may be serious in concrete exposed to freezing and thawing. The aggregate particle becomes saturated and, when frozen, expands. If close to the surface of the concrete the particle will fracture the surface and "pop-outs" result.

Friable particles are weak and cannot resist stresses; therefore, they weaken the concrete. These particles will also tend to break down during handling and mixing operations and may vary the particle-size distribution of the aggregate. Coal and lignite, being soft and light organic materials, do not make good concrete aggregates.

Lightweight Pieces in Aggregate

Purpose Natural aggregates may contain undesirable lightweight materials. Coal and lignite obviously fall in this category. Lightweight cherts and impure limestones have also been found to be deleterious in concrete. These lighter rock types usually have high absorption values. This test will give an indication of these undesirable materials, and specification requirements can limit their use.

Testing procedures Materials that have a specific gravity of less than 1.95 can be removed by immersing a sample in a solution of zinc chloride ($ZnCl_2$), which has a specific gravity of 1.95.

The sample of dry aggregate and the solution are placed in a mixing bowl and stirred vigorously. Floating particles are then skimmed off the surface 1 min after stirring has stopped. Coal and lignite can be separated by inspection.

The percentage of lightweight particles or coal and lignite can be computed as follows:

$$P = \frac{B}{A} 100 \tag{12-5}$$

where P = percentage of lightweight particles
A = grams of original sample (dry)
B = grams of particles skimmed (dry)

12-5 ABRASION OF COARSE AGGREGATE

Purpose

The Los Angeles abrasion test measures the wear resistance of aggregate particles. The wear or loss in the test results from both impact and surface abrasion. Both the toughness and the hardness of aggregate particles will resist the wear and breakdown in this test. The resistance of aggregates to impact and wear does not necessarily mean that portland cement concrete of superior quality will result. It does indicate the quality of atomic bonding (Chap. 2) and/or the degree of weathering within given rock types. For example, limestone as a group will generally show greater loss in the abrasion test than basalts. This does not mean that high-quality concrete cannot be produced with limestone aggregates.

The abrasion resistance is important in asphaltic concrete where stability of an asphaltic concrete pavement depends on the intergranular pressure among the aggregate particles. The test is particularly valuable in identifying those aggregates which will provide the most lasting stability and skid resistance in asphaltic concrete pavements.

Testing Procedure

A 5000-g sample of coarse aggregate, graded in accordance with gradings shown in Table 12-9, is placed in the Los Angeles abrasion machine (Fig. 12-7). The abrasive charge is added: it consists of 12 cast-iron or steel spheres 4.75 cm in diameter with a mass of 390 to 445 g each.

The grams of material which will pass a no. 12 sieve is measured after 500 revolutions of the cylinder.

Again,

$$P = \frac{B}{A} 100 \tag{12-6}$$

where P = percentage loss in abrasion test
B = grams passing no. 12 sieve
A = grams of original sample (5000 g)

Table 12-9 Grading of test samples for abrasion test

Sieve numbers (square openings)		Grams of each size		
Passing	Retained on	Grading A	Grading B	Grading C
$1\frac{1}{2}$	1	1250	—	—
1	$\frac{3}{4}$	1250	—	—
$\frac{3}{4}$	$\frac{1}{2}$	1250	2500	—
$\frac{1}{2}$	$\frac{3}{8}$	1250	2500	—
$\frac{3}{8}$	No. 3	—	—	2500
No. 3	No. 4	—	—	2500

Figure 12-7 Los Angeles abrasion machine and a sieve shaker.

Significance of the Abrasion Test

The abrasion test measures the quality of aggregate particles directly and gives an indication of their toughness and hardness. The test will not have significant variation from sample to sample of the same aggregates and is, therefore, a dependable guide in establishing variations in aggregate types.

12-6 SPECIFIC GRAVITY, DENSITY, AND ABSORPTION OF AGGREGATES

Purpose

The specific gravity is a dimensionless ratio of unit mass to unit volume (g/cm^3). It is useful in converting mass to volume or volume to mass. The solid volume of a given mass of aggregate can then be computed. The specific gravity, when multiplied by 1000, gives the density of the material (kg/m^3). For any given rock type, lower density may be an indication of weathering. Absorption is a measure of surface voids which become filled with water.

Testing procedures

A sample of aggregate is immersed in water and allowed to absorb water for 24 h. The sample is then "surface dried." All surface water is removed, but all voids remain filled (Fig. 12-8). The sample is divided into approximately equal parts, from which two samples are obtained (about 600-g samples for sand and 1200-g samples for gravel). One sample is placed in an oven and dried and is recorded as A.

A ground-glass pycnometer (Fig. 12-9) is filled about three-fourths full of water of known temperature, and the saturated, surface-dry sand sample B is added. Entrapped air is removed by rolling or otherwise agitating the jar. The jar is then completely filled with water. The meniscus above the top of the jar is removed by sliding the disk across the top of the jar. The jar is shaken vigorously to remove all remaining entrapped air, after which the disk is removed and the jar carefully refilled with water. The disk is then replaced, making sure no air voids remain, and the outside surfaces are dried. The jar with disk in place is weighed, and the weight is recorded as W_s.

Computations The bulk specific gravity is computed by one of the following formulas:

$$\begin{array}{c}G\text{, bulk specific gravity}\\ \text{(dry basis)}\end{array} = \frac{A}{W_w + B - W_s} \qquad (12\text{-}7)$$

$$\begin{array}{c}G_{SSD}\text{, bulk specific gravity}\\ \text{(saturated surface dry basis)}\end{array} = \frac{B}{W_w + B - W_s} \qquad (12\text{-}8)$$

$$\text{Density} = G \times 1000 \qquad (12\text{-}9)$$

where A = weight of oven-dry sample
B = weight of SSD sample
W_w = weight of pycnometer filled with water only
W_s = weight of pycnometer filled with water plus sample

$$\text{Percent absorption} = \frac{B - A}{B}100 \qquad (12\text{-}10)$$

Direct measurement apparatus A direct measurement apparatus was developed by the author in the U.S. Bureau of Reclamation laboratories. This apparatus will measure the specific gravity, absorption, and free moisture directly. Since it is particularly useful in the control of concrete mixes and in mix proportioning, it is discussed in Chap. 13.

Significance of Tests

The specific gravity is not usually an indication of quality. The specific gravity of different aggregates will vary widely, depending on the rock types involved.

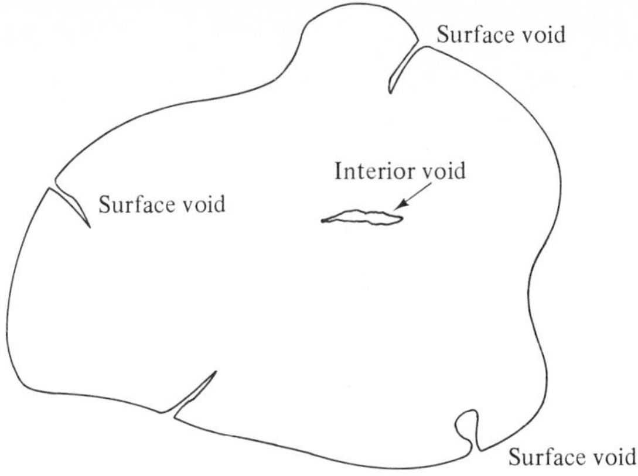

Figure 12-8 Voids in an aggregate particle.

Figure 12-9 Ground-glass pycnometer.

However, for a particular rock type, a specific gravity value lower than average may indicate weathering and deterioration. Potentially harmful chert and other lightweight materials may be distinguished on the basis of specific gravity. Aggregates used in construction of Glen Canyon Dam were processed by the means of heavy media separation to exclude a potentially harmful chert aggregate.

High absorption values may indicate either weathering or an aggregate with a critical void system which contributes to freezing and thawing deterioration of concrete. Aggregate particles having numerous small voids with the ability to absorb and retain moisture will fracture if saturated when frozen and cause pop-outs on concrete surfaces.

12-7 SOUNDNESS OF AGGREGATES USING SODIUM OR MAGNESIUM SULFATE

Purpose and Significance of Test

Sulfate soundness tests provide a rough indication of the ability of concrete aggregate to produce durable concrete. If properly interpreted in light of other tests and field service records, these tests assist engineering judgment in determining the permissibility of using a particular aggregate in a specific application. A specific limit on sulfate test loss, to distinguish between acceptable and unacceptable aggregate, is hard to justify. If the allowable loss is low enough to reject all objectionable aggregates, it will also reject some acceptable ones. If it is high enough to accept all good aggregates, then it will also accept some that should not be used.

Other tests for soundness are more definitive. Service records of structures are the engineer's best criterion for predicting aggregate performance. Aggregates can also be tested in freezing and thawing. The best laboratory information that can be secured is the comparison of concrete specimens made with the aggregates in question and specimens with aggregates of known quality in laboratory freezing and thawing tests. Even these tests must be interpreted in relation to the expected severity of exposure and economic availability. They serve primarily to rank aggregates in order of relative endurance rather than to provide a quantitative measure of life expectancy in the field.

Testing Procedures

Clean, dry samples of aggregate are soaked in a saturated solution of sodium sulfate (or magnesium sulfate) for about 17 h. The sample is drained and then completely dried at 110°C. This process is repeated for the desired number of cycles. The sulfate salt crystals gradually build up in the voids of the aggregate with successive wetting and drying cycles and exert pressure in the voids of the aggregate particle. This is assumed to simulate the expansion of freezing ice in the aggregate void system.

Computations

The percentage loss in sodium or magnesium sulfate soundness test is computed as follows:

$$L = \frac{B}{A} 100 \qquad (12\text{-}11)$$

where L = percentage loss in sodium sulfate
A = original aggregate sample, g
B = grams of material passing designated sieves with openings smaller than original aggregate particles

12-8 POTENTIAL REACTIVITY OF AGGREGATES

Purpose and Significance of Tests

Coarse aggregate for use in concrete that will be subject to wetting, extended exposure to humid atmosphere, or contact with moist ground should not contain any materials that are deleteriously reactive with the alkalies in the cement in an amount sufficient to cause excessive expansion of mortar or concrete. However, if such materials are present in injurious amounts, the coarse aggregate may be used with a cement containing less than 0.6 percent alkalies calculated as sodium oxide or with the addition of a material that has been shown to prevent harmful expansion resulting from the alkali-aggregate reaction.

A number of methods for detecting potential reactivity have been proposed. However, they do not provide quantitative information on the degree of reactivity to be expected or tolerated in service. Therefore, evaluation of potential reactivity of an aggregate should be based on judgment and on the interpretation of test data and examination of concrete structures containing a combination of fine and coarse aggregates and cements for use in the new work. Results of the following tests will assist in making the evaluation.

Petrographic Study

Certain materials are known to be reactive with the alkalies in cements. These include the following forms of silica: opal, chalcedony, tridymite, and cristobalite; intermediate to acid (silica-rich) volcanic glass such as likely to occur in rhyolite, andesite, or dacite; certain zeolites such as heulandite; and certain constituents of some phyllites. Determination of the presence and quantities of these materials by petrographic examination is helpful in evaluating potential alkali reactivity. When present in quantities as little as 1.0 percent or even less, some of these materials render an aggregate deleteriously reactive.

Dissolved Silica

In this test, aggregates represented by points lying to the right of the solid line of Fig. 12-10 usually should be considered potentially reactive.

If $R_c > 70$, the aggregate is considered potentially reactive if $S_c > R_c$.

If $R_c < 70$, the aggregate is considered potentially reactive if $S_c > 35 + R_c/2$.

These criteria conform to the solid-line curve given in Fig. 12-10. The test can be made quickly and, while not completely reliable in all cases, provides helpful information, especially where results of the more time-consuming tests are not available.

Expansion of Concrete Prisms

The results of this test, when made with a high-alkali cement and the aggregates in question, furnish information on the likelihood of harmful reactions occurring. The alkali content of the cement should be substantially above 0.6 percent, and preferably above 0.8 percent, expressed as sodium oxide. Combinations of aggregate and cement which have produced excessive expansions in this test usually should be considered potentially reactive. While the line of demarcation between nonreactive and reactive combinations is not clearly defined, expansion is generally considered to be excessive if it exceeds 0.05 percent at 3 months or 0.10 percent at 6 months. Expansions greater than 0.05 percent at 3 months should not be considered excessive where the 6-month expansion remains below 0.10 percent. Data for the 3-month tests should be considered only when 6-month results are not available.

Expansion of Mortar Bars

Cement-aggregate combinations tested by this procedure whose expansion equals or exceeds 0.2 percent at an age of 1 year may be considered unsatisfactory for use in concrete exposed to wide variations of temperature and degree of saturation with water.

Expansion of Rock Samples Immersed in a Solution of Sodium Hydroxide

The reaction of the dolomite in certain carbonate rocks with alkalies in portland cement paste has been found to be associated with deleterious expansion of concrete containing such rocks as coarse aggregate. Carbonate rocks capable of such reaction possess a characteristic texture and composition. The characteristic texture is that in which relatively large crystals of dolomite are scattered in a finer-grained matrix of calcite and clay. The characteristic composition is that in which the carbonate portion consists of substantial amounts of both dolomite and calcite, and the acid-insoluble residue contains a significant amount of clay. Except in certain areas, such rocks occur relatively infrequently and seldom make

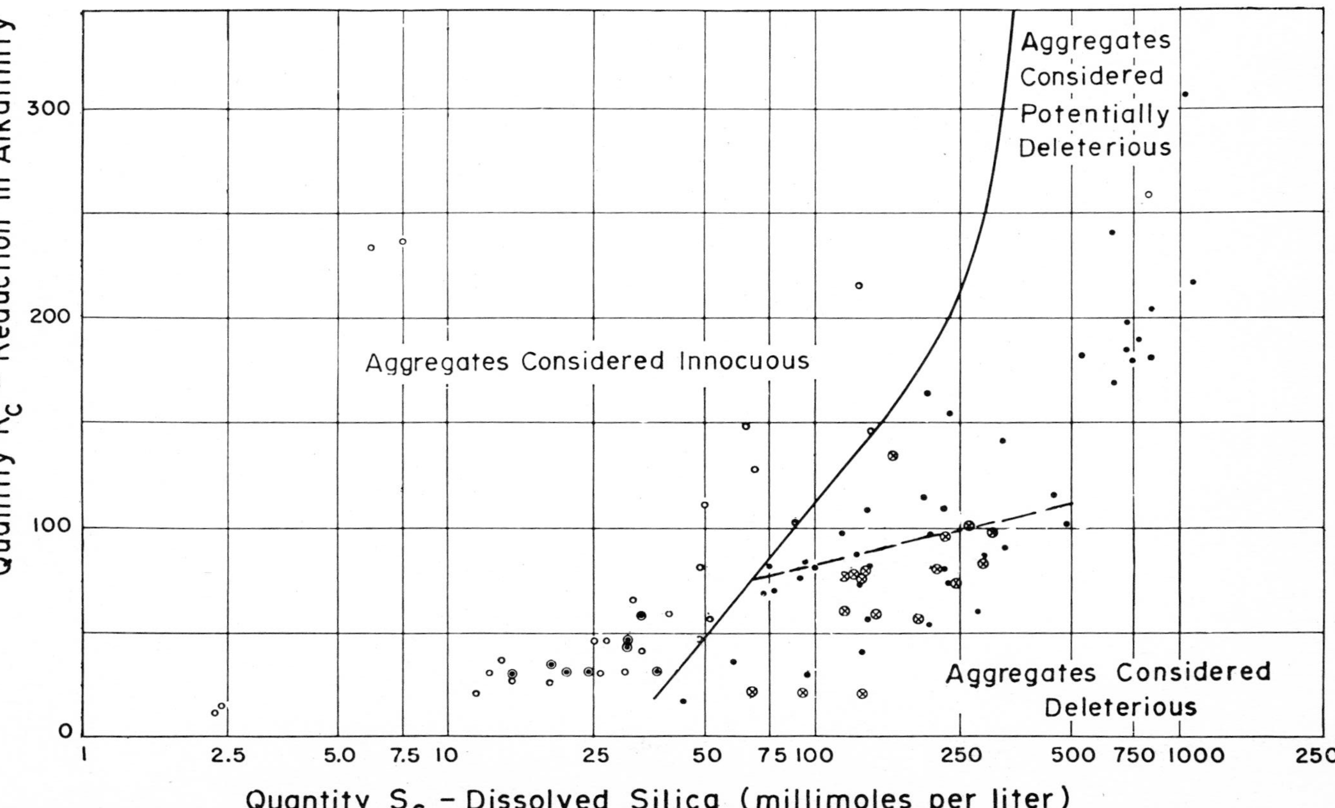

Figure 12-10 Illustration of division between innocuous and deleterious aggregates on the basis of reduction in alkalinity test. (*ASTM C-289.*)

up a significant proportion of the material present in a deposit of rock being considered for use in making aggregate for concrete. Method C-586 has been successfully used in research and preliminary screening of aggregate sources to indicate the presence of material with a potential for deleterious expansions when used in concrete.

12-9 TYPICAL PETROGRAPHIC EXAMINATIONS

A petrographic examination of aggregate samples is performed by trained petrographers qualified by education and experience to recognize the characteristic properties of rocks and minerals and to classify the constituents of an aggregate sample. A petrographic examination is particularly valuable in classifying reactive aggregates and other deleterious materials. Neither the civil engineer nor the architect is usually trained to make a petrographic examination. However, it is important that they be sufficiently familiar with such evaluations to understand and interpret these reports. The following is an example of pertinent information taken from a petrographic examination of aggregate samples from India at the U.S. Bureau of Reclamation laboratories in Denver, Colorado.

Coarse Aggregate

The gravel particles range from rounded to subangular in shape. The particles tend to be somewhat flattened and elongated. Infrequent particles are partially coated with a thin, poor to moderately well bonded coating of calcium carbonate. The gravel is composed predominantly of quartzites, metasandstones, graywackes, sandstones, limestones, and dolomites, as indicated in Table 12-10. Smaller proportions of gneisses, schists, argillites, serpentine rock, chalcedonic sandstone, cherts, siltstones, and andesites are present.

Deeply weathered or otherwise physically unsound particles constitute less than 1 percent of the gravels. Particles of fair physical quality which might tend to decrease the durability of concrete exposed to adverse climatic conditions constitute an average of only 1.7 percent of the analyzed gravels.

Cherts, chalcedonic sandstones, and glassy andesites constitute an average of 2.3 percent of the gravel. These rock types are known to be deleteriously reactive with high-alkali cement, but the amount present in the gravel is less than that considered necessary to produce harmful reactions in concrete (Table 12-11).

Sand

The particles of the sand range from rounded to angular in shape. The coarse fractions of the sand are composed predominantly of the same rock types occurring in the same proportions as in the related gravel. Small amounts of individual grains of quartz and mica are present. The finer fractions of the sand are composed predominantly of fine-grained quartzites, limestones, and individual grains of quartz. Smaller proportions of feldspar grains, serpentine, argillites, cherts, and micas are present.

Table 12-10 Petrographic analysis of coarse aggregate, Bhakra Dam, India

Rock types	Percentage by weight, laboratories no. M-1023		Description of rock types	Physical quality	Chemical quality
	$1\frac{1}{2}$ to $\frac{3}{4}$ in	$\frac{3}{4}$ to $\frac{3}{8}$ in			
Quartzite, quartzose sandstone	25.1	24.2	Hard, tough, medium- to fine-grained rugose surface	Good	Innocuous
Quartzites, metasandstones, graywacke	42.0	46.1	Slightly weathered, infrequent tight fractures	Satisfactory	Innocuous
Sandstone	—	0.9	Moderately friable	Fair	Innocuous
Deeply weathered sandstone	—	0.4	Crumbly	Poor	Innocuous
Limestones and dolomites	12.2	12.8	Medium- to exceedingly fine-grained	Satisfactory	Innocuous
Weathered limestones and dolomites	—	0.6	Slightly porous, moderately weathered	Fair	Innocuous
Deeply weathered limestones and dolomites	—	0.7	Soft, argillaceous, porous	Poor	Innocuous
Chalcedonic sandstone	3.0	0.4	Hard, sand grains cemented by chalcedony	Satisfactory	Deleterious
Cherts	0.6	0.3	Hard, chalcedonic, poor bonding characteristics	Fair	Deleterious
Argillites	5.6	2.7	Fine-grained, tough	Satisfactory	Innocuous
Siltstones	—	1.0	Fine-grained, slightly absorptive	Fair	Innocuous
Gneisses and schists	4.5	2.6	Medium-grained, schistose, hard	Satisfactory	Innocuous
Serpentine rock	7.0	6.9	Hard to firm, slightly porous, fine-grained	Satisfactory	Innocuous
Andesites	—	0.4	Hard, glassy ground mass, porphyritic	Satisfactory	Deleterious

Table 12-11 Summary of quality of coarse aggregate, Bhakra Dam, India

	Percentage by weight, laboratories no. M-1023	
Degree of quality	$1\frac{1}{2}$ to $\frac{3}{4}$ in	$\frac{3}{4}$ to $\frac{3}{8}$ in
Physical quality		
Good	25.1	24.2
Satisfactory	74.3	71.9
Fair	0.0	2.8
Poor	—	1.1
Chemical quality		
Innocuous	96.4	98.9
Deleterious†	3.6	1.1

† Deleterious with high-alkali cement.

Deeply weathered or otherwise physically unsound particles constitute 2 percent or less of any of the various sand fractions.

Chert, a rock type known to be deleteriously reactive with high-alkali cement, constitutes less than 2 percent of the sand.

A small amount of silt-sized particles is present in the sand, but is easily removed by washing.

Gravel and sand comparable to the sample examined are considered suitable from a petrographic standpoint for use as concrete aggregate.

12-10 PERFORMANCE OF AGGREGATES IN CONCRETE OR MORTAR

In the final analysis, the proof as to whether aggregates are suitable for use in concrete or asphaltic concrete is in the quality and characteristics of the concrete or asphaltic concrete produced. In other words, if a concrete has sufficient strength to resist stresses imposed on it, if it is durable against the forces of deterioration, and if it is dimensionally stable, then the obvious conclusion must be that the aggregate is suitable. These tests require considerable time and are generally used to check aggregate quality for large and/or important structures.

The following types of tests are useful in measuring the performance of aggregates. In each case the performances of the aggregates in question are compared with aggregates of proved quality. Identical companion concrete mixes can be made with the aggregate in question and a known standard aggregate.

1. Strength of concrete
2. Stability of asphaltic concrete
3. Resistance of concrete to freezing and thawing deterioration

4. Resistance of asphaltic concrete to freezing and thawing deterioration
5. Tests for expansion of concrete or mortar prisms containing possible reactive aggregates

These tests are discussed in Chaps. 13 and 14.

QUESTIONS AND PROBLEMS

1 (*a*) Explain why the tests for concrete aggregates are essentially the same as tests for aggregates for asphaltic concrete.

(*b*) Name some tests in each case which are not important to the other type of concrete.

2 What aggregate tests are important for concrete, but are not important for asphaltic concrete?

3 What is the most important test for aggregate quality for both concrete and asphaltic concrete?

4 Why is it important that special care be taken to obtain representative samples of materials?

5 Assume that 100 g was added to the amount of material retained on the no. 8 sieve in Table 12-1 (176 g rather than 76 g). How would this affect the FM?

6 (*a*) Explain why there are so many different grading requirements in Table 12-4.

(*b*) Can quality concrete be made with gradings outside the limits shown?

7 Why is the total surface area of aggregate in concrete mixes important?

8 Are all materials finer than 75 μm deleterious in concrete?

9 Can a sand still be used even if it fails the organic impurities test?

10 Why are certain lightweight pieces of aggregate considered harmful in concrete?

11 What does a high loss in the Los Angeles abrasion test indicate?

12 Explain how SI units simplify the use of the terms specific gravity and density.

13 (*a*) What is the purpose of the sodium sulfate soundness test?

(*b*) Is it reliable?

14 How can the reactivity of an aggregate be evaluated?

15 What is the purpose of a petrographic examination?

16 What application does the adage "The proof of the pudding is in the eating" have in the evaluation of aggregates?

CHAPTER
THIRTEEN

TESTING AND EVALUATION OF PORTLAND CEMENT AND CONCRETE

Specifications and tests for concrete and concrete materials are included in Part 14 of the ASTM standards. Standard ASTM tests for concrete may be divided into (1) tests with fresh, plastic concrete made immediately after mixing and (2) tests for the properties of hardened concrete. The following are common tests selected from ASTM, Part 14.

1. *Portland cement*
   - C-150 Specifications for portland cement
2. *Fresh, plastic concrete*
   - C-172 Sampling fresh concrete
   - C-143 Slump of concrete
   - C-138 Test for unit weight (density) yield and air content (gravimetric) of concrete
   - C-231 Test for air content of freshly mixed concrete by the pressure method
   - C-330 Test for unit weight (density) of structural lightweight concrete
   - C-403 Time of setting of concrete mixtures by penetration resistance
3. *Properties of hardened concrete*
   - C-31 Making and curing of concrete compressive- and flexural-strength specimens in the field
   - C-684 Making, accelerated curing, and testing of concrete compression-test specimens
   - C-617 Capping cylindrical concrete specimens
   - C-39 Test for compressive strength of cylindrical concrete specimens

C-78 Test for flexural strength of concrete (using simple beam with third-point loading)
C-496 Splitting tensile strength of cylindrical concrete specimens
C-469 Static modules of elasticity and Poisson's rate of concrete in compression
C-666 Resistance of concrete to rapid freezing and thawing
C-805 Rebound number of hardened concrete

13-1 PORTLAND CEMENT

Specifications for portland cement consist of requirements for chemical composition and physical properties. Each cement plant maintains a testing laboratory and furnishes test results to customers. Tests are seldom made by outside testing laboratories. There are notable exceptions, including large government or state agencies that run their own tests on a particular production run and reserve it in sealed cement silos for their own use.

Chemical Requirements

The only chemical requirements for type I cement limit the percentage of undesirable chemicals, insoluble residue, and loss on ignition (Table 13-1). Type II cement limitations are placed on aluminum and iron compounds with a minimum requirement for SiO_2. These limitations produce cement with moderate sulfate-resisting and moderate heat-producing properties.

The chemical limitations on type III cement are less restrictive and allow much more tricalcium aluminate.

For type IV cement, a maximum limitation is imposed for tricalcium silicate with a minimum for dicalcium silicate.

Type V cement has the greatest restriction on tricalcium aluminate and is the only cement which limits the combination of aluminum and iron compounds. This reduces the susceptibility of the cement to the attack of sulfate alkalies.

Physical Requirements

The physical requirements for portland cement are shown in Table 13-2. These tests indicate the relative physical characteristics of cement and its behavior when mixed with water and in some cases fine aggregate. These tests are rarely made in control laboratories but are furnished by the cement companies or control laboratories, where required. Since these tests are not included in student laboratory exercises, only the purpose and interpretation of the tests will be discussed.

Fineness The fineness of portland cement is indicated by measuring the specific surface of the cement particles (cm^2/g). Cement particles are too fine to measure the particle-size distribution by sieving. The turbidimeter test is based on the fact

Table 13-1 Chemical requirements (ASTM C-150)

	Type I	Type II	Type III	Type IV	Type V
Silicon dioxide (SiO_2), min, percent	—	21.0	—	—	—
Aluminum oxide (Al_2O_3), max, percent	—	6.0	—	—	—
Ferric oxide (Fe_2O_3), max, percent	—	6.0	—	6.5	—
Magnesium oxide (MgO), max, percent	6.0	6.0	6.0	6.0	6.0
Sulfur trioxide (SO_3), max, percent:					
When $3CaO \cdot Al_2O_3$ is 8 percent or less	3.0	3.0	3.5	2.3	2.3
When $3CaO \cdot Al_2O_3$ is more than 8 percent	3.5	—	4.5	—	—
Loss on ignition, max, percent	3.0	3.0	3.0	2.5	3.0
Insoluble residue, max, percent	0.75	0.75	0.75	0.75	0.75
Tricalcium silicate ($3CaO \cdot SiO_2$),† max, percent	—	—	—	35	—
Dicalcium silicate ($2CaO \cdot SiO_2$),† min, percent	—	—	—	40	—
Tricalcium aluminate ($3CaO \cdot Al_2O_3$),† max, percent	—	8	15‡	7	5
Sum of tricalcium silicate and tricalcium aluminate, max, percent	—	58§	—	—	—
Tetracalcium aluminoferrite plus twice the tricalcium aluminate† [$4CaO \cdot Al_2O_3 \cdot Fe_2O_3 + 2(3CaO \cdot Al_2O_3)$], or solid solution ($4CaO \cdot Al_2O_3 \cdot Fe_2O_3 + 2CaO \cdot Fe_2O_3$), as applicable, max, percent	—	—	—	—	20.0

† The expressing of chemical limitations by means of calculated assumed compounds does not necessarily mean that the oxides are actually or entirely present as such compounds.

When the ratio of percentages of aluminum oxide to ferric oxide is 0.64 or more, the percentages of tricalcium silicate, dicalcium silicate, tricalcium aluminate, and tetracalcium aluminoferrite will be calculated from the chemical analysis as follows:

$$\begin{aligned}
\text{Tricalcium silicate} &= (4.071 \times \text{percent CaO}) - (7.600 \times \text{percent } SiO_2) \\
&\quad - (6.718 \times \text{percent } Al_2O_3) - (1.430 \times \text{percent } Fe_2O_3) \\
&\quad - (2.852 \times \text{percent } SO_3) \\
\text{Dicalcium silicate} &= (2.87 \times \text{percent } SiO_2) - (0.7544 \times \text{percent } C_2S) \\
\text{Tricalcium aluminate} &= (2.650 \times \text{percent } Al_2O_3) - (1.692 \times \text{percent } Fe_2O_3) \\
\text{Tetracalcium aluminoferrite} &= 3.043 \times \text{percent } Fe_2O_3
\end{aligned}$$

When the alumina–ferric oxide ratio is less than 0.64, a calcium aluminoferrite solid solution [expressed as *ss* ($C_4AF + C_2F$)] is formed. Contents of this solid solution and of tricalcium silicate will be calculated by the following formulas:

$$\begin{aligned}
ss\,(C_4AF + C_2F) &= (2.100 \times \text{percent } Al_2O_3) + (1.702 \times \text{percent } Fe_2O_3) \\
\text{Tricalcium silicate} &= (4.071 \times \text{percent CaO}) - (7.600 \times \text{percent } SiO_2) \\
&\quad - (4.479 \times \text{percent } Al_2O_3) - (2.859 \times \text{percent } Fe_2O_3) \\
&\quad - (2.852 \times \text{percent } SO_3)
\end{aligned}$$

No tricalcium aluminate will be present in cements of this composition. Dicalcium silicate will be calculated as previously shown.

In the calculation of C_3A, the values of Al_2O_3 and Fe_2O_3 determined to the nearest 0.01 percent will be used. In the calculation of other compounds, the oxides determined to the nearest 0.1 percent will be used.

Values for C_3A and for the sum of C_4AF and $2C_3A$ will be reported to the nearest 0.1 percent. Values for other compounds will be reported to the nearest 1 percent.

‡ When moderate sulfate resistance is required for type III cement, tricalcium aluminate will be limited to 8 percent. When high sulfate resistance is required, the tricalcium aluminate will be limited to 5 percent.

§ This limit applies when moderate heat of hydration is required and tests for heat of hydration are not requested.

Table 13-2 Physical requirements

	Type I	Type II	Type III	Type IV	Type V
Fineness, specific surface, cm^2/g (alternative methods):					
Turbidimeter test:					
Average value, min	1600	1600	—	1600	1600
Minimum value, any one sample	1500	1500	—	1500	1500
Air permeability test:					
Average value, min	2800	2800	—	2800	2800
Minimum value, any one sample	2600	2600	—	2600	2600
Soundness:					
Autoclave expansion, max, percent	0.80	0.80	0.80	0.80	0.80
Time of setting (alternative methods):					
Gillmore test:					
Initial set, min, not less than	60	60	60	60	60
Final set, h, not more than	10	10	10	10	10
Vicat test (method C-191):					
Set, min, not less than	45	45	45	45	45
Air content of mortar, prepared and tested in accordance with method C-185, max, percent, by volume, less than	12.0	12.0	12.0	12.0	12.0
Compressive strength:					
The compressive strength of mortar cubes, composed of 1 part cement and 2.75 parts graded standard sand, by weight, prepared and tested in accordance with method C-109, shall be equal to or higher than the values specified for the ages indicated below:					
1 day in moist air, MPa			12.4		8.3
1 day in moist air, 2 days in water, MPa	12.4	10.3	24.1		
1 day in moist air, 6 days in water, MPa	19.3	17.2		6.9	15.2
1 day in moist air, 27 days in water, MPa	—	—		17.2	20.7

that in a solution large particles settle faster than small particles (Stokes' law). The amount of settlement in a given time period is measured by the amount of light passing through the solution.

The permeability of a small, compacted cylinder of cement is measured by the rate of flow of air through the sample. The specific surface of the cement particles in the sample is a function of the size and quantity of voids which in turn determine the permeability.

Cement fineness is important since the greater the surface area of cement exposed to water, the more rapid cement hydrates. The extra fineness in type III cement contributes to its high early strength.

Soundness When lime and magnesium and other compounds are not completely burned, the chemical combination with SiO_2 is not complete. Cements containing an excess of these compounds are unsound and will cause expansion in small prisms when exposed to high temperatures in an autoclave. The soundness test limits the quantity of these unsound compounds.

Time of setting When portland cement begins to hydrate, the formation of crystals in the silica gel causes it to harden. The Gillmore and Vicat tests measure the time it takes for cement and water paste to stiffen a given amount. This is an arbitrary designation of time of set. Time-of-set designation is not completely realistic since the stiffening process is gradual over a long time.

Air content The air content of a mortar consisting of sand, cement, and water is measured by determining the difference in density between the mortar and the ingredients of the mortar. The amount of air influences other properties of the mortar and must be limited.

Compressive strength The strength of 2 × 2 in mortar cubes at various ages of curing gives the relative strength-producing properties of the cement and requires a minimum strength as indicated in Table 12-2. The difference in the required strength gain among the different types of cement indicates the difference in their hydration rates.

Tensile strength The tensile strength of mortar briquettes varies with the compressive strength and is not used extensively in cement testing.

Heat of hydration Only type II cement has restrictions on the heat of hydration. The purpose of this limitation is to restrict the temperature rise in the concrete.

False set Under certain conditions, cements will set too rapidly and cause problems in mixing and placing the concrete. A similar problem results when the cement paste stiffens prematurely. The false-set test restricts the use of a given cement which has these tendencies.

13-2 FRESH, PLASTIC CONCRETE

Tests most generally made to evaluate fresh concrete being placed in the field include the following (Fig. 13-1):

1. *Slump.* A measure of consistency or wetness of a mix; to some extent, this test indicates how easily concrete can be placed and compacted.
2. *Density* (kg/m^3). This important test is necessary in order to compute the volume of a batch from total amount of ingredients added to a concrete batch.
3. *Percentage of entrained air.* The amount of entrained air in concrete has a significant influence on the freezing and thawing durability of concrete (Chap. 6).
4. *Moisture content of fine aggregate.* The moisture content of fine aggregates will have a significant effect on the properties of a concrete mix. Any "free" moisture (total moisture less absorbed moisture) will combine with the portland cement and change the water-cement ratio. Because of the limited surface area, coarse aggregates retain only a small percentage of surface moisture and will readily drain to an *SSD* condition.

Figure 13-1 Typical laboratory equipment used in making concrete trial mixes.

Sampling Fresh Concrete in the Field

This method covers procedures for obtaining representative, composite samples of fresh concrete, as delivered to the project site, to determine compliance with quality requirements of the specifications under which the concrete is furnished. The method includes sampling from stationary, paving, and truck mixers and from agitating and non-agitating equipment used to transport central-mixed concrete.

General The elapsed time between obtaining the first and final portions of the composite samples should be as short as possible, but in no instance should it exceed 15 min.

Transport the individual samples to the place where fresh concrete tests are to be performed or where test specimens are to be molded. They are then combined and remixed with a shovel to ensure uniformity.

Start tests for slump or air content, or both, within 5 min after the sampling is completed. Complete these tests as expeditiously as possible. Start molding specimens for strength tests within 15 min after fabricating the composite sample.

Keep the elapsed time between obtaining and using the sample as short as possible; and protect the sample from the sun, wind, and other sources of rapid evaporation and from contamination.

Sample size Approximately 70 kg of composite concrete samples should be used for strength tests. Smaller samples may be permitted for routine air content and slump tests, and the size is dictated by the maximum aggregate size.

Sampling from stationary mixers Sample the concrete at two or more regularly spaced intervals during discharge of the middle portion of the batch. Take the samples, so obtained, within the time limit specified and composite them into one sample for test purposes. Do not obtain samples from the very first or last portions of the batch discharge. Perform sampling either by passing a receptacle completely through the discharge stream or by completely diverting the discharge into a sample container. If discharge of the concrete is too rapid to divert the complete discharge stream, discharge the concrete into a container or transportation unit sufficiently large to accommodate the entire batch and then accomplish the sampling in the same manner as given above. Take care not to restrict the flow of concrete from the mixer, container, or transportation unit so as to cause segregation. These requirements apply to both tilting and nontilting mixers.

Sampling from paving mixers Sample the concrete after the contents of the paving mixer have been discharged. Obtain samples from at least five different portions of the pile and then composite into one sample for test purposes. Avoid contamination with subgrade material or prolonged contact with an absorptive subgrade. To preclude contamination or absorption by the subgrade, sample the concrete by placing three shallow containers on the subgrade and discharging the concrete across the containers. Composite the samples so obtained into one sample for test purposes. The containers should be of a size sufficient to provide a composite sample size that is in agreement with the maximum aggregate size.

Sampling from revolving-drum truck mixers or agitators Sample the concrete at two or more regularly spaced intervals during discharge of the middle portion of the batch. Take the samples so obtained within the time limit specified and composite them into one sample for test purposes. In any case, do not obtain samples until after all the water has been added to the mixer; also do not obtain samples from the very first or last portions of the batch discharge. Sample by repeatedly passing a receptacle through the entire discharge stream or by completely diverting the discharge into a sample container. Regulate the rate of discharge of the batch by changing the size of the gate opening.

Slump of Concrete

Purpose The consistency or wetness of concrete is measured by the slump test. The test specimen is formed as the frustum of a cone with a 203-mm-diameter

Rodding and filling cone using three separate layers of concrete

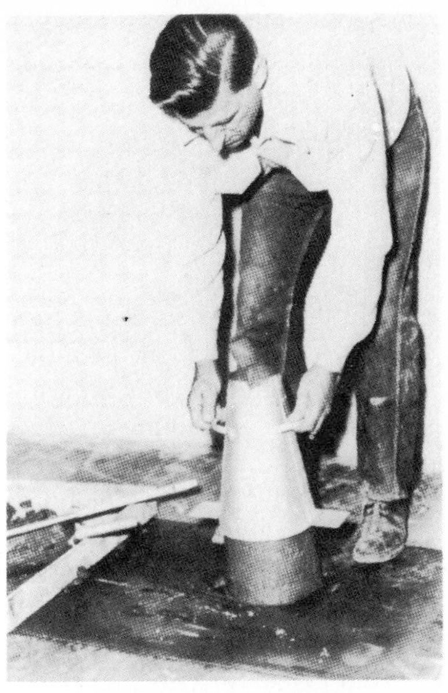

Slow, steady, vertical removal of the mold

Measuring the slump after subsidence

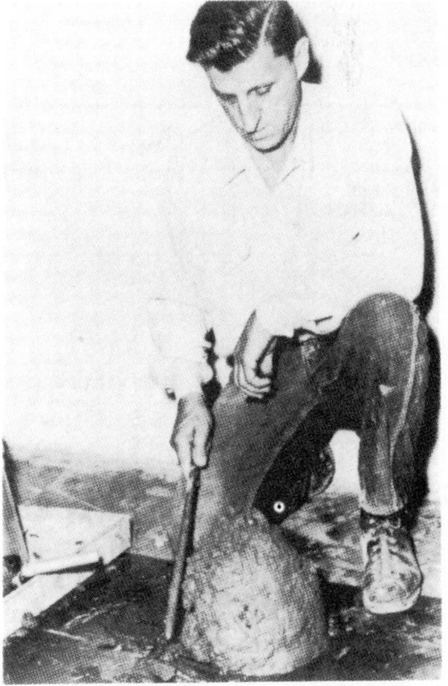

Tapping the concrete to observe the plasticity

Figure 13-2 Making slump test. (*U.S. Bureau of Reclamation.*)

base, a 102-mm-diameter top, and 305-mm height. The base and the top of the mold are open and parallel to each other and at right angles to the axis of the cone. The mold is provided with foot pieces and handles, as shown in Fig. 13-2. The sample should be representative of the entire batch.

Test procedure The mold should be dampened and placed on a flat, moist, nonabsorptive surface, where the operator holds it firmly in place by standing on the foot pieces while it is being filled. The mold is filled in three layers, each approximately one-third the volume of the mold. Each scoopful of concrete should be moved around the top edge of the mold as the concrete slides from it, to ensure symmetrical distribution of concrete within the mold. Each layer is rodded with 25 strokes of a $\frac{5}{8}$-in rod, 24 in long and bullet pointed at the lower end. The strokes are distributed uniformly over the cross section of the mold and should just penetrate the underlying layer. The bottom layer should be rodded throughout its depth. After the top layer has been rodded, the surface of the concrete is struck off so that the mold is exactly filled, and the spilled concrete is cleaned from the base. The mold is immediately removed from the concrete by being raised slowly and carefully in a vertical direction (Fig. 13-2). The slump is measured to the nearest centimeter immediately thereafter by determining the difference between the height of the mold and the average height of the top surface of the concrete after subsidence.

Slump specimens which break or slough off laterally give incorrect results and should be remade with a fresh sample. After the slump measurement is completed, the side of the concrete frustum should be tapped gently with the tamping rod. The behavior of the concrete under this treatment is a valuable indication of its cohesiveness, workability, and placeability. A well-proportioned, workable mix will settle gradually and retain its original identity, while a poor mix will crumble, segregate, and fall apart.

Density of Fresh Concrete†

Purpose The density and volume of a fresh concrete mix at the mixer are an important test for determining the cubic meters of concrete produced in each batch. With the density, computations can also be made for actual cement, water, air, and aggregate contents of the concrete batch (Chap. 5).

Tests for the density of fresh concrete are made in a cylindrical measure, about 0.00708 m^3 ($\frac{1}{4}$ ft^3). Larger measures are used for mixes containing large-size aggregates (Fig. 13-1).

Test procedure

1. The test is made immediately after mixing is completed.

† Usually this test is made at the mixer. But in any situation where it is indicated that more than normal amounts of air are lost as a result of special conditions of handling, transportation, or vibration, it will be desirable to make a check test for air content on a sample of concrete taken after the treatment in question.

2. The measure is dampened and excess moisture removed with a damp cloth just before the test is started.
3. The measure is filled in two layers, each approximately half the volume of the measure. Care should be taken to ensure that only representative concrete is used for the test. If the maximum size of aggregate is larger than no. $1\frac{1}{2}$ sieve, special care must be taken to obtain a representative sample; in mixes containing 6-in-maximum size aggregate, it is advisable to estimate and include the number of cobbles which should be contained in the test concrete. Each layer should be vibrated with the minimum amount necessary to obtain compaction. If a laboratory vibrator is not available for internal vibration, external compaction may be obtained by rodding and then dropping container to the floor in rapid succession from about a 10-cm height.

Because of the small quantity of concrete in the test, the amount of vibration is often greater than may be apparent and, if so, may cause excessive loss of air. Average concrete of medium slump may require no more than 1 or 2 s of in-and-out immersion of the vibrator. Vibration of the second layer should not penetrate more than 1 in into the lower layer. After vibration, the concrete is made level with the top of the container with a steel or hardwood straightedge. Overflow mortar should be thoroughly cleaned from the sides of the measure.

Computations

$$D = \frac{kg}{V} \tag{13-1}$$

where D = density of concrete, kg/m^3
kg = concrete, kg
V = volume of container, m^3

Computation of Other Properties

Volume of batch We have

$$V_B = \frac{I}{D} \tag{13-2}$$

where V_B = volume of batch, m^3
I = total ingredients in batch, kg
D = density of concrete, kg/m^3

Batches per cubic meter Now, we have

$$B = \frac{D}{I} \tag{13-3}$$

where B = batches per cubic meter
D = density, kg/m^3
I = total ingredients in batch, kg

Ingredients, kg/m³

$$\text{kg cement/m}^3 = B \times \text{kg cement/batch} \tag{13-4}$$

$$\text{kg water/m}^3 = B \times \text{kg water/batch} \tag{13-5}$$

$$\text{kg aggregate/m}^3 = B \times \text{kg aggregate/batch} \tag{13-6}$$

Air content The air content of fresh concrete can be computed when the specific gravity of each ingredient is known.

$$A = \frac{V_B - V_I}{V_B} 100 \tag{13-7}$$

where A = percent air
V_B = volume of batch, m³
V_I = combined volume of ingredients, m³

and

$$V_I = \left(\frac{\text{kg, agg}}{\text{sp. gr., agg}} + \frac{\text{kg, cem}}{\text{sp. gr., cem}} + \frac{\text{kg, water}}{1} \right) \Big/ 1000 \tag{13-8}$$

Note: The combined volume of ingredients is divided by 1000 to change the volume from cubic decimeters to cubic meters.

Air Content of Fresh Concrete by Pressure Methods

Purpose The operation of the pressure meter is based on Boyle's law of gases, or $PV = P_1V_1$. A volume of air at a certain initial pressure is allowed to expand into a container of fresh concrete, compressing the entrained-air voids. The reduction in pressure indicates the percentage of air voids in the concrete, the percentage being read directly on a calibrated gauge. Several pressure-type air meters are satisfactory for this test and should be calibrated as recommended by the manufacturer (Fig. 13-3).

Procedure First, the base container is filled with a representative sample of fresh concrete, following the procedure for determining density of concrete (the test for density can be made simultaneously with the test for air content). If the fresh concrete contains aggregate larger than $1\frac{1}{2}$ in nominal size and a $\frac{1}{4}$-ft³ container is used, the sample should be wet-screened over a screen having $1\frac{1}{2}$-in² openings.

Second, the flange of the container and the cover are cleaned, and the cover is clamped in place with the operating and bleeding valves open. Water is added to fill the space between the concrete and the lid in accordance with manufacturer's instructions. Air chamber valves are then closed, and pressure in the air chamber is increased to slightly more than the initial pressure mark. After a few seconds have elapsed so the air can cool, the needle is brought to the initial mark by opening the bleeder valve while tapping the gauge lightly. The valve between the air chamber and the concrete is then opened rapidly.

Figure 13-3 Commercial air meter for measuring air content of fresh concrete.

The gauge is tapped lightly, and after the gauge has stabilized, the percentage of air is read on the dial.

Surface Moisture in Aggregates

Purpose This test is listed with tests made with fresh concrete since the moisture on aggregates will influence the water-cement ratio of the cement paste.

Test procedure for fine aggregate (sand)

1. Select a representative sample of wet sand (about 500 to 700 g).
2. Spread the sample in a thin layer in a large, flat-bottom pan.
3. Dry the sample to *SSD* condition, with a fan frequently collecting and spreading the sand.

Test procedure for coarse aggregate

1. Select a representative sample of wet coarse aggregate (about 5010 kg).
2. Spread the sample out on a towel and remove all free moisture.

Computations

$$M = \frac{A_w - A_{SSD}}{A_{SSD}} 100 \qquad (13\text{-}9)$$

where M = free moisture in aggregate, %
A_w = wet aggregate, g
A_{SSD} = SSD aggregate, g

Direct Measurement Apparatus

The author developed a direct measurement apparatus while employed by the U.S. Bureau of Reclamation—USBR Designation 11 Concrete Manual (Fig. 13-4).

Procedure A representative sample of B g is a constant, determined for each direct measurement on the moisture apparatus at the time the specific-gravity scale is calibrated. The siphon can is filled with water and allowed to discharge to the siphon cutoff point. Discharge water is drained from the glass discharge reservoir and discarded; then the petcock is closed. The specific gravity of the aggregate must be known to measure surface moisture or absorption. For determining surface moisture or absorption, the 0 percent mark of the movable moisture scale is aligned with the aggregate specific gravity on the fixed specific-gravity scale, and the value is read. Several aggregate samples may be tested without emptying the siphon can. However, care should be exercised to see that the siphon can is filled to the siphon cutoff point before each sample is placed in the can.

Surface moisture B g of wet aggregate is placed in a full siphon can. When the siphon stops discharging, the percentage of moisture is read on the moisture scale.

Absorption B g of dry aggregate is placed in a full siphon can. The aggregate is left submerged for 30 min, after which the glass reservoir is drained, the petcock closed, and all discharged water returned to the siphon can. After the second discharge is complete, the percentage of absorption is read on the moisture scale.

Specific gravity B g of SSD aggregate is placed in a full siphon can. The specific gravity is read on the specific-gravity scale after the siphon has discharged.

Rate of Hardening of Concrete Mixture by Penetration Resistance

Purpose The penetration test to determine the degree of hardening of sand cement mortar, or mortar wet-screened from concrete, was developed by the author while

Figure 13-4 Apparatus for direct measurement of surface moisture, absorption, and specific gravity of aggregates.

working in the research laboratories of the U.S. Bureau of Reclamation. The test is based on the gradual stiffening characteristic of concrete as hydration takes place. The unit force required to penetrate the mortar mixture after given periods gives an indication of the concrete mixture's setting and hardening characteristics. This test method was adopted as an ASTM standard in 1957 (ASTM C-403).

The standard method covers determination of the time of setting of concrete with slump greater than zero by testing mortar sieved from the concrete mixture. The method is suitable for use only when tests of the mortar fraction of the concrete will provide the information required. Since the hardening of concrete is a gradual process, any definition of time of setting must necessarily be arbitrary. The temperature of storage of specimens employed in this test is to be selected by the user. Times of initial and final setting of concrete are determined in accordance with this method on the basis of a rate-of-hardening test made by means of penetration-resistant needles on mortar sieved from the concrete mixture.

The method can be used to determine the effects of variables such as temperature, cement, mixture proportions, additions, and admixtures on the time of setting and hardening characteristics of concrete. It may also be used as a part of performance specifications to determine compliance with specified time-of-setting requirements.

Definitions

Time of initial setting The elapsed time, after initial contact of cement and water, required for the mortar sieved from the concrete to reach a penetration resistance of 3.5 MPa is the "time of initial setting."

Time of final setting The elapsed time, after initial contact of cement and water, required for the mortar sieved from the concrete to reach a penetration resistance of 27.6 MPa is the "time of final setting."

Preparation of mortar specimens

1. From the concrete mixture under test, select a representative sample of concrete of sufficient volume to provide enough mortar to fill the test container(s) to a depth of at least 140 mm.
2. Remove essentially all the mortar from the sample of concrete by sieving it through a no. 4 sieve onto a nonabsorptive surface.
3. Thoroughly remix the mortar by hand methods on the nonabsorptive surface, place it in the container(s), and compact by rodding. Distribute the strokes uniformly over the cross section of the specimen. Upon completion of specimen preparation, the mortar surface should be at least 13 mm below the top edge of the container, to provide space for the collection and removal of bleeding water and to avoid contact between the mortar surface and the protective covering specified in step 4.
4. Store and maintain the specimens at the desired temperature of test. To prevent

excessive evaporation of moisture, keep the specimens covered with a suitable material such as damp burlap or a tight-fitting, water-impermeable cover for the duration of the test, except when bleeding water is being removed or penetration tests are being made. The specimens should be shielded from the sun. At least three separate batches should be made for each test condition. One rate-of-hardening test should be made on each batch.

Test procedure Remove bleeding water from the surface of the mortar specimens just prior to making a penetration test by means of a pipette or suitable instrument. To facilitate collection of bleeding water, tilt the specimen carefully to an angle of about 12° from the horizontal by placing a block under one side 2 min prior to removal of the bleeding water.

Insert a needle of appropriate size, depending on the state of hardening of the mortar, in the penetration-resistance apparatus. Bring the bearing surface of the needle into contact with the mortar surface. Gradually and uniformly apply a vertical force downward on the apparatus until the needle penetrates the mortar to a depth of 1 in (25 mm) as indicated by the scribe mark. The time required to penetrate to the 25-mm depth is approximately 10 s. Record the force required and the time of application, measured as elapsed time after initial contact of cement and water. In subsequent penetration tests, take care to avoid areas where the mortar has been disturbed by previous tests. The clear distance between needle impressions should be at least two diameters of the needle being used but not less than $\frac{1}{2}$ in (13 mm). The clear distance between any needle impression and the side of the container should not be less than 1 in.

Make penetration tests at hourly intervals for normal mixtures and normal temperatures, the initial test being made after the elapsed time of 3 to 4 h. For accelerated mixtures or high temperatures, it may be advisable to make the initial test after an elapsed time of 1 or 2 h and subsequent tests at $\frac{1}{2}$-h intervals. For low-temperature conditions or retarded concrete mixtures, the initial penetration test may be deferred for an elapsed time of 4 to 6 h, and perhaps longer. Subsequent tests may be made at intervals of 1 h, unless the rate of increase in penetration resistance indicates that shorter intervals are desirable.

Not less than six penetration-resistance determinations should be made in each rate-of-hardening test, and the time intervals between penetration-resistance determinations should be such as to give a satisfactory rate-of-hardening curve, as indicated by equally spaced points. Continue the tests until one penetration resistance of at least 4000 psi (27.6 MPa) is reached.

Computations and curves Calculate the penetration resistance, in megapascals, as the force required to cause 25-mm depth of penetration of the needle divided by the area of the bearing face of the needle.

For each variable and condition of concrete, the results from each of three or more rate-of-hardening tests are plotted separately, showing penetration resistance in megapascals as the ordinate and elapsed time in hours and minutes as the abscissa.

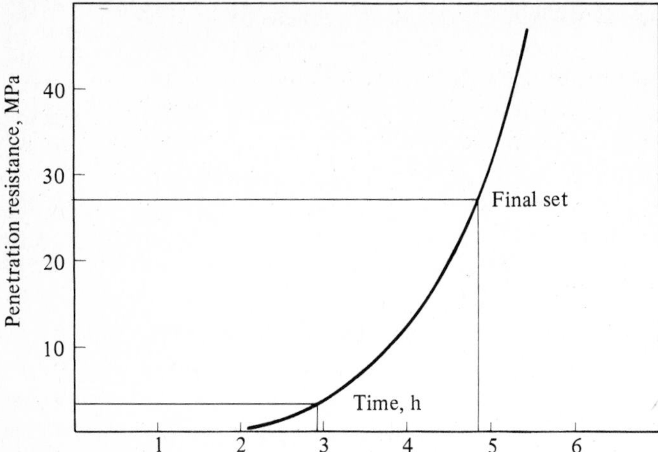

Figure 13-5 Time-of-setting curve shows the rate of hardening of concrete mortar.

Time of setting Times of initial and final setting as defined earlier are calculated by averaging the elapsed times, as determined from the curves, at which penetration resistances of 3.5 and 27.6 MPa, respectively, are reached. Times of setting is reported in hours and minutes to the nearest minute (Fig. 13-5).

Significance of time of setting of concrete The rate of hardening of concrete depends on several factors including temperature, *w/c* ratio, type of cement, and admixtures. In cold weather concrete may set too slow, and in hot weather the set may be too rapid for placing and finishing. The test for setting time provides a means for evaluating and controlling the rate of hardening of concrete.

13-3 TESTS WITH HARDENED CONCRETE

The tests made with hardened concrete are generally more meaningful than tests of the ingredients and fresh concrete since they measure the performance of ingredients and concrete as they exist in service. The quality of concrete produced is the ultimate test of the suitability, compatibility, and performance of the ingredients in concrete and of the concrete itself.

Casting Specimens for Strength Tests

For casting cylinders 6 × 12 in cylinder molds are standard for compressive-strength test specimens. These are approximately 15 × 30 cm in size, which will undoubtedly become the standard-size cylinder as conversion is made to SI units. All molds should be provided with machined base plates. Care should be taken to obtain tight molds so that mixing water will not escape during molding. The inside surfaces of molds should be greased or oiled before using.

Casting Cylinders Using Cast-Iron Molds

Vibration compaction The fresh concrete is placed in the mold in two layers, each approximately one-half of the volume of the mold. Each layer is consolidated by vibrating with an immersion-type laboratory vibrator. In consolidating the bottom layer, the vibrator should not be allowed to rest on the bottom of the mold. While the top layer is vibrated, the vibrating element should penetrate approximately 1 in into the bottom layer.

The period of vibration will depend on the slump of the concrete and the effectiveness of the vibrator. (Three insertions of 3 or 4 s each are usually sufficient.) The vibration can be judged adequate when the top surface of the concrete exhibits a shiny, wet appearance. In placing each scoopful of concrete, the scoop should be moved around the top edge of the mold as the concrete slides from it in order to ensure a symmetrical distribution of concrete. The mold should not be filled so full that mortar runs over the top when the vibrator is inserted. After vibration of the second layer, enough concrete should be added and worked into the underlying concrete with a trowel to bring the level about $\frac{1}{8}$ in above the top of the mold. The specimen is then moved to the curing room, struck off flush, and smoothed with a trowel.

Molding specimens, hand compaction If concrete is compacted by hand-rodding, the mold is filled in three layers, each approximately one-third the volume of the mold. Each layer is rodded 25 strokes with a $\frac{5}{8}$-in-diameter rod 24 in in length, bullet-pointed at the lower end. The strokes are distributed in a uniform manner over the cross section of the mold and should just penetrate into the underlying layer. The bottom layer should be rodded throughout its depth. After the top layer has been rodded, the specimen is removed to the curing room and the excess concrete struck off with a trowel.

Storage and handling of specimens Specimens should be removed from the molds 18 to 24 h after casting, weighed, and returned to the curing room.

Specimens made in the field at the site of placement should be kept, as nearly as practicable, at 23°C and protected from the sun and from moisture loss.

Casting Cylinders in the Field Using Molds Made of Steel or Cardboard

Molds The can or mold should be 6 in $\pm \frac{1}{16}$ in in diameter and 12 in $\pm \frac{1}{8}$ in high. Smaller lids and openings in cans are acceptable, but they should provide sufficient area for easy troweling. The lids should be tight-fitting. The molds should be round and true to shape. Bottoms of cans should be completely flat on the inside without beads or other profile (Fig. 13-6).

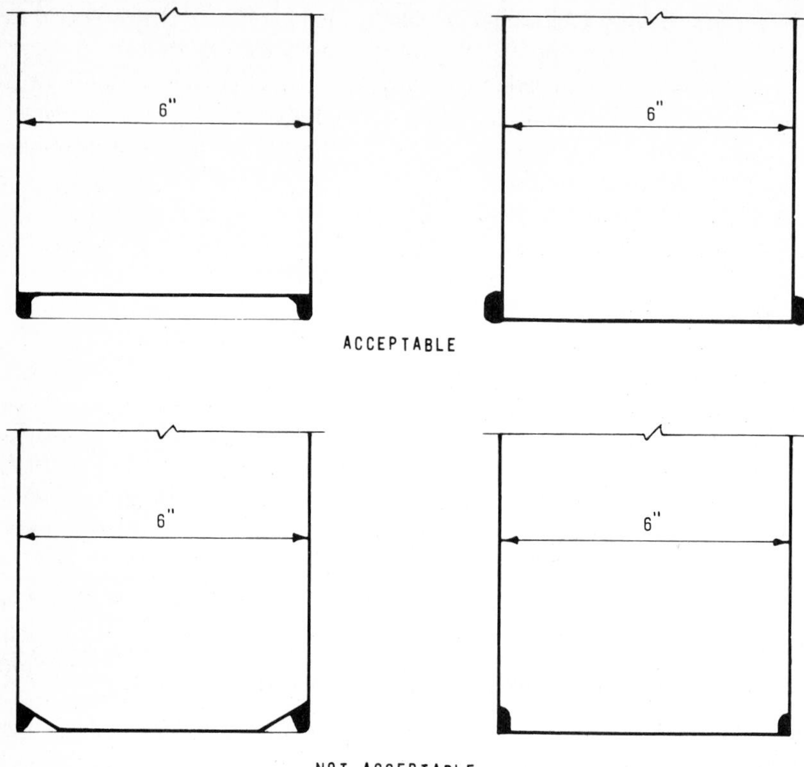

Figure 13-6 Acceptable metal molds for making field cylinders. (*U.S. Bureau of Reclamation.*)

Procedure

1. The fresh sample is mixed thoroughly before concrete is placed in the can or mold.
2. Before the specimen is cast, the mold should be placed on a smooth, level surface that is free from vibration. If the cylinder is to be transported immediately after fabrication, it must be done by hand and in a vertical position. The specimen should then be allowed to set on a level surface for at least 6 h and preferably 24 h, during which time it must be protected from extreme temperatures.
3. The mold is filled in three layers, each approximately one-third the total volume. Each layer is compacted by hand-rodding 25 strokes with a $\frac{5}{8}$-in-diameter rod 24 in in length, bullet-pointed at the lower end. The strokes are distributed in a uniform manner over the cross section of the can and should penetrate into the underlying layer. The bottom layer should be rodded throughout its depth, with care being taken not to strike the bottom of the can hard enough to dent or mar it. Convex ends on cylinders and bottoms damaged

by rodding will be avoided if each can, during filling and until the concrete has hardened, is rested symmetrically on a wooden or metal disk $5\frac{1}{2}$ in in diameter. After the top layer has been rodded, its surface is smoothed off. A small trowel with a rounded point should be used for this purpose when cans are used. Particular care should be taken to secure smooth cylinder ends that are perpendicular to the axis of the cylinder.

4. Specimens should be stored where the temperature of the concrete will be maintained at approximately 23°C. Before testing, cylinders should be capped on both ends.

Capping Concrete Cylinders

The ends of all concrete specimens which have not been ground smooth or which have not been cast against a machined base plate should be capped with a melted mixture of sulfur and finely ground, screened material. Milled fire clay has been found to be the best material to use with sulfur for capping. Commercial capping materials specially compounded are suitable provided they develop compressive strength equal to or greater than the anticipated strength of the specimen at time of test.

Preparation before capping All loose particles and high points are removed from the end of the cylinder with a wire brush and carburundum stone; the end should be free from laitance and moisture.

Capping procedure A mixture of 3 parts of sulfur by weight to 1 part of fine sand is heated at an approximate temperature of 150°C until the mixture is thick and viscous. The right temperature of the mixture for capping is determined through observation and experience with the mixture used. If a commercial preparation is used, the manufacturer's recommendation should be followed as to temperature. Overheating of the mixture should be avoided because these practices tend to make the cap rubbery rather than brittle as desired. Enough material to make the cap is poured on a lightly greased capping plate, and the specimen is pressed firmly into the melted material. This operation should be done quickly before solidification begins. Caps should be as thin as practical and should not flow or fracture when the specimen is tested. After the cap has hardened, the cylinder may be loosened by a twisting force or by striking the edge of the plate.

If any holes in the end of the cylinder are more than 0.5 cm deep, they should be partially filled by pouring capping material into them and allowing it to harden prior to forming the full cap.

Significance of proper cylinder capping Unless the axial load of the compression forces are spread uniformly over the end surface of the cylinder being tested, erroneous and erratic test results will be obtained. Concentrated stresses on a high point on the surface, for example, will greatly weaken the cylinder.

The capping material should have a modulus of elasticity approximately equal to that of the concrete. Excessive deformation of the material will allow stress concentrations to develop.

Cylinders which are not capped properly will usually produce a strength lower than its true value. This discrepancy favors the owner rather than the contractor in concrete quality control.

Compressive Strength

Moist-cured concrete test specimens should be tested for compressive strength as soon as practicable after they are removed from the curing room. When the cylinder size is not accurately known, the cylinder should be carefully measured first. When a check on the mix proportions of the concrete is desired, the density of the cylinder should be determined. If the specimens are to be sulfur-capped, they should be weighed and measured first, then capped and returned to the curing room until tested. If elasticity tests are to be made, the strength tests are made immediately following the elasticity tests or, in case of delay, the specimens are returned to the curing room. Sealed specimens do not require curing-room storage, except when more than 6 h is to elapse between stripping and testing.

All foreign material must be removed from the ends of the specimen before testing.

Procedure Compressive-strength tests are made in the testing machine (Fig. 13-7). A spherical bearing block should be used to transmit the load to the specimen. The diameter of the bearing block should be the same as or slightly larger than that of the test specimen. The test specimen should be carefully centered with respect to the bearing block.

The load should be applied uniformly and without shock at a rate of 0.14 to 0.34 MPa/s. It is important that no adjustment be made in the controls of the testing machine while a specimen is yielding rapidly immediately before failure.

Some factors which affect compressive strength

1. *Effect of wet screening and type of curing.* Cylinders of concrete used for compressive-strength tests are generally 6 in in diameter and 12 in long. The strength of mass concrete in a structure may be estimated from the strength of 6 × 12 in cylinders by applying appropriate factors. Figure 13-8 shows the strength relationship of mass concrete containing large aggregate, tested in small cylinders. The relationship between mass-cured and standard fog-cured mass concrete is also given. These factors are useful in interpreting results obtained from field tests of wet-screened mass concrete.
2. *Cylinder size.* The test data from tests shown in Fig. 13-9 are typical of the relative strengths to be expected when the same concrete is tested in cylinders varying in size from 2 × 4 in to 36 × 72 in.
3. *Cylinder height.* A standard test cylinder has a diameter one-half of its height. There are occasions, however, when the available specimens do not have these

Figure 13-7 Universal testing machine. (*Utah State University.*)

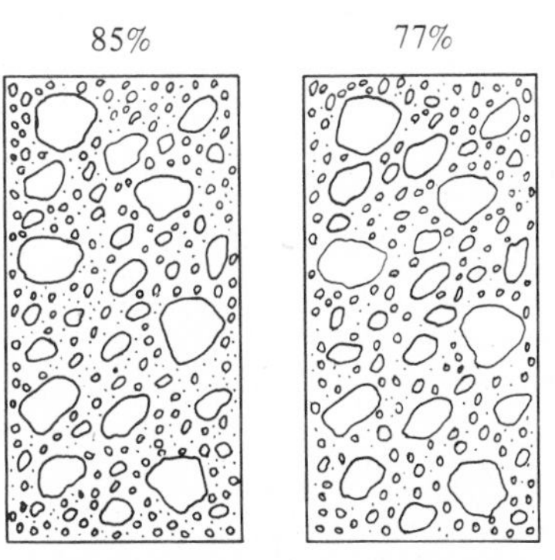

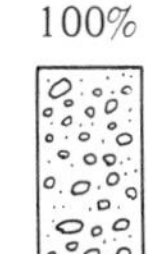

Figure 13-8 Relative strength of large cylinders using large aggregates versus the strength of standard cylinders using wet-screened concrete. (*After U.S. Bureau of Reclamation* Concrete Manual, *8th ed.*)

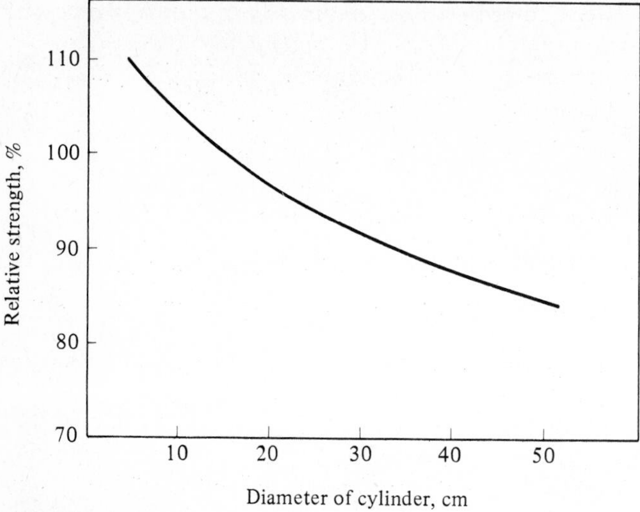

Figure 13-9 Effect of cylinder size on strength. (*After Bureau of Reclamation* Concrete Manual, *8th ed.*)

relative dimensions. In these cases the curve in Fig. 13-10 may be used to correct indicated strengths so that they will be comparable with those obtained from standard specimens. Since the curve is quite flat for ratios of 1.5 and over, small variations in height of specimen do not greatly affect strength.

Significance of the compressive strength of concrete The compressive-strength test has limitations and does not measure directly the resistance to loads imposed on concrete structures. This test does provide valuable information and is used universally as a measure of concrete quality.

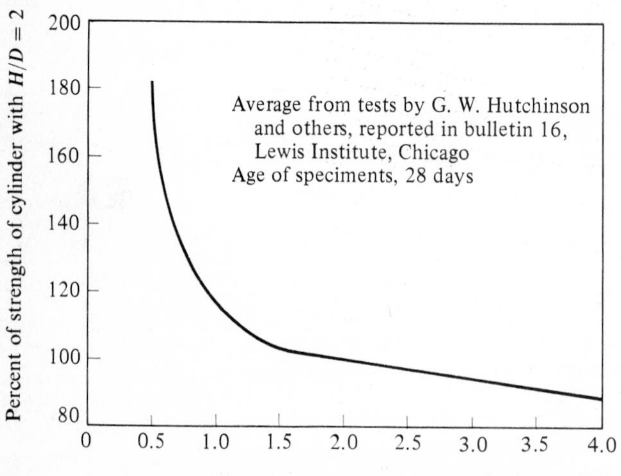

Figure 13-10 Effect of height/diameter ratio on strength.

The relationship between compressive strength and w/c ratio has been well established. Most desirable properties of concrete increase with a decrease in w/c ratio. The compressive strength is, therefore, an indirect measure of concrete quality. The variability of the strength test results is used as a measure of concrete uniformity (Chap. 11).

Flexural Strength (Using a Simple Beam with Third-Point Loading)

This method covers determination of the flexural strength of concrete by use of a simple beam with third-point loading.

Test procedure Turn the test specimen on its side with respect to its position as molded and center on the bearing blocks. Center the loading system in relation to the applied force. Bring the load-applying blocks in contact with the surface of the specimen at the third points between the supports (Fig. 13-11).

The load may be applied rapidly, up to approximately 50 percent of the breaking load. Thereafter, apply the load continuously at a rate which constantly increases the extreme fiber stress between 8.61 and 12.07 kPa/min, until rupture occurs.

Measurement of specimens after test Take three measurements across each dimension (one at each edge and at the center) to the nearest 1.3 mm to determine the average width, average depth, and line of fracture location of the specimen at the section of failure.

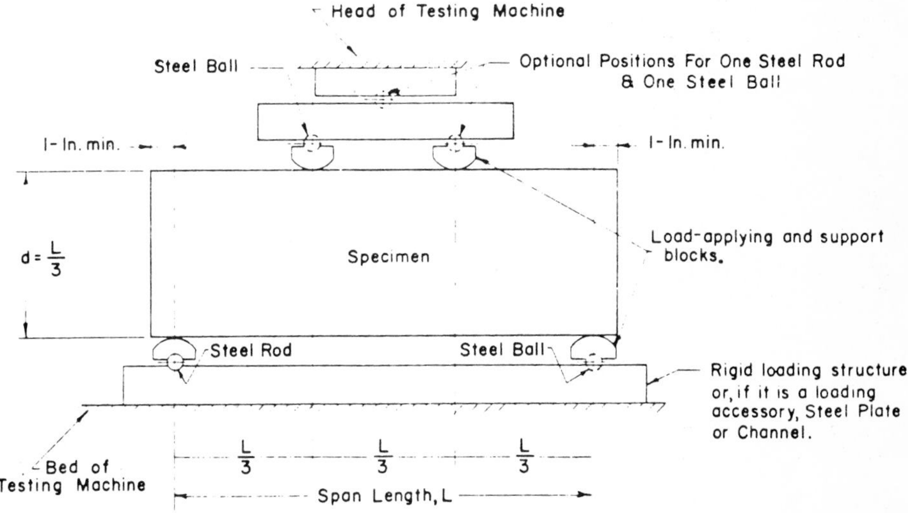

NOTE—This apparatus may be used inverted. If the testing machine applies force through a spherically seated head, the center pivot may be omitted, provided one load-applying block pivots on a rod and the other on a ball.
NOTE—1 in. = 25.4 mm.

Figure 13-11 Flexural-strength test. (*ASTM C-78.*)

Computations If the fracture initiates in the tension surface within the middle third of the span length, calculate the modulus of rupture as follows:

$$R = \frac{Pl}{bd^2} \tag{13-10}$$

where R = modulus of rupture, MPa
P = maximum applied load indicated by testing machine, N
l = span length, mm
b = average width of specimen, mm
d = average depth of specimen, mm
N = kg × 9.86 (or pounds × 2.205 × 9.86)

Significance of the flexural strength of concrete With the exception of unreinforced pavements, concrete is not required to resist the tension forces of flexure. In reinforced-concrete design, reinforcing steel is used to carry these stresses.

The flexural strength is approximately one-tenth of the compressive strength but reaches a maximum of about 5 MPa. This test is only used where specific information is desired.

Splitting Tensile Strength of Cylindrical Concrete Specimens

This method covers the determination of the splitting tensile strength of cylindrical concrete specimens such as molded cylinders and drilled cores. This information may be important in the evaluation of bond between the aggregate particles and the cement paste.

Test procedure Two bearing strips of nominal $\frac{1}{8}$-in-thick plywood, free of imperfections, approximately 25 mm wide, and of a length equal to or slightly longer than that of the specimen should be provided for each specimen. The bearing strips are placed between the specimen and both the upper and lower bearing blocks of the testing machine or between the specimen and supplemental bars or plates (Fig. 13-12).

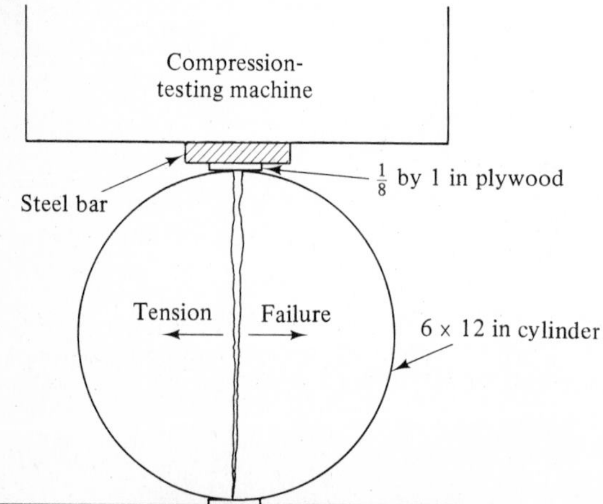

Figure 13-12 Splitting tension test. (*ASTM C-496.*)

1. *Marking.* Draw diametral lines on each end of the specimen using a suitable device that will ensure that they are in the same axial plane. Center one of the plywood strips along the center of the lower bearing block. Place the specimen on the plywood strip and align so that the lines marked on the ends of the specimen are vertical and centered over the plywood strip. Place a second plywood strip lengthwise on the cylinder, centered on the lines marked on the ends of the cylinder.
2. *Rate of loading.* Apply the load continuously and without shock, at a constant rate within the range of 690 to 1400 kPa/min splitting tensile stress until failure of the specimen. Record the maximum applied load indicated by the testing machine at failure. Note the type of failure and appearance of fracture.

Computations Calculate the splitting tensile strength of the specimen as follows:

$$T = \frac{2P}{\pi l d} \tag{13-11}$$

where T = splitting tensile strength, kPa
P = maximum applied load indicated by testing machine, kN
l = length, m
d = diameter, m

Significance of the splitting tensile strength of concrete The tensile strength of concrete is difficult to measure and varies widely depending on the bond between the aggregate particles and the hardened paste, which is influenced by the size of the aggregate particles, the shape of the aggregate particles, and their surface texture.

Although not a true tension test, the splitting test fails in tension and is used to indicate the tensile strength of concrete.

Resistance of Concrete to Rapid Freezing and Thawing

Purpose This method covers the determination of the resistance of concrete specimens to rapidly repeated cycles of freezing and thawing. The procedure is not intended to provide a quantitative measure of the length of service that may be expected from a specific type of concrete, but does indicate relative durability as compared with other concretes.

Freezing-and-thawing apparatus The freezing-and-thawing apparatus consists of a suitable chamber in which the specimens may be subjected to the specified freezing-and-thawing cycle, together with the necessary refrigerating and heating equipment and controls to produce continuously and automatically reproducible cycles within the specified temperature requirements (Fig. 13-13).

Test specimens This method contemplates the use of prisms not less than 76 mm nor more than 137 mm in width and depth and not less than 356 mm nor more

Figure 13-13 Rapid freezing and thawing equipment for measuring durability of concrete. (*Utah State University*.)

than 406 mm in length. Difficulty may be experienced in complying with the requirements of the method if specimens are used which differ appreciably from the above dimensions.

Test specimens may also be cores or prisms cut from hardened concrete. If so, the specimens should not be allowed to dry to a moisture condition below that of the structure from which they were taken. This may be accomplished by wrapping in plastic or by other suitable means.

For this test the specimens are stored in saturated lime water from the time of their removal from the molds until freezing-and-thawing tests are started. All specimens to be compared with one another initially should be of the same nominal dimensions.

Test procedure Immediately after the specified curing period, usually 14 days moist curing, test for fundamental transverse frequency (Fig. 13-14), weigh, and measure. Protect the specimens against loss of moisture between the time of removal from curing and the start of the freezing-and-thawing cycles.

Start freezing-and-thawing tests by placing the specimens in the thawing water at the beginning of the thawing phase of the cycle. Remove the specimens from the apparatus, in a thawed condition, at intervals not exceeding 36 cycles of exposure to the freezing-and-thawing cycles; test for fundamental transverse frequency at a temperature of $5.6 \pm 2.8°C$; weigh; and return them to the appar-

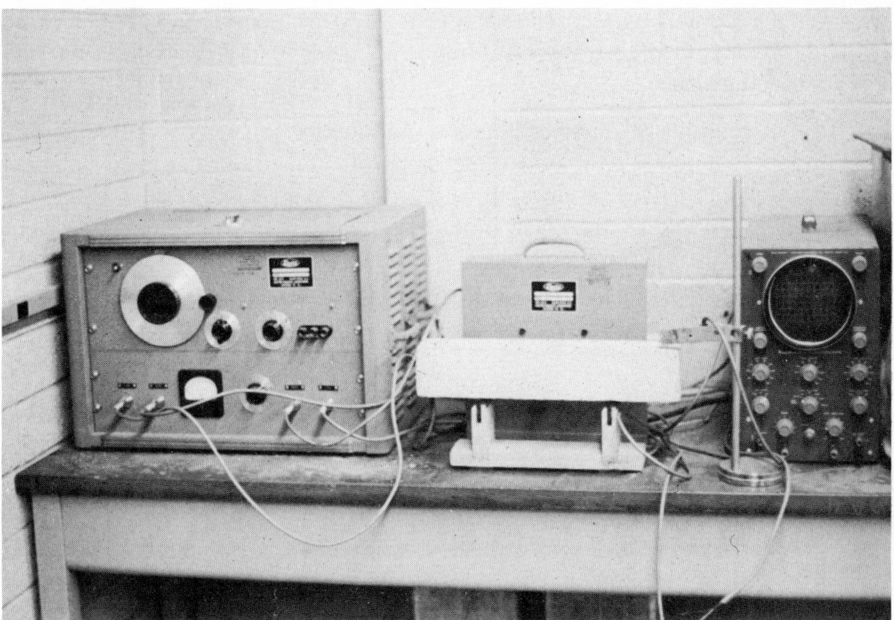

Figure 13-14 Apparatus for measuring fundamental frequency of vibration of a concrete prism.

atus. To ensure that the specimens are completely thawed and at the specified temperature, place them in the tempering tank or hold them at the end of the thaw cycle in the freezing-and-thawing apparatus for a sufficient time for this condition to be attained throughout each specimen to be tested. Protect the specimens against loss of moisture while out of the apparatus, and turn them end for end when returned. Rinse out the container and add clean water. Return the specimens either to random positions in the apparatus or to positions according to some predetermined rotation scheme that will ensure that each specimen that continues under test for any length of time is subjected to conditions in all parts of the freezing apparatus. Continue each specimen in the test until it has been subjected to 300 cycles or until its relative dynamic modulus of elasticity reaches 60 percent of the initial modulus, whichever occurs first. Each time a specimen is tested for fundamental frequency, make a note of its visual appearance and make special comment on any defects that develop.

Computations

Relative dynamic modulus of elasticity Calculate the numerical values of relative dynamic modulus of elasticity as follows:

$$P_c = \left(\frac{n_1^2}{n^2}\right)100 \tag{13-12}$$

where P_c = relative dynamic modulus of elasticity, after c cycles of freezing and thawing, percent

n = fundamental transverse frequency at 0 cycles of freezing and thawing
n_1 = fundamental transverse frequency after c cycles of freezing and thawing

This calculation of relative dynamic modulus of elasticity is based on the assumption that the weight and dimensions of the specimen remain constant throughout the test. This assumption is not true in many cases because of disintegration of the specimen. However, if the test is to be used to make comparisons between the relative dynamic moduli of different specimens or of different concrete formulations, P_c as defined is adequate for the purpose.

Durability factor

$$\mathrm{DF} = \frac{PN}{M} \tag{13-13}$$

where DF = durability factor of test specimen
P = relative dynamic modulus of elasticity at N cycles, percent
N = number of cycles at which P reaches the specified minimum value for discontinuing test or specified number of cycles at which exposure is to be terminated, whichever is less
M = specified number of cycles at which the exposure is to be terminated

Loss of weight Another method of determining durability is to measure the loss of weight as the specimens deteriorate:

$$\mathrm{DF}_w = \frac{W_n}{W} 100$$

where DF_w = durability factor as measured by weight loss after n cycles
W_n = weight of specimen after n cycles of freezing and thawing
W = original weight of specimen

Significance of rapid freezing-and-thawing durability of concrete Although the rapid freezing-and-thawing test cannot be used to accurately predict the life of a structure exposed to freezing and thawing under field conditions, it is valuable in determining the comparative durability of aggregates, portland cements, admixtures, and other variables.

When certain materials have known durability records in actual service, comparison of the relative durability of these materials and of unknown materials will provide definitive information.

Accelerated Curing of Concrete Compression Test Specimens

Purpose Concrete specimens are exposed to elevated temperatures and to moisture conditions adequate to develop a significant portion of their ultimate strength within 24 to 48 h depending on the procedure selected. Procedures 1 and 2 utilize storage of specimens in heated water at elevated curing temperatures without moisture loss. The primary function of the moderately heated water used in procedure 1 is to serve as insulation to conserve the heat generated by hydration. The temperature level employed in procedure 2 provides thermal acceleration. Procedure 3 involves storage of specimens in insulated curing containers in which the elevated temperature is obtained from heat of hydration of the cement. The sealed containers also prevent moisture loss. Sampling and testing procedures are the same as for normally cured specimens.

The accelerated curing procedures provide, for a particular combination of materials at the earliest practical time, an indication of the potential strength of the concrete. They also provide information on the variability of the production process for use in process control.

Correlation between accelerated early strength of test specimens and strength at some later age achieved by conventional curing methods depends on the materials comprising the concrete and the specific procedure employed. Any strength value provided by companion specimens, no matter how obtained, has a dubious relation to the actual strength of the concrete in place in the structure and has value only as an indicator of a probability that the desired load-bearing capability has been or can be obtained in the structure by use of a particular formulation. There is, therefore, no fundamental reason why the accelerated early strength obtained from any one of the three procedures outlined in this method cannot be used in the design and evaluation of concrete strengths in the same way conventional 28-day strengths have been used in the past, with suitable changes in the expected numbers used to describe strength values. However, since the practice of using strength values obtained from standard-cured cylinders at 28 days is long established and widespread, it is recognized that many people will wish to use the results of strength tests on specimens cured by accelerated methods to make "predictions" of strength that might be obtained at later ages. Such predictions should be limited to concretes using the same materials as those used for establishing the correlation.

The ratio of accelerated strength to conventionally obtained strength of test specimens at later ages increases with the cement content and initial mixture temperature.

Summary of accelerated curing methods Three procedures are currently in use for making, curing, and testing specimens of concrete stored under conditions intended to accelerate the development of strength. The choice of procedure should be made by the user on the basis of experience and local conditions. The three procedures are as follows: procedure 1, warm water method; procedure 2, boiling water method; and procedure 3, autogenous curing method.

Procedure 1: warm water method The accelerated curing tank may be of any configuration suitable for the number of cylinders to be tested, and the cylinders may be arranged in any configuration provided clearances of at least 50 mm between the side of the cylinder and the side of the tank and at least 100 mm between adjacent cylinders are maintained.

The tank should be capable of providing the specified water temperature. The temperature at any point in the water should be maintained within ±3°C of that specified.

Cover the top of the specimen to prevent loss of mortar to the water bath.

Place the specimen in the curing tank. The water at the time of immersion and throughout the curing period should be 35 ± 3°C. The temperature of the curing water should be periodically measured throughout the curing period.

After curing for 23½ h ± 30 min, remove the cylinder from the tank and strip the mold.

Procedure 2: boiling water method In *initial curing*, cover the cylinders to prevent loss of moisture and store them so that they will not be disturbed or subjected to vibration or jarring. In the storage area the temperature adjacent to the cylinders is maintained at 21 ± 6°C. In *accelerated curing*, place the covered cylinder molds in the water tank at 23 h ± 15 min after molding. The temperature of the water at the time of immersion and throughout the curing period should be at boiling. The temperature of the curing water should be measured at regular intervals throughout the curing period.

After curing for 3½ h ± 5 min, remove the cylinder from the boiling water, remove the mold, and allow the cylinder to cool for not less than 1 h at room temperature prior to capping.

Procedure 3: autogenous method The container consists of thermal insulation closely surrounding the concrete test cylinder. The container is capable of being opened to permit insertion and withdrawal of the cylinder and where required should have an outer casing and inner liner to protect the insulation from mechanical damage.

Provision must be made to keep the container securely closed during the specified curing period.

Immediately after molding, cover the mold with a metal plate or a tightly fitted cap and place in a heavy-duty plastic bag from which as much of the entrapped air as possible is expelled prior to tying the neck. The plastic bag should be of sufficient weight and strength to resist punctures and serve as a lifting grip for removal of the cylinder from the autogenous container.

Record the time of molding to the nearest 15 min and the temperature of the fresh concrete.

For at least 12 h after molding, the container should not be moved, disturbed, or subjected to vibration or jarring and should be stored out of the sun, preferably at a temperature of 21 ± 6°C.

At the age of 48 h ± 15 min after the time at which the cylinder was molded, remove the cylinder from the container and strip the mold. Allow to stand for 30 min at room temperature.

Interpretation of results Because strength requirements in existing specifications and codes are not based on accelerated curing, results from this method in the prediction of specification compliance of strengths at later ages must be applied with great caution. The variability of the method is the same or less than that of traditional methods. Thus, results can be used in rapid assessment of variability for process control and signaling the need for indicated adjustments. On the other hand, the magnitude of the strength values obtained is influenced by the specific combination of materials, so that the use of the results from either conventional tests at any arbitrary age or those from this method must be supported by experience or correlations developed by the specific agency for the existing local conditions and materials. Factors influencing relationships between measured strengths and those of concrete in place are no different from those affecting conventional strength tests.

Rebound Number of Hardened Concrete

Scope This method covers the determination of a rebound number of hardened concrete using a spring-driven steel hammer.

Significance The rebound number determined by this method may be used to assess the uniformity of concrete in situ; to delineate zones or regions (areas) of poor quality or deteriorated concrete in structures; and to indicate changes with time in characteristics of concrete such as those caused by the hydration of cement, so that it provides useful information in determining when forms and shoring may be removed.

This method is not intended as an alternative for strength determination of concrete.

Apparatus

1. *Rebound hammer* consists of a spring-loaded steel hammer which, when released, strikes a steel plunger in contact with the concrete surface. The spring-loaded hammer must travel with a fixed and reproducible velocity. The rebound distance of the steel hammer from the steel plunger is measured in a linear scale attached to the frame of the instrument.
2. *Abrasive stone* consists of medium-grain texture silicon carbide or equivalent material.

Test area Concrete members to be tested should be at least 100 mm thick and fixed within a structure. Smaller specimens must be rigidly supported. Areas exhibiting honeycombing, scaling, rough texture, or high porosity should be avoided. Concretes should be approximately the same age and have the same moisture conditions in order to be compared. Dry concretes give higher rebound numbers than wet concretes, and the surface layer of concrete may be densified, yielding higher rebound numbers. The form material against which the concrete was placed should be similar. Troweled surfaces generally exhibit higher rebound numbers than screeded or formed finishes. If possible, structural slabs should be tested from the underside to avoid finished surfaces. Heavily textured, soft surfaces with loose mortar should be ground smooth.

Procedure Hold the rebound hammer firmly perpendicular to the surface of concrete. Gradually increase the pressure on the plunger until the hammer impacts. Record the rebound number. Take a minimum of 10 readings in the area to be tested.

Computations Discard readings more than 7 units from the average and average the remaining readings. If there are excessive variations in the readings, discard all readings.

QUESTIONS AND PROBLEMS

1 Why are tests for portland cement seldom performed in construction control laboratories?

2 Why is the fineness of cement important in concrete?

3 Is the compressive strength of 2 × 2 in mortar cubes a good indication of the strength-producing properties of cement in concrete?

4 Tests made with samples of fresh, plastic concrete are used extensively as acceptance tests for the concrete. Why is this true?

5 Why are samples for fresh concrete from mixers taken from two or more regularly spaced intervals from the middle portion of the batch?

6 What is the relationship between density of concrete and its unit weight?

7 Assume concrete mix proportions are 1 : 2 : 4, with the corresponding specific gravities of 3.15, 2.65, and 2.7 for cement, sand, and gravel. If the w/c ratio is 55 percent, compute the density of the concrete.

8 What law of physics is used in measuring air content by pressure methods?

9 What is meant by "free moisture" in aggregates?

10 What is meant by initial set and final set?

11 Why is the compressive-strength test considered the most important of all evaluation and control tests of concrete?

12 List several factors which have an influence on the compressive strength.

13 Is the flexural-strength test important in testing concrete?

14 Will freezing-and-thawing tests indicate the length of life of concrete in a given environment?

15 What is the basis of the accelerated-strength test?

16 When is the rebound test for concrete strength useful?

CHAPTER
FOURTEEN
TESTING AND EVALUATION OF ASPHALT CEMENT AND ASPHALTIC CONCRETE

There are certain tests by which the engineer can determine the suitability of asphalt cement and asphaltic concrete.

Asphalt Cement

Important tests for asphalt cement for pavement construction are listed in ASTM specifications D-946 as follows:

D-140 Test for sampling bituminous materials
D-5 Test for penetration of bituminous materials
D-113 Test for ductility of bituminous materials
D-92 Test for flash and fire points by Cleveland open cup
D-1754 Test for effect of heat and air on asphaltic materials
D-2042 Test for solubility of bituminous materials in organic solvents

Aggregates for Asphaltic Concrete

Tests for aggregates for asphaltic concrete are discussed in Chap. 12.

Asphaltic Concrete

Tests for asphaltic concrete are primarily concerned with the following:

D-2726 Density of asphaltic concrete from which the degree of compaction and void content can be determined
D-2172 Percent of asphalt cement in asphaltic concrete by quantitative extraction
D-1074 Test for compressive strength for bituminous paving mixtures
D-1559 Test for resistance to plastic flow of bituminous mixtures

A. ASPHALT CEMENT

14-1 SAMPLING BITUMINOUS MATERIALS

Purpose of sampling asphalt cement Asphalt cement should be sampled for one of two purposes: (1) to represent as nearly as possible an average of the materials being sampled and (2) to ascertain variations in characteristics of the material from one sample to the next.

Size of samples The size of samples of asphalt cement will depend on the size of storage facility being sampled. From bulk storage it is 1 gal; from barrels or drums it is 1 qt.

Sampling at Place of Manufacture

Two sampling methods are used to sample vertical tanks not capable of being agitated.

Sampling-valve method Valves are located in the top third, the middle third, and the bottom third of the tank. The top half should be at least 1 m from the top and the bottom valve at least 1.1 m from the bottom of the tank. A minimum of 4 dm^3 is drawn from each valve and discarded before the samples are taken. Samples of 1 to 4 dm^3 are then extracted from each valve.

Throw-away container method Samples are taken from the top third, the middle third, and the bottom third of a storage tank by lowering a stoppered can to the proper location and then pulling the stopper out. After the can is full, it is pulled to the surface and its contents are emptied into a clean sample can. The original container is then thrown away.

Samples from storage tanks can be tested separately to check for stratification, or they can be combined to obtain an average sample. When storage tanks containing liquid asphalt cement are equipped with mechanical agitators, a single sample taken by any approved method will be suitable for tests.

Sampling from Tank Cars, Vehicle Tanks, Distribution Trucks, or Recirculating Storage Tanks

Samples may be taken from sample valves or taps when provided. Before the sample is taken, 4 dm^3 of material should be drawn through the sample valve and discarded.

Samples of liquid materials may be taken by the dip method using a clean wide-mouth or friction-top can with a suitable holder. A clean container should be used to take the sample and then transferred to another new clean container.

Significance of Proper Sampling Methods

Because numerous types and grades of bituminous materials are shipped and stored in the same or similar containers, the opportunity for contaminating these containers is ever-present. Numerous opportunities do exist for obtaining samples which are not representative. Continuous precautions should be exercised in sampling these materials.

14-2 PENETRATION OF BITUMINOUS MATERIALS

Purpose of the Penetration Test

The "penetration grade" of asphalt cement is defined as the consistency of a bituminous material expressed as the distance in tenths of a millimeter that a standard needle vertically penetrates a sample of material under specified conditions of loading, time, and temperature (Fig. 14-1). This test provides a means of specifying the type and grade of asphalt cement for a given project. Different grades will be specified for different mean ambient temperatures—softer cements

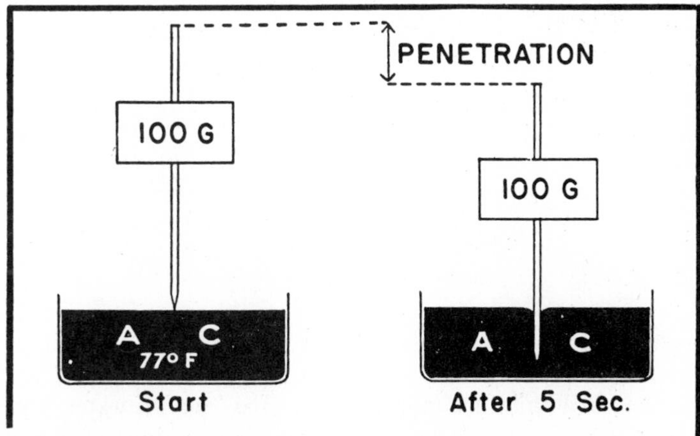

Figure 14-1 Penetration test for asphalt cement. (*Asphalt Institute.*)

for cold climates, so they will not become too brittle, and harder cements for warm climates, so they will not become too soft. The penetration of asphalt cement at a given temperature largely depends on the percentage of the more volatile oils remaining in the cement after distillation.

Test Procedure

Between 1 and $1\frac{1}{2}$ h after the sample has been poured in, a test can is placed in a 25°C bath. The penetration test is performed 1 to $1\frac{1}{2}$ h after the sample has been placed in the bath.

The penetrometer shaft should weigh 100 g including a 50-g weight placed on the shaft. The needle is lowered to within about 5 mm of the asphalt surface with the needle at least 10 mm away from the edge of the cup. A lamp is placed to the rear of the machine so that the reflection of the needle may be seen in the asphalt. The needle is lowered until the point of the needle appears to be resting on the point of its image. The shaft is released for exactly 5 s, and the penetration reading on the dial is recorded. The test is repeated until three tests have been obtained which do not differ by more than 4 mm between the maximum and minimum. Points on the surface at which the penetrations are made must be at least 10 mm apart. The average of the three penetrations is reported to the nearest whole number.

Significance of the Penetration Test

The penetration test is one of the most useful tests in the control of asphalt cement. It provides a basis for specifying and controlling asphalt grades. The test can also be used to check the uniformity of a given tank and of different shipments. The penetration test can be made in a field laboratory.

14-3 DUCTILITY OF BITUMINOUS MATERIALS

Purpose of the Ductility Test

The ductility of asphalt cement gives an indication of the cracking tendencies of asphaltic concrete pavements. This is particularly important in cold climates where the asphaltic cement may become too brittle to perform properly in flexible pavements.

Test Procedure

Between 30 and 40 min after the sample has been poured into the molds (Fig. 14-2), the specimens are placed in a water bath at a specified temperature (usually 25°C). At the end of 30 min, the molds are removed from the water bath, and the excess asphalt is cut from the top of the molds by means of a hot, straight-edged spatula or putty knife so that they are just level full. Place the plate

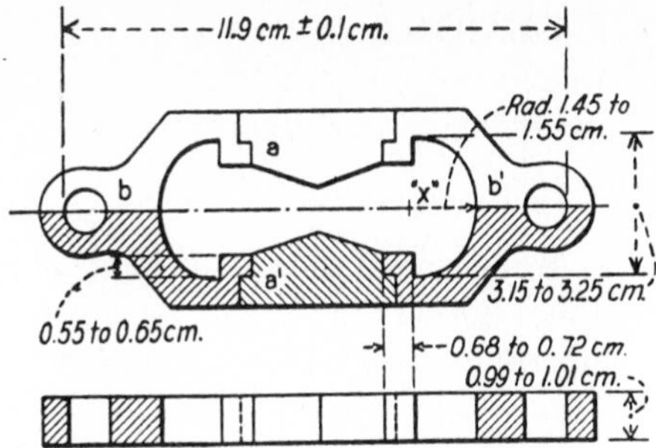

Note.—The opening in the end of each clip, as indicated by "x," shall be half an ellipse having a transverse axis of 3.2±0.05 cm and half of the longitudinal axis shall be 1.45 to 1.55 cm.

Figure 14-2 Molds for ductility test. (*ASTM D-113.*)

with the specimens back in the water bath. They are to remain in the bath for 85 to 95 min before the ductility test is run. Fill the ductility bath with water at 25°C.

After the specimens have remained in the water bath for 85 to 95 min, the mold side plates are carefully removed and the moving head of the ductility machine is adjusted so that the pointer is at zero, the specimens are hooked onto the machine, and the motor is started. The reading under the pointer at which each strand breaks is recorded. The average of the reading on the two test strands is reported as the ductility (Fig. 14-3).

Significance of the Ductility Test

Unless asphalt cement has sufficient ductility, it may become too brittle and crack. The ductility test is useful in determining compliance with specifications. The test does not lend itself to field testing and control and is usually performed in control laboratories.

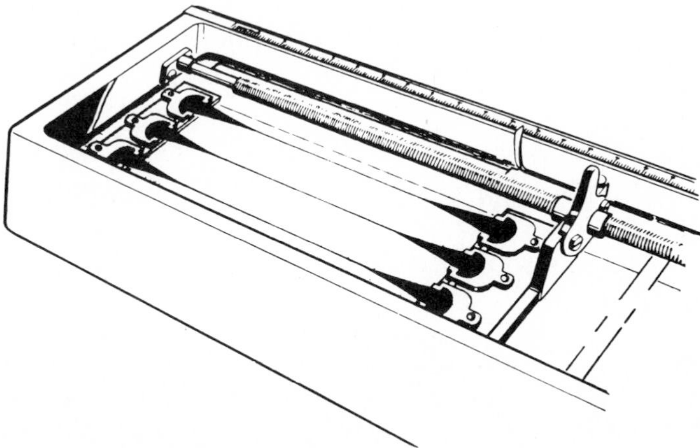

Figure 14-3 Ductility test. (*Asphalt Institute.*)

14-4 FLASH POINT FOR ASPHALT CEMENT BY MEANS OF OPEN CUP

Purpose of the Flash-Point Test

Although most volatile oils are usually distilled from asphalt cement, there may be enough to vaporize and create a fire hazard in a hot-mix plant. The flash-point determination will indicate the relative temperature at which there may be a danger of fire.

Test Procedure

The filled Cleveland flash cup (Fig. 14-4) should be placed on a special heating plate and supported on a tripod or ring and ring stand. The bottom of the thermometer bulb should be 6 mm from the bottom of the cup and halfway between the center and back of the cup. The test flame is adjusted so that it is approximately 3.2 to 4.8 mm in diameter. The asphalt may be heated rapidly to about 120°C (but not exceeding 15°C/min), after which the flame is adjusted so that the rate of temperature rise is 5 to 6°C per minute. After the temperature has reached about 148°C, try for a flash for each 2°C increase in temperature as follows: Pass the flame across the center of the cup at right angles to the diameter and in a horizontal plane not more than 2 mm above the edge of the cup. The time for passage of the test flame across the cup should be approximately 1 s.

The flash point is the temperature read on the thermometer when a flash appears at any point on the surface of the asphalt.

Significance of the Flash-Point Test

The flash-point test is used to determine the properties of the material being tested. Although it is an indication of potential fire hazard, the test is not intended to regulate fire hazards under actual fire conditions.

14-5 LOSS OF PENETRATION BY HEATING ASPHALT CEMENT

Purpose

Since asphalt cements are manufactured by removing controlled amounts of lighter, more volatile oils, there is a possibility of changing the composition and characteristics of asphalt when it is heated in a hot plant in the manufacture of asphaltic concrete. This test is designed to determine whether the asphalt cement changes during production of asphaltic concrete.

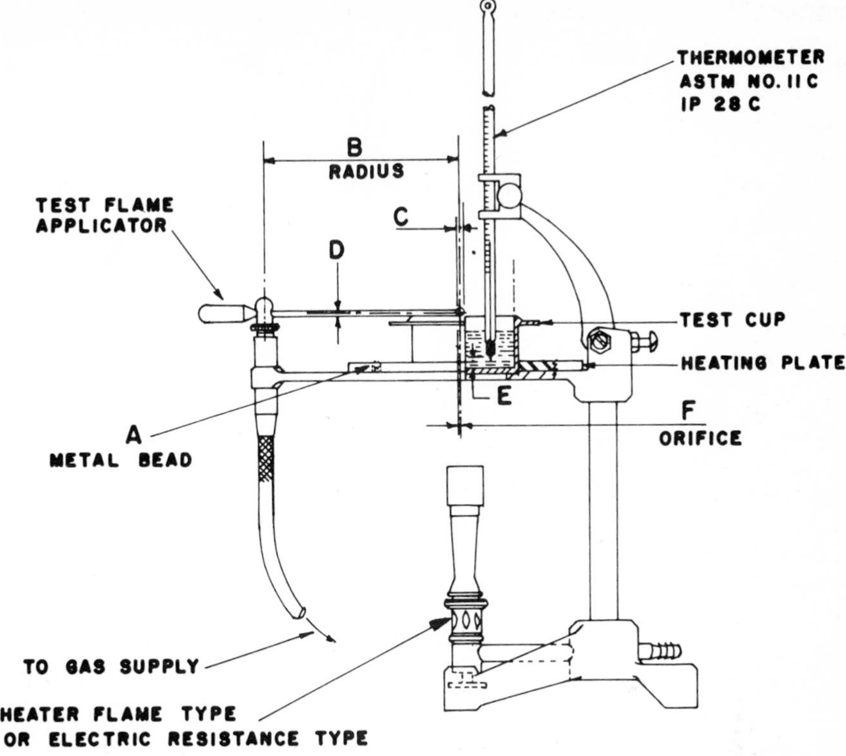

	millimetres	
	min	max
A—Diameter	3.2	4.8
B—Radius	152	nominal
C—Diameter	1.6	nominal
D		2
E	6	7
F—Diameter	0.8	nominal

Figure 14-4 Cleveland flash cup. (*ASTM D-92.*)

Test Procedure

The sample is heated in an area held at a temperature of 163 ± 1°C. The grams of the original sample is determined at room temperature to the nearest 0.01 g and recorded.

The sample is placed in one of the recesses of the circular rotating shelf. The sample is left in the oven at 163°C for 5 h.

At the end of 5 h, the sample is allowed to cool and grams of sample is again determined. The percentage loss on heating is computed. The penetration is determined as described in Sec. 14-2 and compared with the penetration value of the original sample.

Significance of the Test for Loss on Heating

If the properties of asphalt cement change significantly during the manufacture of asphaltic concrete, the properties of the resulting concrete may not be suitable. This may necessitate changes in the product or in manufacturing procedures. The test for loss of penetration on heating provides an indication of the behavior of asphalt cement during the manufacture of hot-mix asphaltic concrete.

14-6 SOLUBILITY OF ASPHALT CEMENT IN TRICHLOROETHYLENE

Purpose of the Solubility Test

By definition, a bituminous material is one that is soluble in carbon bisulfide. This is also true of trichloroethylene, which is used as a substitute because it is less dangerous to handle. The solubility test determines the percentage of insoluble impurities in asphalt cement.

Test Procedure

To a flask containing the sample 100 mL of trichloroethylene is added, and the flask is agitated until all lumps disappear and no asphalt adheres to the bottom. The flask is set aside for about 1 h in subdued light.

Gentle suction is applied to the filter flask equipment, and the contents of the flask are poured slowly into the gooch crucible. The flask is washed with successively smaller portions of trichloroethylene, followed by scrubbing with a rubber policeman and pouring the washings through the crucible. Washing is continued until all color is gone from the flask and until the walls of the crucible and the material passing through the crucible are clean.

After washing, the crucible is placed in the oven and dried at a temperature of 100 to 121°C for 20 min.

Computations

$$I = \frac{C - T}{S} 100 \qquad (14\text{-}1)$$

where I = insoluble residue, percent
C = insoluble residue plus crucible, g
T = crucible, g
S = original sample, g

Significance of Solubility Test

The solubility test is included in specifications in order to reject asphalt cements which contain insoluble impurities. The test is more important when natural asphalts are considered. As much as 20 percent insoluble impurities are found in natural asphalts.

The amount of insoluble impurities found in asphalt cement from a modern refinery is usually negligible.

B. ASPHALTIC CONCRETE

The manufacture of asphaltic concrete is complete after it has been mixed in a hot plant, spread on the road base, compacted, and allowed to cool. At this time the thickness of the pavement and the degree of compaction "density" can be checked. The grading of aggregates can be checked as discussed in Chap. 12. The percentage of asphalt cement in the mix can be checked by the "extraction test," and the relative stability can be measured.

14-7 BULK DENSITY

Purpose of the Density Test

The density (kg/m^3) is an important property of asphaltic concrete. With the density, the mix proportions, and specific gravity of the ingredients, the degree of compaction can be determined on a core taken from pavement of compacted asphaltic concrete or a sample of broken pavement.

Test Procedure

The mass of a sample of asphaltic concrete is determined to the nearest 0.01 kg. A container sufficiently large to completely immerse the sample is placed on a balance and filled with water. Kilograms of water is determined to nearest 0.01 kg.

This sample is suspended on a wire and immersed in the water. The sample should be completely covered with water without touching sides or bottom. The total kilograms with sample immersed is determined.

Computations

$$G = \frac{S}{W_s - W} \tag{14-2}$$

and

$$V = W_s - W \tag{14-3}$$

where G = bulk specific gravity of sample
S = sample, kg
W = water in container, kg
W_s = water plus force of immersed sample, kg
V = volume of specimen, dm^3

Density D is

$$D = G \times 1000 \text{ kg/m}^3 \tag{14-4}$$

14-8 QUANTITATIVE EXTRACTION OF BITUMEN FROM BITUMINOUS PAVING MIXTURES

Purpose of the Extraction Test

The percentage of asphalt cement in an asphaltic concrete mix is critical to the stability and durability of the concrete in service. By extracting and measuring the asphalt cement content it is possible to determine whether specifications have been complied with.

Test Procedure

The moisture content of the sample is first determined. The asphalt cement can be extracted from the asphaltic concrete by centrifuging after the asphalt cement is dissolved or by the recommended method of dripping condensed trichloroethylene over the sample of asphaltic concrete until the asphalt cement is removed.

When the extraction apparatus (Fig. 14-5) is assembled, the asphaltic concrete sample is placed in the cone with filter paper so that only dissolved asphalt cement passes through.

Into the glass jar is placed 500 mL of trichloroethylene, and then the frame with the supporting legs is put in the jar. The solvent level must be below the tip of the cone in this frame. The top frame is placed on the bottom frame so that the stub legs fit into the round holes in the top rim of the lower frame.

The loaded jar is placed on an electric hot plate with an asbestos pad. The jar is covered with a condenser, and a gentle steady flow of cold water is circulated through the condenser. The heat is adjusted so that the solvent boils gently and a steady flow of condensed solvent drips into the top cone. The extraction is continued until the solvent running from the tip of the lower cone appears a light straw color when viewed against a white background.

Computations

The percentage of bitumen in the sample is computed as follows:

$$B = \frac{W_1 - W_2}{W_1} 100 \tag{14-5}$$

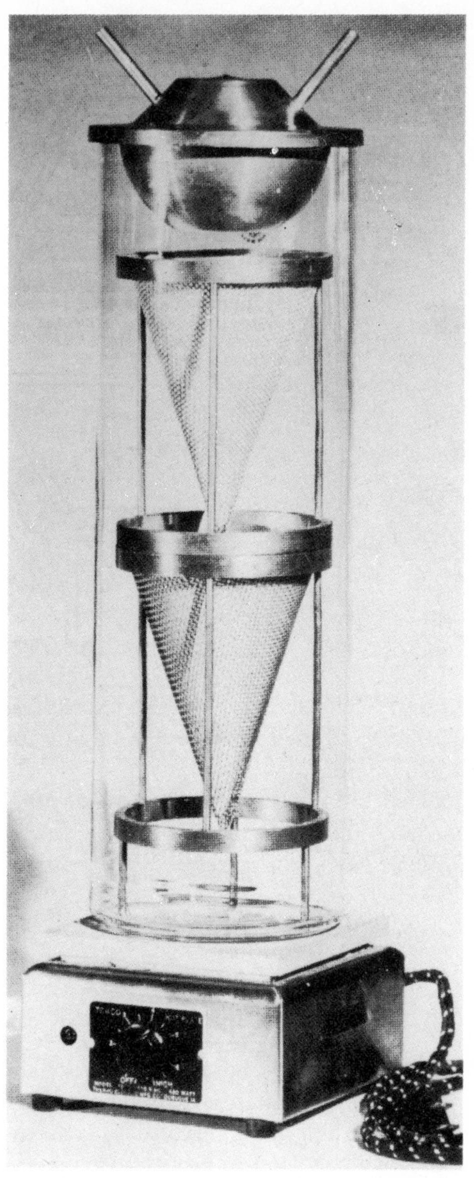

Figure 14-5 Extraction apparatus. (*ASTM D-2172.*)

where B = bitumen, percent
W_1 = asphaltic concrete sample, g
W_2 = insoluble aggregate and residue, g

Significance of the Extraction Test

The extraction test is one of the tests that can be used to evaluate asphaltic concrete after it is in place in a pavement. Cores taken from the pavement can be tested for stability and strength and then broken up, and the percentage of asphalt cement in the sample can then be determined. When this information is compared with the stability and asphalt content of laboratory trial mixes, valuable information is obtained regarding compliance with specifications and the correlation of field and laboratory samples.

14-9 COMPRESSIVE STRENGTH OF BITUMINOUS MIXTURES

Purpose of the Compressive-Strength Test

Although asphaltic concrete is not rigid and will deform under load, an indication of its stability and ability to carry loads can be measured by testing it in unconfined axial compression.

The simple strength test is for compacted bituminous mixtures of the hot-mixed, hot-laid type for use in pavement surfaces and base courses, and it provides a measure of the compressive strength of these paving mixtures.

Molding and Curing Test Specimens

The test specimens are usually cylinders 102 mm in diameter and 102 $\pm$ 2.5 mm in height.

When the molding pressure is first applied, the temperature of hot asphalt mixtures is 124 $\pm$ 2.8°C. As soon as the materials have been thoroughly mixed and have reached this temperature, approximately one-half of the mixture is placed in the molding cylinder. The cylinder, together with the top and bottom plunger, should be preheated in a water bath maintained at a temperature just under the boiling point. The molds and plungers should be wiped with a clean cloth that has a few drops of oil on it. With the bottom plunger in place and the molding cylinder supported temporarily on the two steel bars, the mixture is spaded vigorously 25 times with a heated spatula, with 15 of the blows being delivered around the inside of the mold to reduce honeycomb. The remaining half of the mixture is added to the molding cylinder, and the spading action is repeated. The mixture should be penetrated with the spatula as deeply as possible. The mixture is compressed between the top and bottom plungers, under an initial load of about 1 MPa, to set the mixture against the sides of the mold. The support bars are removed to permit full double-plunger action, and the entire molding load of 20.7 MPa is applied for 2 min. The specimen is then removed from the mold with an ejection device that provides a smooth, uniform rate of travel for the ejection head.

After removal from the mold, the specimens are oven-cured for 24 h at 60°C.

Test Procedures

The bulk specific gravity of the test specimens is determined, and they are brought to the test temperature, 25 ± 1°C, by being stored in an air bath for not less than 4 h.

The specimens are tested in axial compression without lateral support at a uniform rate of vertical deformation.

The compressive strength, in pounds per square inch, is determined by dividing the maximum vertical load obtained during deformation by the original cross-section area of the test specimen. Not less than three specimens should be prepared for each mixture, and the average of the three is reported as the compressive strength.

Significance of the Compressive-Strength Test for Asphaltic Concrete

The compressive-strength test for asphaltic concrete cannot be compared with the compressive strength of concrete since asphalt cement flows under load whereas portland cement paste fractures. The compressive-strength test is not an indication of stability since in confined compression such as a pavement the load is carried by intergranular pressure among the aggregate particles.

Testing asphaltic concrete in unconfined compression will give an indication of the strength and stiffness of the asphalt cement; as such, it is an indication of stability and another measure of the penetration grade of asphaltic cement.

14-10 RESISTANCE TO PLASTIC FLOW OF BITUMINOUS MIXTURES USING MARSHALL APPARATUS

Purpose of the Marshall Test

This method covers the measurement of the resistance to plastic flow of cylindrical specimens of bituminous paving mixture loaded on the lateral surface by means of the Marshall apparatus (Fig. 14-6). This method is for use with mixtures containing asphalt cement, asphalt cutback or tar, and aggregate up to 25.4-mm maximum size.

Figure 14-6 Marshall test apparatus. (Design and Construction of Asphalt Pavement, *McGraw-Hill, 1958.*)

Materials

Dry aggregates to constant weight at 105 to 110°C, and separate the aggregates by dry-sieving into the following size fractions:

1 to $\frac{3}{4}$ in (25.0 to 19.0 mm)
$\frac{3}{4}$ to $\frac{3}{8}$ in (19.0 to 9.5 mm)
$\frac{3}{8}$ in to no. 4 (915 to 4.75 mm)
No. 4 to no. 8 (4.75 to 2.36 mm)
Passing no. 8 (2.36 mm)

The temperatures to which the asphalt cement must be heated to produce a viscosity of 170 ± 20 cSt will be the mixing temperature. The temperature to which asphalt cement must be heated to produce a viscosity of 280 ± 20 cSt will be the compacting temperature.

Preparation of Mixtures

Aggregates are heated to approximately the mixing temperature of asphalt cement and mixed in. A crater is formed in the dry, blended aggregate, and the preheated required amount of asphalt cement is poured into the mixture. The aggregates and asphalt are mixed rapidly until the aggregates are thoroughly coated.

Compaction of Specimens

The entire batch of asphaltic concrete is placed in a preheated mold. The mixture is then vigorously spaded with a heated spatula or trowel 15 times around the perimeter and 10 times over the interior. The mold assembly is placed on the compaction pedestal, and 50 blows with the compaction hammer is applied with a free fall of 457.2 mm. The specimen is reversed top to bottom, and the same number of compaction blows is applied to the face of the reversed specimen. After the sample is extracted, it is allowed to stand overnight at room temperature after which it is weighed, measured, and tested.

Test Procedure

The asphaltic concrete specimens are brought to the specified temperature by being immersed in the water bath 30 to 40 min or placed in the oven for 2 h at 60 ± 1.0°C. The testing-head temperature should be maintained between 21.1 and 37.8°C. The test specimens are placed in the lower segment of the breaking head. The upper segment of the breaking head is placed on the specimen, and the complete assembly is placed in position on the testing machine.

The load is applied to the specimen by means of the constant rate of movement of the testing-machine head at 50.8 mm/min until the maximum load is reached and the load decreases as indicated by the dial. The maximum load is noted on the testing machine. The dial reading is noted at the instant the maximum load begins to decrease, and the indicated flow value is noted.

Significance of the Marshall Test

In order for a flexible asphaltic concrete pavement to perform properly, it must be stable under loading. This stability is achieved in pavement design by compacting the pavement so that the aggregates distribute the load by point-to-point contact. The Marshall test and other tests for stability measure directly the performance of the asphaltic concrete under load. The performance of the pavement in service can thus be predicted.

QUESTIONS AND PROBLEMS

1 What is the most important test made with asphalt cement?

2 Why is ductility important in asphalt cement?

3 What penetration grade would you specify for pavements in southern Arizona?

4 Is the flash-point test used to control fire hazards in a hot plant?

5 Do many modern asphalt cements fail the solubility test?

6 Why is bulk density important in testing asphaltic concrete?

7 The extraction test is used to determine the percent of asphalt cement in asphaltic concrete. Isn't this already known from the mix proportions?

8 Does the compressive-strength test indicate the stability of asphaltic concrete pavements?

9 How does the Marshall test differ from the compressive-strength test?

10 Is the Marshall test the only test used to measure the stability of asphaltic concrete?

CHAPTER

FIFTEEN

TESTING AND EVALUATION OF METALS

Many of the basic materials of modern society are made from metals and metal alloys. Steel is the most common alloy, and it has thousands of uses. Testing and evaluation of the many various metals require hundreds of tests and specifications. The ASTM book of standards has 10 parts (volumes) dealing with various metals. Part 4 covers various steel products.

Since this text is primarily interested in structural materials, Chap. 15 is limited to tests and evaluation of the structural and mechanical properties of metals. Structural steel and reinforcing steel are the common forms of metals used in construction with smaller amounts of other metals and alloys.

Although ASTM lists many tests covering various metals and metallic products, the most common mechanical tests are listed in ASTM A-370 as follows:

- E-8 Tension testing of metallic materials
- A-15 Bend test of metallic materials
- E-10 Test for Brinell hardness of metallic materials
- E-18 Tests for Rockwell hardness and Rockwell superficial hardness of metallic materials
- E-23 Notched-bar impact testing of metallic materials
- E-110 Test for indentation hardness of metallic materials by portable hardness testers

15-1 TENSION TEST

Purpose

The tension test is the most important test for determining the structural and mechanical properties of metals. From this test the tensile strength, yield strength, modulus of elasticity, Poisson's ratio, ductility characteristics, and other properties can be determined.

Test Procedures

The tension test is performed by gripping the opposite ends of a test specimen and pulling it apart. Standard ASTM test specimens (Fig. 15-1) can be sheared,

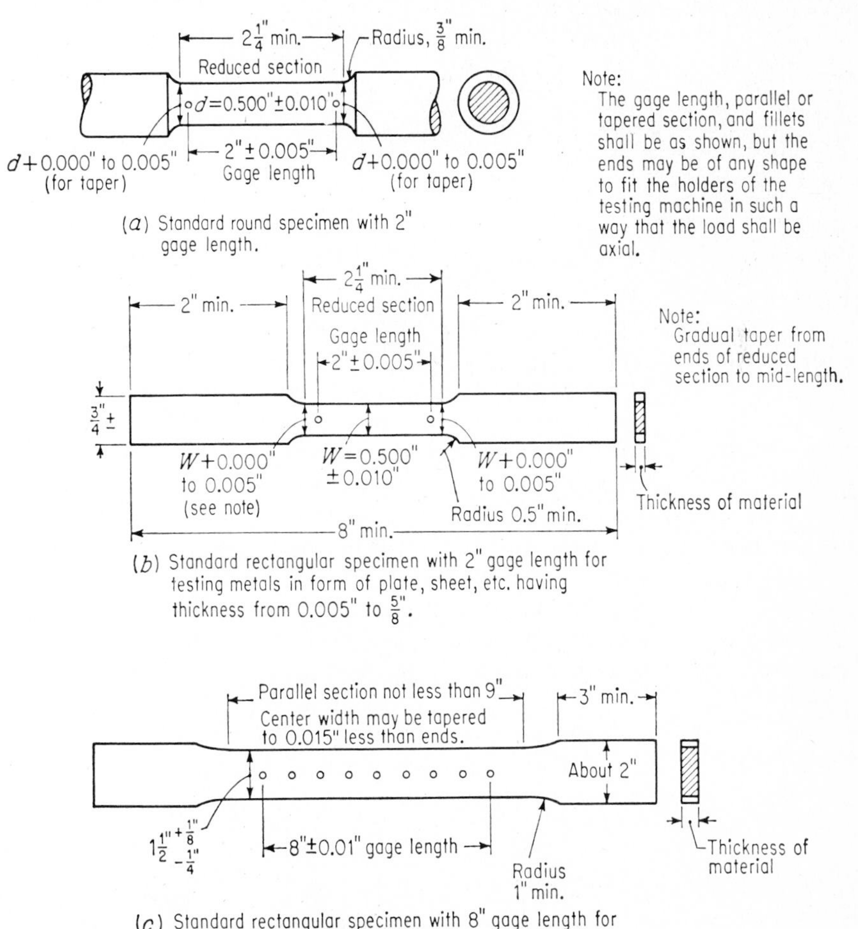

Figure 15-1 ASTM standardized forms of (ductile) metal tension—test specimen. (*ASTM E-8.*)

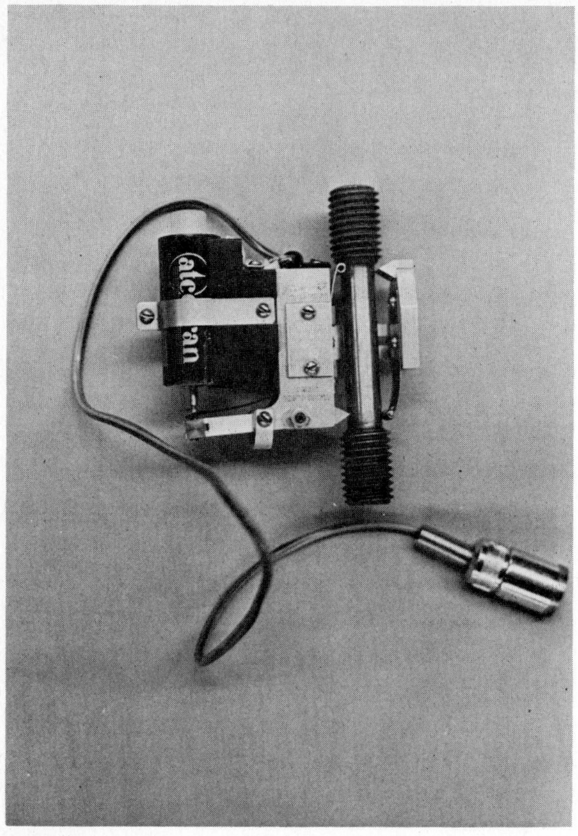

Figure 15-2 Electronic strain gauge for tension test.

blanked, sawed, trepanned, or oxygen-cut from the material being tested. Care should be taken to remove by machining all distorted, cold-worked, or heat-affected areas. A short section of reinforcing steel, machined to standard size, provides a good test specimen. Test specimens are usually machined to reduce the cross section at midlength and to localize the zone of fracture (Fig. 15-1). The specimen should be gauge marked in order to determine elongation.

The rate of loading metal specimens is not critical, but should not exceed 690 MPa/min. Modern testing machines are equipped with electronic strain gauges (Fig. 15-2). When this gauge is fastened to the tension specimen, a load-strain diagram is plotted automatically as the load is applied. Stress-strain diagrams can also be plotted by measuring the strain as the load is applied (Fig. 15-3).

Significance of the Tension Test

Different types of fractures are produced in the tension test with different metals (Fig. 15-4). Mild steel, for example, has a ductile cup-cone type of fracture, wrought iron has a ragged fibrous fracture, and cast iron usually shows a flat

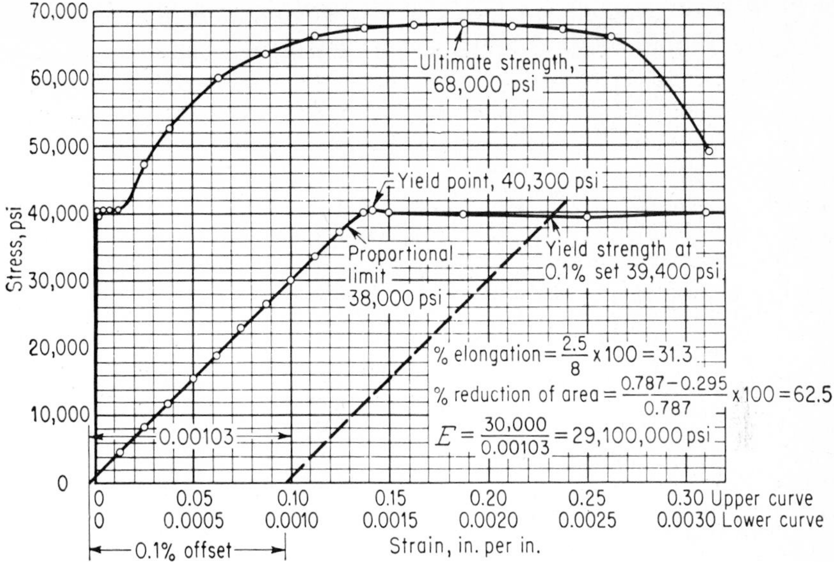

Figure 15-3 Typical stress-strain chart for mild steel. (*ASTM E-8.*)

granular fracture. The type of fracture may also indicate nonuniformity and imperfections in the metal.

Tensile strength The tensile strength of metals is the ultimate stress, before failure, based on the original cross-sectional area of the specimen (Fig. 15-3). The strength increases and reaches a maximum in mild steel, after extensive elongation and necking. Working stresses in design cannot be based on ultimate strength, because excessive strain cannot be permitted. Creep in metals in tension is not usually a consideration in design and becomes important only at elevated temperatures.

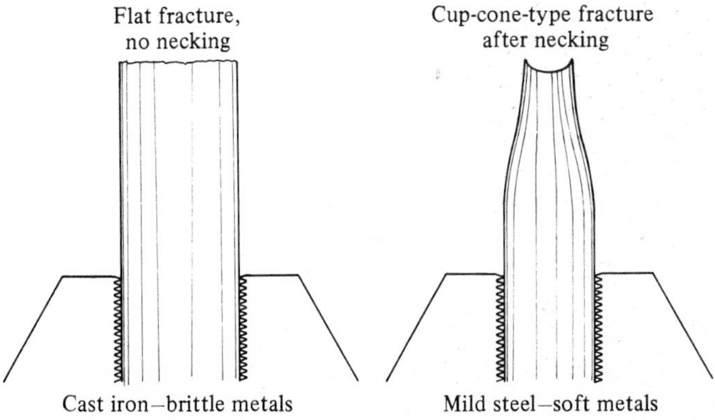

Figure 15-4 Typical tensile fractures of metals. (*ASTM E-8.*)

Ductility Ductility is the ability of a material to deform in the inelastic or plastic range. This property is important in steel design and is particularly important in the design of reinforced concrete. The ratio of deformation at failure to deformation at yield is called the ductility ratio.

Yield point The yield point is the first load at which an increase in strain occurs without an increase in stress. This is characterized by a sharp knee in the stress-strain curve for mild steel (Fig. 15-3). Most metals do not have a yield point, and the offset method of determining yield strength is employed. The yield point is not used directly in design except for materials which may exhibit unique characteristics in the stress-strain relationship.

Proportional limit Metals are elastic until the proportional limit is reached; i.e., the stress is no longer proportional to strain. The proportional limit has significance in the elastic stability of columns and shells, since it indicates the point where the material changes from an elastic material to an inelastic material (Fig. 15-3).

Yield strength The yield strength is usually measured at some offset in strain on the stress-strain curve (Fig. 15-3).

Working stresses used in design are usually some factor of the yield strength. The ultimate strength of the specimen is important in plastic design, but working stresses must be below the yield strength to avoid excessive and possibly permanent deformation of structural members. In consideration of plastic deformation, the yield–ultimate strength ratio is important.

Modulus of elasticity The modulus of elasticity (Young's modulus) is the ratio of unit stress to unit strain in the elastic range of stress-strain curve:

$$E = \frac{\text{stress, psi}}{\text{strain, in/in}} \tag{15.1}$$

or in SI units,

$$E = \frac{\text{MPa}}{\text{cm/cm}} \tag{15.2}$$

The modulus of elasticity is particularly important in design, since it is proportional to the deflection of structural members under load.

Elongation Elongation is the total strain at failure and is a measure of the ductility of the metal.

Modulus of resilience The area under the stress-strain curve up the proportional limit is called the modulus of resilience. This indicates the capacity of a material to absorb energy without permanent deformation.

Modulus of toughness The area under the entire stress-strain curve is called the modulus of toughness and indicates the capacity of a material to absorb energy without fracture.

15-2 THE BEND TEST

Purpose

The bend test is a simple method of measuring ductility. The test is primarily qualitative and is used only in proof testing. The measure of failure is the development of cracks and the angle at which they develop. The test is useful in testing reinforcing steel and the ductility of welds, and it serves as a specification requirement for rods, steel plate, and structural steel.

Test Procedure

The bend test consists of sharply bending the test specimen through a large angle and noting the development of cracks (Fig. 15-5). The severity of the test is varied by using pins of different diameter.

The "nick-bend" test is made by nicking the specimen with a cold chisel or hacksaw, then clamping it in a vise and bending it with a hammer.

Significance of the Bend Test

The bend test is a rather crude measure of ductility. Reinforcing steel, for example, must be able to stand severe cold bending without loss of strength. The test is also useful in eliminating brittle steels. Brittle steels or steels with coarse crystalline structure or internal defects will fracture rather than bend.

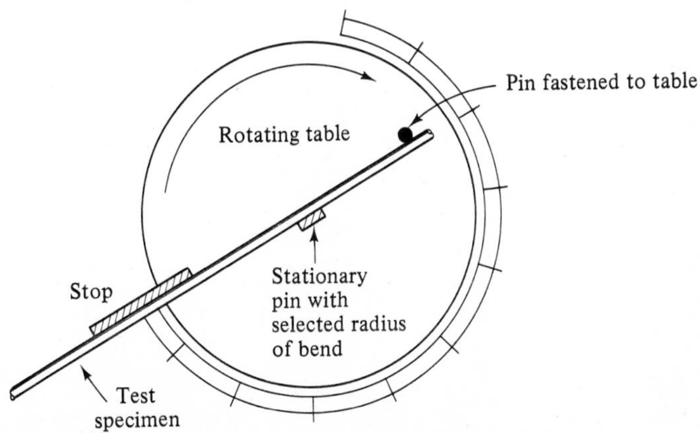

Figure 15-5 Diagram of cold bend test. (*ASTM A-15.*)

15-3 HARDNESS TESTS

Purpose

Hardness tests have a wide field of application. This is not because hardness of a material can be utilized directly in design or analysis, but because the hardness, in ferrous metals, can be correlated with tensile strength and other properties. For workers with previous experience, hardness tests provide a quick, simple means of checking the following:

1. Uniformity of steel in structural members
2. Effectiveness and uniformity of heat treatment
3. Quality level of materials
4. Need for more complete tests
5. Tensile strength

Hardness tests for metals determine resistance to penetration. There are several methods of determining hardness; the most common are Brinell and Rockwell tests.

The Brinell Test Procedure

A specified load is applied to a flat surface of the specimen to be tested, through a hard ball of specified diameter (Fig. 15-6). The average diameter of the indentation is used as a basis for calculation of the Brinell hardness number. The quotient of the applied load divided by the area of the surface of the indentation, which is assumed to be spherical, is termed the "Brinell hardness number" (HB) in accordance with the following equation:

$$HB = \frac{P}{(\pi D/2)(D - D^2 - d^2)} \tag{15-3}$$

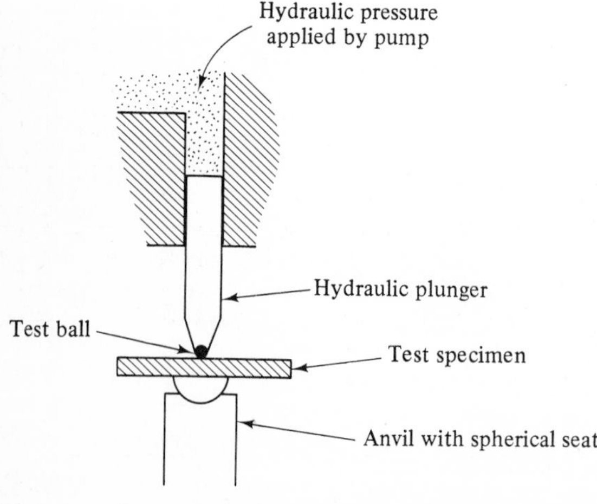

Figure 15-6 Features of a hydraulic-type Brinell machine. (*ASTM E-10.*)

Table 15-1 Approximate relation of Brinell and Rockwell hardness numbers to tensile strength

Brinell indentation diameter, mm	Brinell hardness number: Standard ball	Brinell hardness number: Tungsten carbide ball	Rockwell hardness number: B scale	Rockwell hardness number: C scale	Rockwell superficial hardness number, superficial diamond penetrator: 15-N scale	30-N scale	45-N scale	Tensile strength (approximate), MPa
2.50		601		57.3	89.0	75.1	63.5	2262
2.60		555		54.7	87.8	72.7	60.6	2055
2.70		514		52.1	86.5	70.3	47.6	1890
2.80		477		49.5	85.3	68.2	54.5	1738
2.90		444		47.1	84.0	65.8	51.5	1586
3.00	415	415		44.5	82.8	63.5	48.4	1462
3.10	388	388		41.8	81.4	61.1	45.3	1331
3.20	363	363		39.1	80.0	58.7	42.0	1220
3.30	341	341		36.6	78.6	56.4	39.1	1131
3.40	321	321		34.3	77.3	54.3	36.4	1055
3.50	302	302		32.1	76.1	52.2	33.8	1007
3.60	285	285		29.9	75.0	50.3	31.2	952
3.70	269	269		27.6	73.7	48.3	28.5	897
3.80	255	255		25.4	72.5	46.2	26.0	855
3.90	241	241	100.0	22.8	70.9	43.9	22.8	800
4.00	229	229	98.2	20.5	69.7	41.9	20.1	766
4.10	217	217	96.4					710
4.20	207	207	94.6					682
4.30	197	197	92.8					648
4.40	187	187	90.7					621
4.50	179	179	89.0					607
4.60	170	170	86.8					579
4.70	163	163	85.0					566
4.80	156	156	82.9					552
4.90	149	149	80.8					503
5.00	143	143	78.7					490
5.10	137	137	76.4					462
5.20	131	131	74.0					448
5.30	126	126	72.0					434
5.40	121	121	69.0					414
5.50	116	116	67.6					400
5.60	111	111	65.7					386

Note: This table gives the approximate relationship of Brinell and Rockwell hardness values and corresponding approximate tensile strengths of steel. It is possible that steels of various compositions and processing histories will deviate in hardness–tensile strength relationship from the data presented in this table. The data in this table do not represent a conversion from hardness to approximate tensile strength for the austenitic, ferritic, or martensitic stainless steels. Where more precise conversions are required, they should be developed specially for each steel composition, heat treatment, and part.

where HB = Brinell hardness number
P = applied load, kg
D = diameter of steel ball, mm
d = average diameter of indentation, mm

The Brinell hardness number is conveniently secured from standard tables (Table 15-1), which show numbers corresponding to the various indentation diameters.

The standard Brinell test using a 10-mm ball employs a 3000-kg load for hard materials and a 1500- or 500-kg load for thin sections or soft materials. Other loads and different-size indenters may be used when specified. In reporting hardness values, the diameter of the ball and the load must be stated except when a 10-mm ball and 3000-kg load are used.

Brinell hardness may be required when tensile properties are not specified. When agreed upon, hardness tests can be substituted for tension tests in order to expedite testing of a large number of duplicate pieces from the same lot.

Portable Testers

Under certain circumstances, it may be desirable to substitute a portable Brinell testing instrument, which is calibrated to give results equivalent to those of a standard Brinell machine. Correlation is made on a comparison test bar of approximately the same hardness as the material to be tested.

The Rockwell Test Procedure

In the Rockwell test a hardness value is obtained by using a direct-reading testing machine which measures hardness by determining the depth of penetration of a diamond point or a steel ball into the specimen under certain arbitrarily fixed conditions (Fig. 15-7). A minor load of 10 N is first applied, which causes an initial penetration, sets the penetrator on the material, and holds it in position. A major load which depends on the scale being used is applied, increasing the depth of indentation. The major load is removed; with the minor load still acting, the Rockwell number, which is proportional to the difference in penetration between the major load, is read directly on the dial gauge. This is an arbitrary number

Table 15-2 Load scales for Rockwell hardness test

Scale symbol	Penetrator	Major load, N	Minor load, N
B	1.6-mm steel ball	100	10
C	Diamond brale	150	10

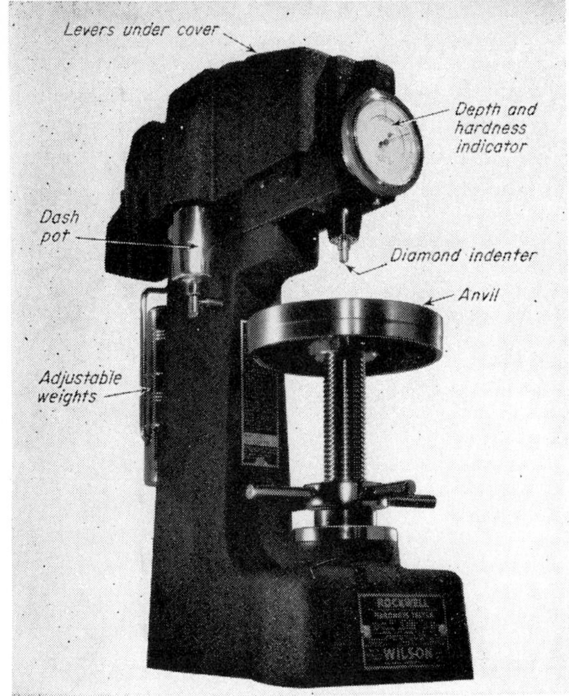

Figure 15-7 Rockwell hardness tester. (*ASTM E-18.*)

which increases with increasing hardness. The scales most frequently used are shown in Table 15-2.

Rockwell superficial hardness machines are used for the testing of very thin shell or thin surface layers. Loads of 15, 30, or 45 N are applied on a hardened steel ball or diamond penetrator, to cover the same range of hardness values as for the heavier loads. See Table 15-3.

Table 15-3 Superficial hardness scales

Scale symbol	Penetrator	Major load, N	Minor load, N
15T	1.6-mm steel ball	15	3
30T	1.6-mm steel ball	30	3
45T	1.6-mm steel ball	45	3
15N	Diamond brale	15	3
30N	Diamond brale	30	3
45N	Diamond brale	45	3

Significance of Hardness Tests

The basis for most hardness tests for metals is resistance to indentation of a variety of instruments. Because of their simplicity and the fact that hardness tests are nondestructive and require relatively little experience, they are one of the most important quality-control tests for metals. By correlation, tensile-strength tests and, after experience in their variability and limitations, hardness tests can be used as a rapid estimate of tensile strength.

15-4 IMPACT TESTS

Purpose of Impact Tests

Impact tests are useful in measuring the toughness of metals. Toughness depends primarily on the strength and ductility of a metal. Tests for strength and ductility do not take into consideration the rate at which energy is absorbed, however, which may influence the behavior of a metal. A different measure of toughness may be obtained from impact loading than from static loading and adds another measure of metal behavior. In steel production, minimum impact requirements are generally specified only for quenched and tempered normalized and tempered or normalized materials.

Test Procedures

Probably the most common impact tests are the Charpy and the Izod tests. These tests are similar and are based on a swinging pendulum in which a moving mass has sufficient kinetic energy to rupture a specimen in its path. In the Charpy test, the specimen is supported on both ends and the specimen fractures because of simple beam flexure. In the Izod test, the specimen is held securely on one end and failure occurs because of cantilever bending. Figure 15-8 shows a Charpy impact machine, and Fig. 15-9 shows various types of specimens.

The specimen, which is usually $10 \times 10 \times 55$ mm, is placed horizontally between the two anvils. The pendulum is raised to its topmost position and then released. As the pendulum falls, it ruptures the specimen, and then continues on an upward swing, depending on the toughness of the specimen. In its upward swing, the pendulum carries a friction pointer which measures the angle of rise.

The energy used in rupturing the specimen may be computed from Fig. 15-10 as follows:

$$\text{Initial energy} = WR(1 - \cos A) \qquad (15\text{-}4)$$

$$\text{Energy after rupture} = WR(1 - \cos B) \qquad (15\text{-}5)$$

$$\text{Energy to rupture specimen} = W(H - H') = WR(\cos B - \cos A) \qquad (15\text{-}6)$$

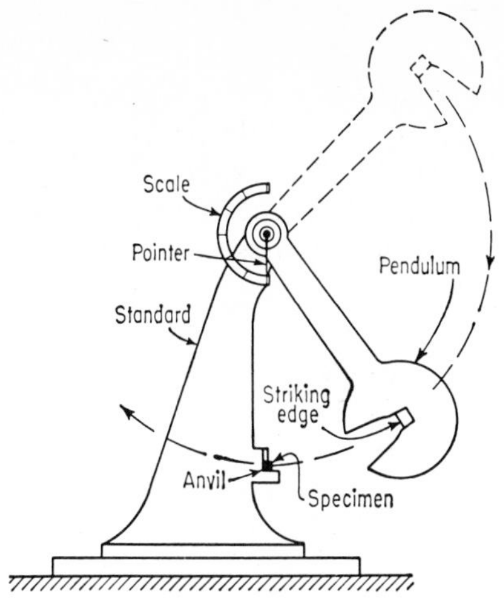

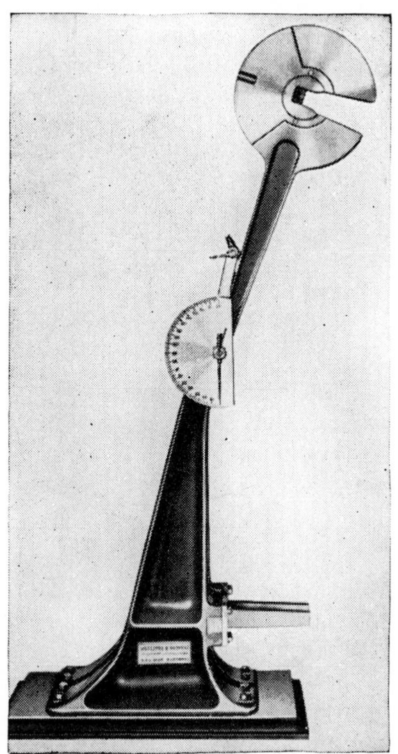

Figure 15-8 Charpy impact machine. (*ASTM E-23.*)

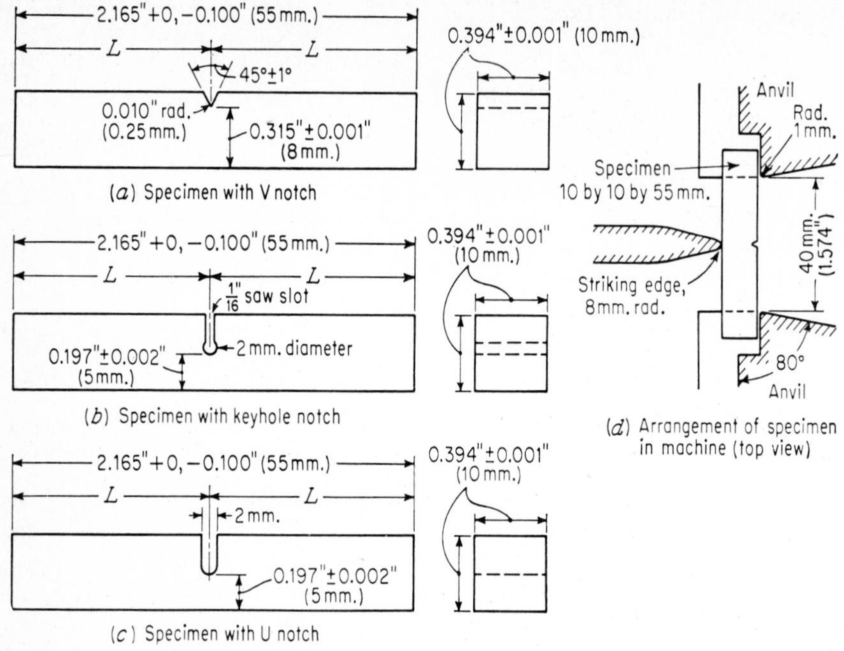

Figure 15-9 Various types of Charpy impact machine specimens. (*ASTM E-23.*)

where W = weight of pendulum
H = height of fall of center of gravity of pendulum
H' = height of rise of center of gravity of pendulum
A = angle of fall
B = angle of rise
R = distance from center of gravity of pendulum to axis of rotation

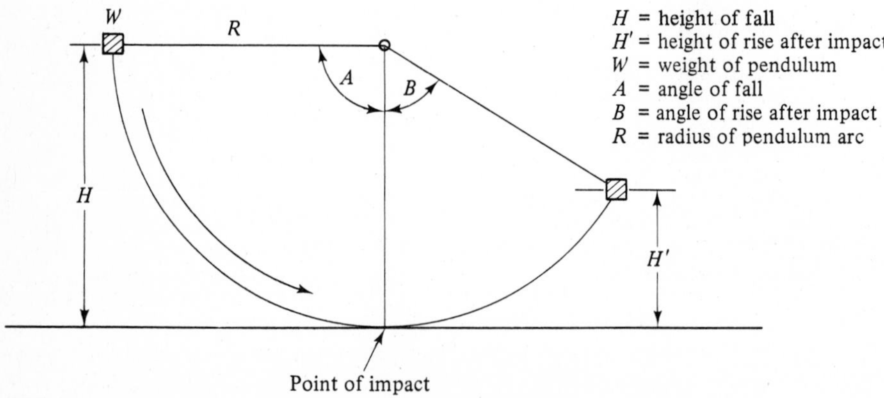

Figure 15-10 Space relations for pendulum machine.

Significance of Impact Tests

The impact tests are not intended to simulate shock loading in service, but are used to indicate differences in metals that are not indicated by other tests. The tests are particularly sensitive to variations in the structure of the metal caused by the following:

1. Heat treatment
2. Compositions that cause brittleness
3. Sulfur and phosphorus content
4. Various alloys

Although there is no direct correlation between impact tests and shock loading in service, these tests could supply additional information regarding failure of structural members during earthquakes, floods, tornadoes, and other disasters.

QUESTIONS AND PROBLEMS

1 What is the most important test used to evaluate metals? Why?

2 Steel is an elastic material. At what point in the tension test does steel become inelastic?

3 What is the difference between the yield point and the yield strength of steel?

4 Why is the bend test important?

5 Why are the hardness tests important, since hardness is not usually a basic property of design?

6 List some of the items which can be checked with hardness tests.

7 What property of metals does the impact test measure?

8 Explain how the energy required to rupture a specimen can be measured with a Charpy impact machine.

9 Explain the difference between modulus of resilience and modulus of toughness.

10 Name the properties of mild steel that can be evaluated from the stress-strain diagram.

11 What causes the strength of metals to increase after they reach the inelastic range?

12 Why is the yield strength determined by the offset method?

13 What is the difference in the type of tensile fracture you might expect in cast iron and mild steel?

14 How can the bend test be used in the evaluation of metals?

15 What tests will measure brittleness in metals?

CHAPTER
SIXTEEN
TESTING AND EVALUATION OF WOOD

The great variety of species, the variability of the material, the continually changing conditions of supply, and many other factors affecting test results all combine to make the technique of testing wood unique in its complexity.

Because many thousands of tests are made under a single comprehensive plan by the U.S. Forest Service, the Forest Products Laboratories of Canada, and other similar organizations, naturally the test methods conform closely to those used by these institutions. Standard test methods are the outgrowth of a study of both American and European experience and methods. Their general adoption will tend toward a worldwide unification of results.

The difficulty in obtaining samples which are representative and the complex nature of the tests themselves preclude the practicability of performing useful tests for construction control in small laboratories.

16-1 TYPES OF COMMON TESTS FOR WOOD†

Small, Clear Specimens

ASTM D-143 outlines a comprehensive testing program for small, clear specimens of timber which includes collection, selection, preparation, and testing of samples. The following mechanical tests are listed in this standard:

Static bending
Compression parallel to grain

† There are many standard tests covering wood, wood products, and related materials in Part 22 of ASTM. Only tests covering some mechanical properties of wood are included in this chapter.

Impact bending
Toughness
Compression perpendicular to grain
Hardness
Shear parallel to grain
Cleavage
Tension parallel to grain
Tension perpendicular to grain
Nail withdrawal
Specific gravity and shrinkage in volume
Radial and tangential shrinkage
Moisture determination

Static Tests of Timbers in Structural Sizes

ASTM standard D-198 includes five static tests used to evaluate structural sizes of timber made of solid or laminated wood:

Flexure
Compression parallel to grain (short column, no lateral support, $l/r < 17$)
Compression parallel to grain (crushing strength of laterally supported long member, effective $l'/r < 17$)
Tension parallel to grain
Torsion

16-2 PURPOSE OF TESTS MADE ON WOOD

Small, Clear Specimens

Tests made on small, clear specimens will provide the following data:

1. Data for comparing mechanical properties of various species
2. Data for establishment of correct strength functions which, in conjunction with timbers in structural sizes, afford the basis for fixing allowable stresses
3. Data used in determining the influence on mechanical properties of such factors as density, locality of growth, position in cross section, height of timber in the tree, change of properties with seasoning, change from sapwood to heartwood and changes in moisture content.

Structural Sizes of Timber

Tests made with structural sizes will provide the following:

1. Data for use in development of grading rules and specifications
2. Data for use in development of working stresses for structural members

3. Data on the influence of imperfections on the mechanical properties of structural sizes
4. Data on strength properties of different species or grades of various structural sizes
5. Data for use in checking existing formulas or hypotheses relating to structural behavior of beams
6. Data on the effects of chemical or environmental conditions on the mechanical properties
7. Data on effects of fabrication variables such as depth, taper, notches, and type of end joint in laminations
8. Data on relationships between mechanical and physical properties

Student Tests

Tests used for student laboratory instruction should include several common tests made with small, clear specimens, which demonstrate the mechanical properties of wood. Although the practicing engineer or architect will not use tests on wood to check conformance with specifications, the student will better understand the performance and properties of wood after conducting laboratory tests. The following tests are important in establishing the mechanical properties of wood.

16-3 TENSION PARALLEL TO THE GRAIN

The tensile strength parallel to the grain is much greater than that perpendicular to the grain, because of the difference between the strength within the annular rings and between annular rings.

Test Procedure

It is difficult to grip wood specimens for tension tests. Failure may occur under the grips before failure in tension. For this reason, tension specimens are slender in the gauge area in comparison to the gripping area (Fig. 16-1). It is important that the specimen is made so that the annular rings are perpendicular to the cross-sectional dimension.

The specimen is loaded continuously at a rate of 1 mm/min. After failure the type of failure is sketched and a specimen 7.5 cm in length is weighed and dried to constant weight to measure the moisture content.

Significance of Tension Test Parallel to the Grain

Wood is strong in tension parallel to the grain and serves well as tension members in construction. The greatest difficulty in the use of wood is designing

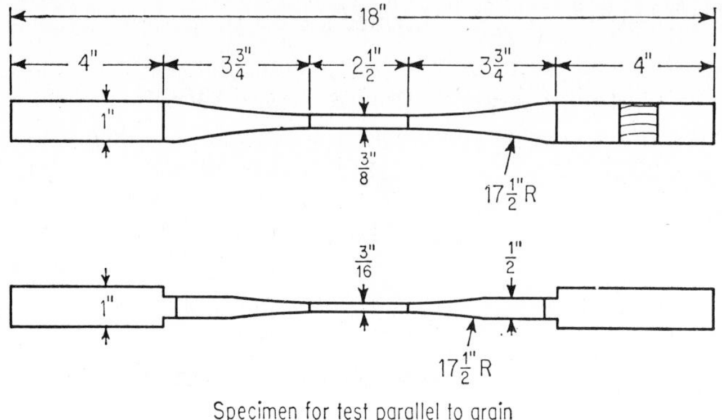

Figure 16-1 ASTM standard tension-test specimens for wood. (*ASTM D-143.*)

connections which will develop the full tensile strength of wood, both in testing and in practice, since the speed of testing and the moisture content have significant influence on the results of most tests for wood. It is important that these be carefully controlled.

16-4 TENSION PERPENDICULAR TO THE GRAIN

The tensile strength of wood perpendicular to the grain is low in comparison to that parallel to the grain, since the annular rings are simply being pulled apart.

Test Procedure

The 2 × 2 in specimen shown in Fig. 16-1 is fastened in appropriate grips.

The load is applied continuously throughout the test at a rate of motion of the crosshead of 2.5 mm/min. The maximum load only is recorded. The failure is sketched on the data sheet.

One of the pieces remaining after failure is used as a moisture specimen.

Significance of Tension Perpendicular to the Grain

This test is optional in ASTM C-143 and has little significance in design. Tension stresses would never be applied perpendicular to the grain except in unusual circumstances. The test does demonstrate the weakness of wood in tension between the annular rings and could indicate what might be expected in resistance to horizontal shear in bending.

16-5 STATIC BENDING

Test Procedure

The static bending tests are made on 5 × 5 × 76 cm specimens. Center loading and a span length of 70 cm is used. Both supporting knife edges are provided with bearing plates and rollers of such thickness that the distance from the point of support to the central plane is not greater than the depth of the specimen (Fig. 16-2). The knife edges are adjustable laterally to permit adjustment for slight twist or warp in the specimen. Alternatively, the method of supporting the specimen in trunnion-type supports that are free to move in a horizontal direction may be employed.

The specimen is placed so that the load is applied through the bearing block to the tangential (flat-sawed) surface nearest the pith.

The load is applied continuously throughout the test at a rate of motion of the movable crosshead of 2.5 mm/min. After failure the moisture content is determined with a 2.5-cm specimen cut from near the failure.

Load-Deflection Curves

Load-deflection curves are usually taken beyond the maximum load for all static bending tests. In at least one-third of the tests, the curves should be continued to a 15-cm deflection, or until the specimen fails to support a load of 90 kg.

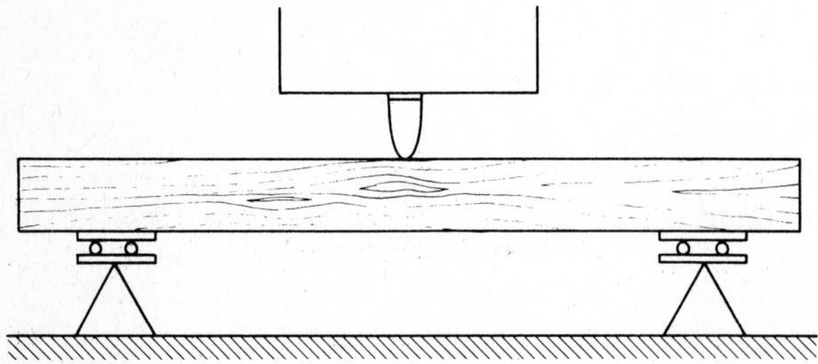

Figure 16-2 Loading and supporting devices for beam tests. (*ASTM*.)

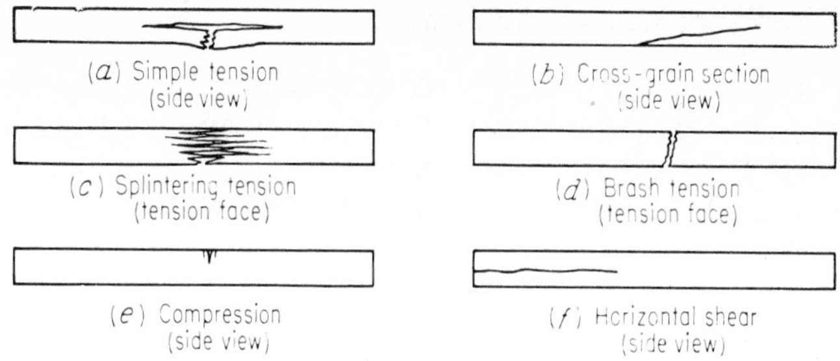

Figure 16-3 Various modes of failure in wood beams. (*ASTM D-143*.)

Description of Static Bending Failures

Static bending (flexural) failures are classified according to the appearance of the fractured surface and the manner in which the failure develops (Fig. 16-3). The fractured surfaces may be roughly divided into "brash" and "fibrous," the term "brash" indicating abrupt failure and "fibrous" indicating a fracture showing splinters.

Significance of Static Bending Tests

Large wood beams usually have some defects such as checks and knots, whereas specimens are made of clear, straight-grained wood. The possible variations in defects which may occur make it impossible to assign values for the actual strength of wood based on tests of small wood specimens. Correlation with tests made on structural-size timbers is necessary.

The bending test is one of the important tests made with wood, since wood is often used for beams.

16-6 COMPRESSION PARALLEL TO THE GRAIN

Test Procedure

The compression-parallel-to-grain tests are made on 5 × 5 × 20 cm specimens. The actual cross-sectional dimensions and the length are measured.

Special care must be taken in preparing the compression-parallel-to-grain test specimens to ensure that the end grain surfaces will be parallel to one another and at right angles to the longitudinal axis. If deemed necessary, at least one platen of the testing machine should be equipped with a spherical bearing to obtain uniform distribution of load over the ends of the specimen. The load is applied continuously throughout the test at a rate of motion of the movable crosshead of 0.003 cm/cm of specimen length per minute.

Load-Compression Curves

Load-compression curves are taken over a central gauge length not exceeding 15 cm and preferably on all the specimens. Load-compression readings are continued until the proportional limit is well passed, as indicated by the curve.

Deformations are read to 0.002 mm.

Position of Test Failures

In order to obtain satisfactory and uniform results, it is necessary that the failures be made to develop in the body of the specimen. With specimens of uniform cross section, this result can best be obtained when the ends are at a very slightly lower moisture content than the body. With green material it will usually suffice to close-pile the specimens, cover the body with a damp or wet cloth, and expose the ends for a short time. For air-dry material, it may sometimes be advisable to pile the specimens in a similar manner and place them in a desiccator, should the failures in test indicate that a slight end-drying is necessary.

Description of Compression Failures

Compression failures are classified according to the appearance of the fractured surface (Fig. 16-4). In case two or more kinds of failures develop, they are described in the order of their occurrence, thus shearing followed by splitting. The failure is also sketched in its proper position on the data sheet.

Weight and Moisture Content

The specimen is weighed immediately before test. After the test a moisture section approximately 2.5 cm in length is cut from the body near the failure. This specimen is dried to constant weight and the percent moisture computed.

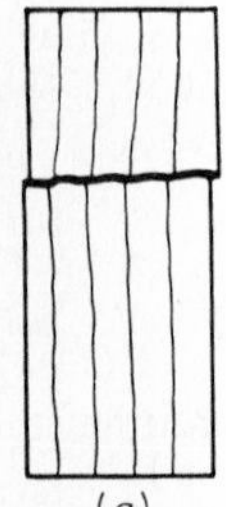

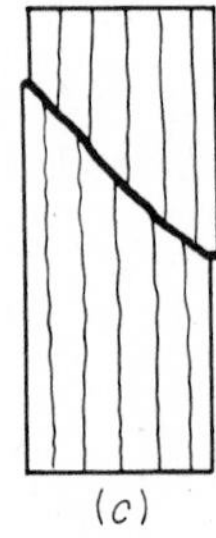

(*a*) Crushing (plane of rupture approximately horizontal).
(*b*) Wedge split (note direction of split: radial or tangential).
(*c*) Shearing (plane of rupture at acute angle with horizontal).
(*d*) Splitting.
(*e*) Shearing and splitting parallel to grain. (Usually occurs in cross-grained pieces).

Figure 16-4 Types of failure in wood under compression parallel to the grain. (*ASTM D-143.*)

Ring and Summer Wood Measurement

When practicable, the number of rings per centimeter and the proportion of summer wood are measured over a representative centimeter of cross section of the test specimen. In determining the proportion of summer wood, it is essential that the end surface be prepared so as to permit accurate summer wood measurement. When the fibers are broomed over at the ends from sawing, a light sanding, planing, or similar treatment of the ends is recommended.

Significance of Compression Tests Parallel to the Grain

The type of failure of wood under compression parallel to the grain is unique. Wood is composed of cells, formed by organic growth, which align themselves to form columns in the direction of the grain. The elastic limit is relatively low, there is no definite yield point, and considerable set takes place before failure. Rupture often occurs because of collapse of the tubular columns.

16-7 COMPRESSION PERPENDICULAR TO THE GRAIN

Test Procedure

The test is made with a 5 × 5 × 15 cm specimen. The load is applied through a metal bearing plate 5 cm wide placed at equal distances from the ends and at right angles to the length (Fig. 16-5). The load should be applied through a radial (quarter-sawed) surface.

The rate of loading of a movable crosshead should be 0.3 mm/min. After failure, a 2.5-cm specimen for testing the moisture content is cut from a section adjacent to the part under load.

Significance of Compression Test Perpendicular to the Grain

This test is useful in measuring the resistance to crushing of wooden beams at the supports or in locations where heavy loads are applied. The compression

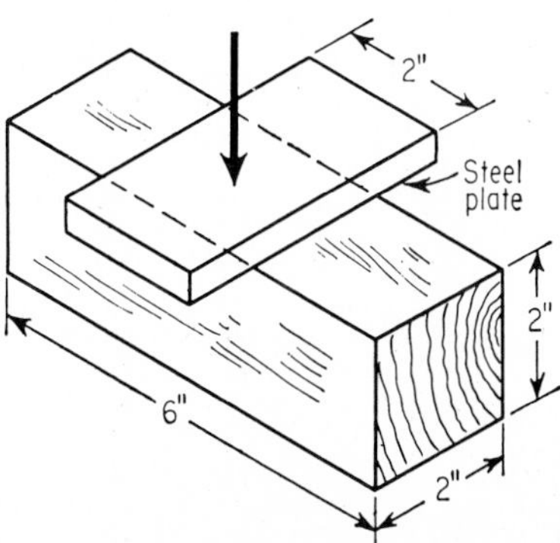

Figure 16-5 Method of compression test for wood perpendicular to the grain. (*ASTM D-143.*)

perpendicular to the grain is lower than when the stress is parallel to the grain, since the load causes lateral collapse of the columner tubes or fibers. Failure occurs due to crushing.

16-8 IMPACT BENDING

The Hatt-Turner impact machine is used for flexure impact tests of wood (Fig. 16-6).

Test Procedures

The impact test is made on a specimen 5 × 5 × 76 cm with center loading and a span length of 70 cm. The specimen is placed so that the load will be applied by a tup weighing 22.5 kg through a bearing block, as shown in Fig. 16-6. The tup is held by an electromagnet and is raised by a motor.

The first drop is made at 2.5 cm and is increased in increments of 2.5 cm until a drop at 10 cm is made. Successive drops are then continued at 5-cm increments until failure occurs or a deflection of 15 cm is reached. The height of the drop causing failure or 15-cm deflection is recorded. The failure is sketched on the data sheet. After failure, a test for moisture is made with a 2.5-cm specimen cut near the failure.

Significance of the Impact Test

The height of drop at failure is a measure of toughness of the wood specimen. The fibrous nature of wood makes it resistant to impact. In comparison with its weight, wood can be considered a tough material.

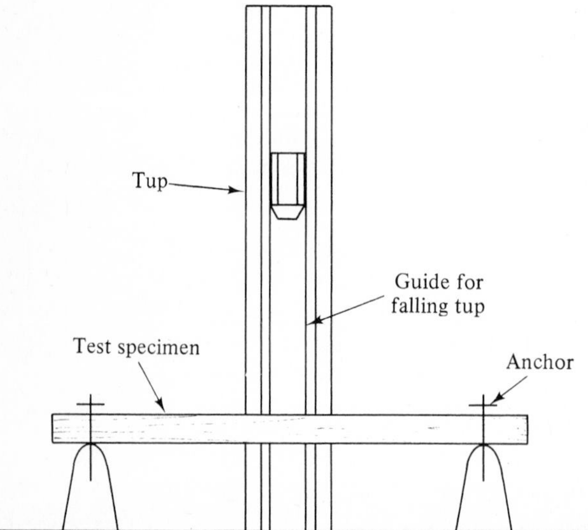

Figure 16-6 Method of supporting specimens in Hatt-Turner test. (*ASTM D-143.*)

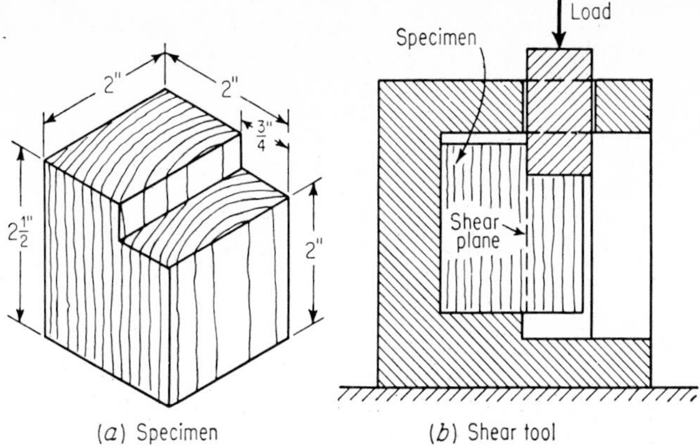

Figure 16-7 Method of testing wood in direct shear. (*ASTM D-143.*)

From the test data obtained from the impact test, the average elastic resilience, the proportional limit, and the modulus of elasticity can be computed.

16-9 SHEAR PARALLEL TO THE GRAIN

The shear test is made on a specimen 5 × 5 × 6.3 cm notched as illustrated in Fig. 16-7.

Test Procedures

The shear test is made in a shear tool (Fig. 16-7). The load is applied continuously throughout the test at a rate of motion of the crosshead of the testing machine of 6 mm/min.

The maximum load on the shear tool is recorded, and the failure is sketched on the data sheet (ASTM D-143).

Significance of the Direct Shear Test

In wooden beams failure sometimes occurs because of failure in horizontal shear (Fig. 16-3). This is particularly true in short, deep beams. The shear test will give an indication of the various shear strengths among various woods.

The direct shear test is also useful in measuring the efficiency of glued laminated joints and adhesives. For shear tests of glued joints, a specimen similar to that shown in Fig. 16-7 is glued along the shear plane and then loaded.

QUESTIONS AND PROBLEMS

1 Why is the testing of wood complex and unreliable compared to other materials?

2 How can wood be used with confidence in design if tests may not be representative of the particular piece of lumber being used?

3 List some common types of tests for wood.

4 What would you say would be a problem in testing wood specimens in tension which is not true of other materials?

5 ASTM D-143 lists tests for small, clear specimens. What other types of specimens are used in testing wood?

6 Why is the tension and compression strength different when a load is applied parallel to the grain and when it is applied perpendicular to the grain?

7 What are the dimensions of a "2 by 4"?

8 Why are glued laminated beams better than natural timber for structural members?

9 What effect would knots have on the strength of timber?

10 Why do wooden beams often fail in horizontal shear?

CHAPTER

SEVENTEEN

TESTING AND EVALUATION OF PLASTICS

Plastics are not generally considered to be structural materials, but since about 1935 the many and varied uses for various materials classed as plastics have been significant to modern society. Standard ASTM tests for plastics are included in Part 35, and under mechanical properties 34 standard test methods are listed.

Probably because of the many varied uses and requirements for different plastic materials, ASTM has not included specifications for the mechanical properties of plastics. The following test methods common for other engineering materials are included in Part 35 of ASTM.

D-695 Compressive properties of rigid plastics
D-790 Flexural properties of plastics and electrical insulating materials
D-785 Hardness, Rockwell, of plastics and electrical insulating materials
D-256 Impact resistance of plastics and electrical insulating materials
D-732 Shear strength of plastics
D-747 Stiffness of plastics by means of a cantilever beam
D-638 Tensile properties of plastics

Many of the tests for plastics have been adopted from similar tests for metals and other materials. Since these tests have already been discussed in other chapters, the discussion of various mechanical tests for plastics will be limited to comments on the purpose and significance of such tests and the adaptation of such tests to plastics.

17-1 COMPRESSIVE PROPERTIES OF RIGID PLASTICS

Purpose and Significance of the Compressive-Strength Test

The compressive-strength test for plastics is specified for rigid plastics only because specimens will only flatten without fracturing with most types of plastics. When the material does not fail in compression by a shattering fracture, the compressive strength is arbitrary, depending on the degree of distortion that is regarded as failure. Many plastics will continue to deform until a flat disk is produced, with the load rising steadily in the process.

The compressive-strength test can be useful in measuring bearing strength, yield strength, proportional limits, and other properties. The test will demonstrate the unusual properties of various types of plastics.

The fact that some plastics deform without fracturing demonstrates their atomic structure and bonding, as discussed in Chap. 2. As crosslinking occurs and primary bonds are developed among the organic molecules, the plastics become brittle and will fracture in the compressive-strength test. As long as the bonding among molecules is composed of secondary bonds, the plastic will deform without breaking.

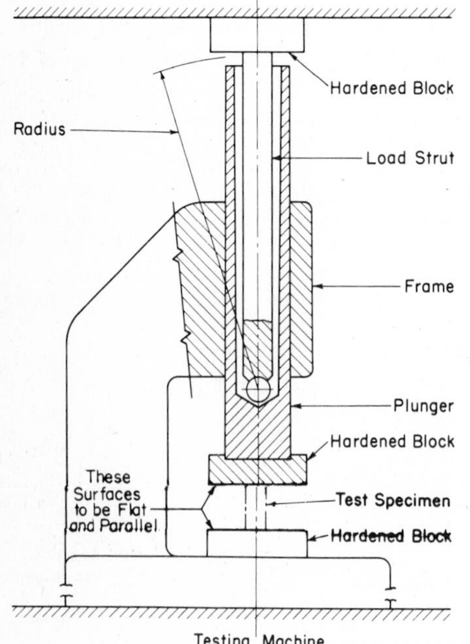

NOTE—Devices similar to the one illustrated have been successfully used in a number of different laboratories. Details of the device developed at the National Bureau of Standards are given in the paper by Aitchison, C. S., and Miller, J. A., "A Subpress for Compressive Tests," Natl. Advisory Committee for Aeronautics, Technical Note No. 912, 1943.

Figure 17-1 Example of subpress for testing the compressive strength of plastics. (*ASTM D-695.*)

Test Procedures

The compressive test for plastics is similar to that used for other materials with the exception of the size of specimens. The preferred specimens are either a cylinder 12.7 mm in diameter and 25.4 mm in height or a prism 12.7 × 12.7 × 25.4 mm. Such small specimens require special equipment such as a subpress, supporting jigs, and/or compression tools (ASTM D-695). One type of subpress is shown in Fig. 17-1.

17-2 ROCKWELL HARDNESS OF PLASTICS

Purpose and Significance of the Hardness Test for Plastics

The hardness test for plastics is based on ASTM E-18 (Chap. 15) for metals, and the Rockwell hardness machine (Fig. 15-7) is adapted to plastics. The hardness test provides valuable information regarding the properties of plastics:

1. A Rockwell hardness number is directly related to the indentation hardness of a plastic material.
2. The results of the hardness test are not generally a measure of abrasion resistance of plastics.
3. Indentation hardness is used as an indication of cure of some thermosetting plastics.
4. Indentation hardness may be used as a control test for indicating punching quality of laminated sheet stock.
5. Special attention must be given in testing certain types of plastics which have creep and recovery tendencies. The time factor has considerable effect on the test results.

17-3 IMPACT RESISTANCE OF PLASTICS

Purpose and Significance

Both the Charpy impact testing machine discussed in Chap. 15 and the Izod impact tester are recommended for use in testing plastics. Testing procedures are similar to those for metals discussed in Sec. 15-4 and are useful in measuring the relative toughness of various plastics. The results of all tests are reported in terms of energy absorbed per unit of specimen width.

17-4 STIFFNESS OF PLASTICS

Purpose and Significance

One form of bending test is useful in testing plastics. ASTM D-747 specifies that the bending moment, as well as the angle of bend, be observed. This is accomplished by using a mechanical system which will show the angle of bend and the bending moment simultaneously on two separate scales (Fig. 17-2).

Test Procedure

The method provides a means of deriving an index of stiffness of a material by measuring force and angle of bend of a cantilever beam. Under actual test conditions, the deformation has both elastic and plastic components, and the true value for elastic modulus cannot be calculated. The apparent value obtained from the following formula is called the "stiffness" of the material:

$$E = \frac{4S}{Wd^3} \frac{\text{max load reading}}{100\phi} \tag{17-1}$$

where E = stiffness, Pa
S = span length, m (measured from center of rotation of pendulum weighing system to contacting edge of bending specimen)
W = specimen width, m
d = specimen depth, m
M = total bending moment, N · m
ϕ = angular deflection, rad

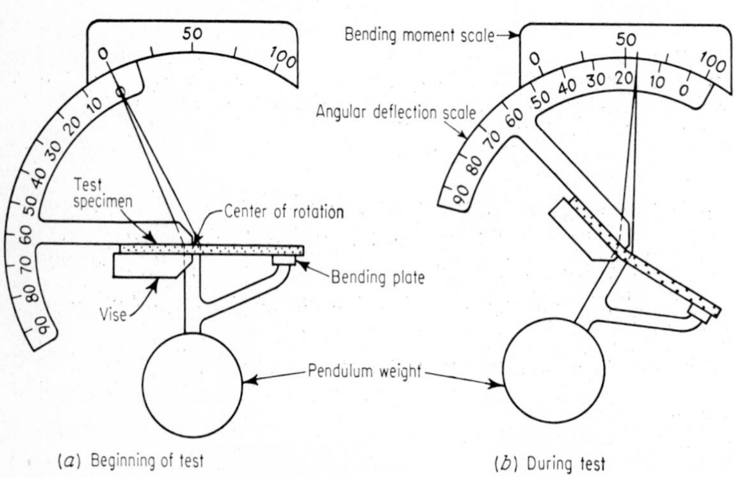

Figure 17-2 Mechanical systems of stiffness tester. (*ASTM D-747.*)

17-5 TENSILE PROPERTIES OF PLASTICS

Purpose and Significance of the Tensile Test for Plastics

The tensile properties for plastics can be obtained in a similar manner as for metals. A high degree of sensitivity is exhibited by many plastics to rate of testing, temperature, humidity, and other conditions. If tensile properties of plastics are to be used for engineering design purposes, testing should be performed over a broad load-time scale, including impact and creep. Figure 17-3 shows typical stress-strain curves for various plastics and designations of yield and tensile strength.

Table 17-1 shows the wide range in tensile and elastic properties for common plastics.

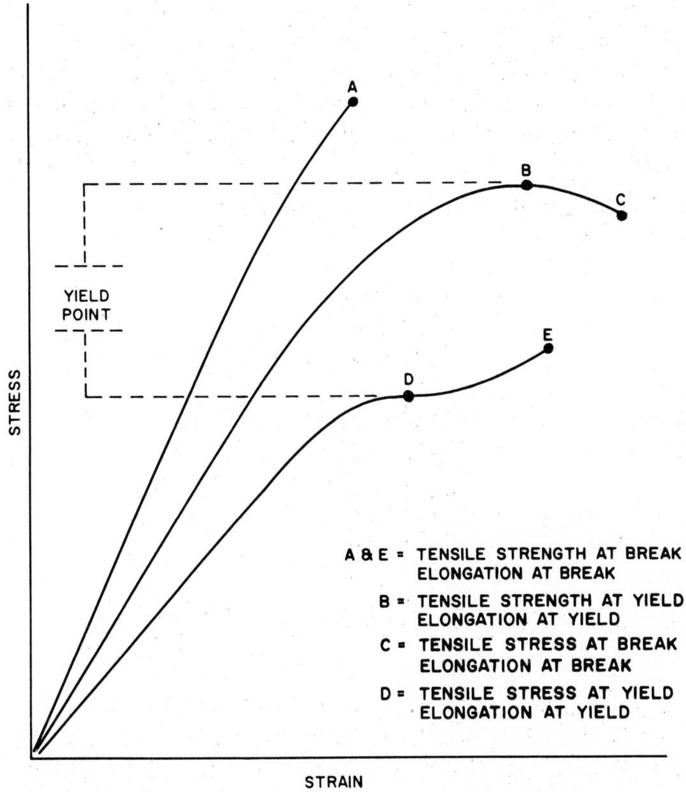

Figure 17-3 Stress-strain tensile designations for plastics. (*ASTM D-638.*)

Table 17-1 Mechanical properties of common plastics

Material	Modulus of elasticity, MPa	Tensile strength, MPa	Tensile elongation, percent
Epoxy	2413	28–90	3–4
Nylon	1034–2760	48–83	25–300
Polyethylene:			
Low-density	138–276	6.9–14	90–800
High-density	414–1034	21–35	15–100
Polymethyl methacrylate (Plexiglas)	2413–3448	55–76	2–7
Polystyrene	2760–3448	35–62	1–2
Polytetrafluorethylene (Teflon)	414	14–31	200–400
Polyvinyl chloride (PVC)	2069–4137	35–62	2–40
Flexible PV		10–21	200–400

QUESTIONS AND PROBLEMS

1 Why is it difficult to establish standard specifications for plastics?

2 What type of test is used to evaluate the mechanical properties of plastics?

3 What type of failure will occur if a nonrigid plastic is tested in compression?

4 What is meant by stiffness in plastics?

5 What precautions must be taken in making a tensile-strength test on plastics?

6 Is the stress-strain curve for plastics similar to that for metals?

7 Why is the hardness test used in testing plastics?

APPENDIX

I

STUDENT LABORATORY EXERCISES

Laboratory exercises can be valuable in several different ways in training students. The primary purpose of laboratory tests is to acquaint students with the behavior and evaluation of materials; it is not the intent to train engineering students and architects to become laboratory technicians.

1. The student is exposed to the behavior and properties of materials and the inconsistencies of test results.
2. The student gains an appreciation of tests as tools to use in arriving at engineering decisions.
3. The student can gain an understanding of why tests are made and their relative value in accepting or rejecting materials.
4. By performing tests, the student can better understand their variability and reliability.
5. Laboratory exercises provide an opportunity to expose the student to actual practical problems encountered in the evaluation of materials.
6. A technical report (Appendix III) gives the student an opportunity to learn to communicate laboratory experiences in a form which will be acceptable in engineering practice.

I-1 TYPES OF LABORATORY EXERCISES

There are at least two different approaches to laboratory courses.

General Laboratory Testing

In some courses the primary objective is to acquaint the student with the behavior and physical and mechanical properties of materials. Selected tests should be made with each engineering material. A report on the test results should be made, and the behavior and important properties of each material should be discussed.

The following selected tests are suggested for civil engineers and architects, but can be adjusted by the laboratory instructor as time and facilities dictate.

- Aggregates (Chap. 12):
  - Los Angeles abrasion test
  - Particle-size distribution
  - Specific gravity and absorption
- Fresh, plastic concrete (Chap. 13):
  - Slump
  - Density
  - Air content
- Hardened concrete (Chap. 13):
  - Compressive strength
  - Modulus of elasticity
  - Poisson's ratio
  - Flexural strength
- Metals (Chap. 15):
  - Tensile strength
  - Yield point
  - Proportional limit
  - Yield strength
  - Hardness test
  - Impact test
- Asphalt cement (Chap. 14):
  - Penetration test
  - Ductility test
- Asphaltic concrete (Chap. 14):
  - Compressive strength
  - Stability
- Wood (Chap. 16):
  - Tensile strength
    - Parallel to grain
    - Perpendicular to grain
  - Flexural strength
  - Compressive strength
    - Parallel to grain
    - Perpendicular to grain
  - Shear parallel to grain

Plastics (Chap. 17):
 Tension test
 Impact test
 Hardness test
 Compressive test

A Practical Problem in Materials Investigation

Experience indicates that students gain an appreciation for the value of laboratory tests if they participate in a practical materials investigation for a typical engineering project.

The student is assigned to investigate a concrete aggregate source for use in a selected structure and to design a suitable concrete mix for that structure. This will require the following:

1. Locate a possible source of aggregate.
2. Obtain representative samples.†
3. Determine the suitability of the aggregates for use in concrete.
4. Make sufficient concrete tests to establish the strength–w/c ratio relationship (The current ACI Building Code requires that the relationship between the compressive strength of concrete and the w/c ratio be established for each combination of ingredients, by actual experience on previous projects or by laboratory tests. The laboratory tests require strength tests from a minimum of three trial mixes made with three different w/c ratios.)
5. Evaluate concrete mixtures. Sufficient concrete mixes should be made to evaluate the aggregate content–slump relationship, as discussed in Chap. 5.
6. Hardened concrete tests. The most common test made with hardened concrete is of the compressive strength of standard cylinders. The standard test cylinder can also be used for other tests made with hardened concrete: compressive strength, modulus of elasticity and Poisson's ratio, and tensile strength using the cylinder-splitting test.
7. Uniformity of tests. Test results from the entire class can be combined and evaluated for (1) uniformity of similar mixes, (2) overall relationships between strength and w/c ratio, and (3) the relationship between aggregate content and slump.
8. Laboratory report. In practice no investigation is complete until a suitable laboratory report has been prepared. Technical reports are discussed in Appendix III.

† May be supplied by instructor.

I-2 EXAMPLE OF A LABORATORY ASSIGNMENT OF A PRACTICAL MATERIALS INVESTIGATION

CEE 328 Laboratory Assignment

Assume you are employed by a consulting firm. You have been assigned to investigate the suitability of a source of aggregate for a reinforced-concrete bridge. [$f'_c = 20$ MPa. Strength is not considered critical (see Chap. 5).]

First, select the most likely source of aggregate in your area and conduct a laboratory investigation of its suitability for use in the bridge. Since the aggregate source has been used for a number of years and examination of structures indicates there is no unusual durability problems, the following tests are considered necessary (Chap. 2):

1. Sampling aggregate source
2. Identification of rock types
3. Grading analysis of sand and gravel
4. Deleterious materials
   (*a*) Organic impurities
   (*b*) Material finer than the no. 200 sieve
   (*c*) Clay lumps, coal lignite
   (*d*) Lightweight pieces
5. Specific gravity and absorption
6. Abrasion of coarse aggregate

Second, after a suitable source of aggregate is established, make sufficient trial mixes to establish the strength–*w*/*c* ratio relationship and the slump–aggregate content relationship (Chap. 5). Assume $\bar{X}_r = 20 + 1.5\sigma$ (Chap. 11) and $\sigma = 3$ MPa.

Third, prepare a technical report to your superior with your findings, conclusions, and recommendations (Appendix III).

APPENDIX

II

SPECIFICATIONS FOR MATERIALS

II-1 GENERAL

Specifications are written statements containing minute descriptions of what the owner, or buyer, wants and will accept. These desires are translated into understandable specifications by the specification writer. Specifications should be written by the most experienced and best informed engineer available.

Good specifications will be

1. Technically adequate
2. Economically sound
3. Definite and certain
4. Fair and just

It is important that specifications be in a form that preserves the "owner–independent contractor" relationship. This can be accomplished by specifying performance (what the contractor produces) rather than materials and methods (how the contractor produces it). When the specifications writer includes details concerning materials and methods for the contractor to follow, the liability of the contractor for strict performance of the finished product is limited. The best specification from a legal standpoint is one which merely specifies the end result desired.

Most materials are manufactured before they reach the job, and specifications need only refer to standard products and specifications. Concrete is the most notable exception since the final steps in proportioning, mixing, placing, and curing occur on the job.

II-2 STANDARD SPECIFICATIONS FOR MATERIALS

The American Society for Testing and Materials includes in each of their volumes standard specifications for materials based on standard ASTM tests. Reference to these specifications can be inserted in any specification, and the materials required are clearly defined. Standard specifications have the distinct advantage of the test of time and general acceptance. Pertinent details and unusual requirements which apply to a specific project can be added to the standards as needed.

II-3 SELECTED ASTM STANDARD SPECIFICATIONS

Concrete aggregates	ASTM C-33
Aggregates for asphaltic concrete	ASTM D-5
Portland cement	ASTM C-150
Ready-mixed concrete	ASTM C-94
Air-entraining admixtures	ASTM C-260
Chemical admixtures	ASTM C-494
Reinforcing steel	ASTM C-615, C-616, C-617
Structural steel	ASTM A-94
Asphalt cement	ASTM D-946

II-4 TYPICAL SPECIFICATIONS FOR CONCRETE

Since the manufacture of concrete occurs on the job, specifications must be written for the materials and conditions peculiar to that job. Standard specifications are not available and would not apply. In Chap. 11 we discussed the use of statistical tools in specifications and control. The use of probability makes it possible to write realistic specifications which take into consideration variations in concrete ingredients and variations which occur during construction.

Ingredients

1. *Aggregates.* Aggregates used in concrete must conform to the minimum requirements of ASTM C-33 with the following additions:
   (*a*) The abrasion loss (ASTM C-535) must not be greater than 30 percent after 500 revolutions.
   (*b*) The specific gravity of aggregates shall not be less than 2.60.
   Note: These additional requirements were added for this particular project in order to limit the use of a deposit of deeply weathered, friable granite which would otherwise pass the requirements of ASTM C-33.
2. *Portland cement* must meet the requirements of ASTM C-150 for type II cement.
3. *Air-entraining admixtures* must be used in all exposed concrete which may be saturated in freezing weather and must meet the requirements of ASTM C-260.

4. *Water-reducing admixtures* must be used in all concrete and must meet the requirement of ASTM C-494. Water-reducing admixtures must be equal in performance and quality to Zeecon LS manufactured by Crown Zellerbach Corp., Camas, Washington.

Classes of Concrete

Two classes of concrete must be used as shown on the plans.

Class 1 Strength is critical to the safety of structural members, and the minimum allowable strength equals f'_c.

Class 2 Strength is not critical to the safety of structural members, and the allowable probability of a strength test falling below f'_c equals 1 in 10.

Typical Examples of Strength Requirements

The strength of concrete must be determined in accordance with ASTM standards C-31, C-39, and C-683.

1. *Class 1 concrete*
   (*a*) The average strength of concrete must be equal to $\bar{X}_r$:

$$\bar{X}_r = f'_c + 3\sigma$$

where $\bar{X}_r$ = average of all strength tests
f'_c = strength used in design
σ = standard deviation

Example: Assume $f'_c = 20$ MPa and $\sigma = 4.14$. Then

$$\bar{X}_r = 20 + 3.0 \times 4.14 = 32.4 \text{ MPa (4700 psi)} \qquad \text{(II-1)}$$

   (*b*) σ must be computed for a minimum of 30 tests. If sufficient tests are not available, a value of σ of 4.0 MPa may be assumed until sufficient tests are available.
   (*c*) No strength test must fall below f'_c.

2. *Class 2 concrete*
   (*a*) The average strength of concrete must equal $\bar{X}_r$ where

$$\bar{X}_r = f'_c + 1.282\sigma \qquad \text{(II-2)}$$

   (*b*) The value of σ may be computed for a minimum of 10 tests if the value of $\bar{X}_r$ is computed as follows:

$$\bar{X}_r = f'_c + 1.4\sigma\dagger \qquad \text{(II-3)}$$

   (*c*) The average of any three consecutive strength tests must not fall below f'_c.

† The value of $\bar{X}_r$ is increased because it must be assumed that σ is not reliable (Chap. 15).

APPENDIX

III

TECHNICAL REPORTS

The purpose of a technical report of materials investigation is to communicate completely, clearly, and precisely all pertinent information which may be useful. Anything that tends to be verbose or involved should be avoided.

Most of the emphasis in composition courses in grade school, high school, and even universities is in writing for the enjoyment and entertainment of the reader. This style of writing only confuses and clutters a technical report.

III-1 FORMAT

There is no "correct" format for technical reports. Different organizations prefer different arrangements. The following outline has several advantages, however, and is used by many technical organizations.

III-2 OUTLINE

The following outline lists the sections of the report in descending order of importance.

1. Introduction
2. Conclusions and recommendations
3. Discussion of test results
4. Test results, tables, charts, and miscellaneous useful information

III-3 ADVANTAGES OF PROPOSED FORMAT

Technical reports are usually written to enable executives, project engineers, or supervisors to make decisions regarding the materials being investigated. The busy architect or project engineer need read only items 1 and 2 of the prepared report.

1. The introduction tells the purpose, scope, and authorization of the investigation.
2. The conclusions tell what was learned from the investigation and what action is recommended. With this information the project engineer or architect can make the appropriate decisions.
3. If the engineer is interested in why the conclusions and recommendations were made, he or she can continue and read section 3.
4. If the engineer is interested in the supportive test results and figures, she or he can then read section 4.

III-4 WRITING STYLE

A technical report is not the place to demonstrate one's literary talents or vocabulary. All sentences should be short and have only one thought. Paragraphs should also be short and contain only one main idea. A report is easier to read if headings and subheadings are used extensively to separate the sections. No words should be used that will not be clearly understood by the reader.

III-5 EXAMPLE OF TECHNICAL REPORT

Appendix IV is an example of a typical report of the investigation of the suitability of a concrete aggregate deposit and concrete trial mixes.

APPENDIX

IV

EXAMPLE OF A TYPICAL TECHNICAL REPORT

INVESTIGATION OF THE SUITABILITY OF THE PARSON AGGREGATE DEPOSIT FOR CONSTRUCTION OF THE BEAR RIVER BRIDGE†

IV-1 INTRODUCTION

The Parson aggregate deposit at Smithfield, Utah, was proposed for use in the construction of the Bear River Bridge on highway I-15. In accordance with the memorandum dated June 1, 1977 from district engineer D. W. Blodgett, a materials investigation was conducted to establish the suitability of this deposit. The deposit is readily accessible from highway 91.

IV-2 CONCLUSIONS AND RECOMMENDATIONS

1. Test results show that suitable concrete aggregate can be produced from the Parson deposit, Smithfield, Utah.
2. It will be necessary to wash the sand to remove an excess amount of silt and fines.

† By G. R. Hales and R. W. Lee.

3. The deposit contains 24.6 percent oversize rock. It is recommended that this material be crushed to appropriate sizes to balance the excess amount of sand in the deposit.
4. The aggregate and ideal type I cement will produce a compressive strength of 28 MPa with a *w/c* ratio of 0.54.

IV-3 DISCUSSION

Physical Properties

The aggregates from the Parson Smithfield deposit are composed of quartzitic sandstones, quartzites, sandstones, limestone with small amounts of granite, and other coarse-grained, igneous rocks. Only a small percentage of weathered particles were found.

1. *Silt content.* The average silt content was 6.3 percent, which is greater than allowed by ASTM specification C-33. This will necessitate washing the sand.
2. *Grading.* The grading of the gravel falls within ASTM C-33 requirements with the exception of oversize rock. In addition to too much silt, the sand shows an excess of material on the no. 100 and no. 50 sieves. Vigorous washing should correct this deficiency.
3. *Abrasion.* The 24.2 percent loss in the abrasion test indicates the gravel particles are hard and tough.
4. *Color.* The color test indicates a negligible amount of organic impurities in the sand.

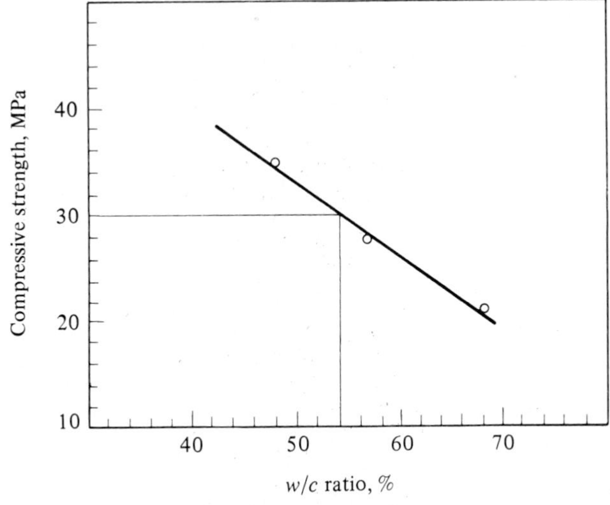

Figure IV-1 Relationship between strength and *w/c* ratio.

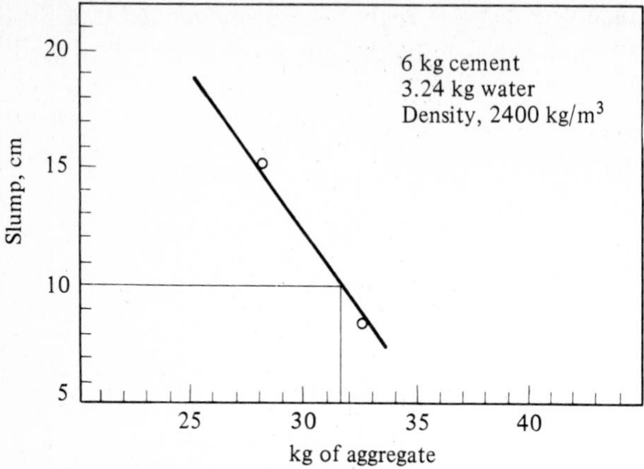

Figure IV-2 Relationship between slump and aggregate content.

Properties of Concrete

1. *Strength.* The relationship between strength and the *w/c* ratio is shown in Fig. IV-1. The three-point curve was proposed in accordance with the requirements of ACI 318 and indicates that the strength-producing properties of the aggregates from the Parson deposit are better than average sources of aggregate as indicated by ACI Committee 211.
2. *Aggregate and cement content.* Figure IV-2 shows the relationship between the aggregate content and slump, using aggregates from the Parson deposit and a *w/c* ratio of 54 percent selected from Fig. IV-1.

IV-4 TEST RESULTS

The following results were obtained from tests made with samples from the Parson deposit, Smithfield, Utah.

Percent passing the no. 200 sieve:

Sand:	6.3
Gravel:	0.8

Specific gravity and absorption:

	Specific gravity	*Percent absorption*
Sand:	2.63	1.5
Gravel:	2.66	0.9
Washed sand:	2.65	1.1

Deleterious materials:

Sand:	negligible
Gravel:	negligible

Table IV-1 Results of tests made with sand

Sand grading

Sieve number	Retained, g	Percent retained	Percent passing	ASTM C-33
4	18	3.0	97.0	95 to 100
8	76	12.7	87.3	80 to 100
16	157	26.2	73.8	50 to 85
30	274	45.7	54.3	25 to 60
50	377	62.8	37.2	10 to 30
100	538	89.7	10.3	2 to 10
Pan	600	100		

FM = 2.40

Gravel grading: pit run

Sieve number	Retained, kg	Percent retained	Percent passing	ASTM C-33
$1\frac{1}{2}$	1.23	24.6	75.4	95 to 100
$\frac{3}{4}$	3.04	60.8	39.4	35 to 70
$\frac{3}{8}$	4.23	84.6	15.5	10 to 30
4	4.84	96.8	3.2	0 to 5
Pan	5.0	100.0		

Without oversize + $1\frac{1}{2}$

Sieve number	Retained, kg	Percent retained	Percent passing	ASTM C-33
$1\frac{1}{2}$	0	0	100	95 to 100
$\frac{3}{4}$	2.39	47.8	52.2	35 to 70
$\frac{3}{8}$	3.97	79.4	20.6	10 to 30
4	4.79	95.8	4.2	0 to 5
Pan	5.00	100.0		

Concrete trial mixes. Figures IV-1 and IV-2 show the results of trial mixes made with Parson aggregate and ideal type I cement. The final mix proportions which should be used on the Bear River Bridge are as follows:

Cement content	287.5 kg/m^3
Water content	155.3 kg/m^3
Aggregate	1513.6 kg/m^3
Slump	10 cm
w/c ratio	54 percent

INDEX